FIRST EDITION

Solutions Manual and Additional Problems for Organic Chemistry

A TWO-SEMESTER COURSE OF ESSENTIAL
ORGANIC CHEMISTRY

BY PETER GRUNDT, SANGEETA MEREDDY,
AND VIKTOR ZHDANKIN

UNIVERSITY OF MINNESOTA - DULUTH

cognella | ACADEMIC PUBLISHING

Bassim Hamadeh, CEO and Publisher
Kassie Graves, Director of Acquisitions
Jamie Giganti, Senior Managing Editor
Miguel Macias, Senior/ Graphic Designer
Amy Stone, Acquisitions Editor
Sean Adams, Project Editor
Luiz Ferreira, Licensing Coordinator

Printed in the United States of America

ISBN: 978-1-5165-2456-3 (pbk) / 978-1-5165-2457-0 (br)

CONTENTS

Preface.. v

CHAPTER 1
Covalent Bonding and Structure of Molecules   1
1.1. Chapter 1 Problems and Solutions................................ 1
1.2. Additional Problems for Chapter 1 11

CHAPTER 2
Proton Transfer Reactions in Organic Chemistry   13
2.1. Chapter 2 Problems and Solutions............................... 13
2.2. Additional Problems for Chapter 2 18

CHAPTER 3
Alkanes and Cycloalkanes   19
3.1. Chapter 3 Problems and Solutions............................... 19
3.2. Additional Problems for Chapter 3 26

CHAPTER 4
Stereochemistry   29
4.1. Chapter 4 Problems and Solutions............................... 29
4.2. Additional Problems for Chapter 4 33

CHAPTER 5
Nucleophilic Substitution and β-Elimination Reactions   35
5.1. Chapter 5 Problems and Solutions............................... 35
5.2. Additional Problems for Chapter 5 47

CHAPTER 6
Alkenes   49
6.1. Chapter 6 Problems and Solutions............................... 49
6.2. Additional Problems for Chapter 6 61

CHAPTER 7
Alkynes   63
7.1. Chapter 7 Problems and Solutions............................... 63
7.2. Additional Problems for Chapter 7 73

CHAPTER 8
Alcohols   75

    8.1. Chapter 8 Problems and Solutions 75

    8.2. Additional Problems for Chapter 8 86

CHAPTER 9
Spectroscopy of Organic Compounds   89

    9.1. Chapter 9 Problems and Solutions 89

    9.2. Additional Problems for Chapter 9 106

CHAPTER 10
Organometallic Compounds and Transition Metal Catalysis 109

    10.1. Chapter 10 Problems and Solutions 109

    10.2. Additional Problems for Chapter 10 113

CHAPTER 11
Aldehydes and Ketones   115

    11.1. Chapter 11 Problems and Solutions 115

    11.2. Additional Problems for Chapter 11 134

CHAPTER 12
Carboxylic Acids and Their Derivatives   137

    12.1. Chapter 12 Problems and Solutions 137

    12.2. Additional Problems for Chapter 12 157

CHAPTER 13
Noncyclic Conjugated Systems   159

    13.1. Chapter 13 Problems and Solutions 159

    13.2. Additional Problems for Chapter 13 165

CHAPTER 14
Benzene and Aromatic Compounds   167

    14.1. Chapter 14 Problems and Solutions 167

    14.2. Additional Problems for Chapter 14 185

CHAPTER 15
Amines   187

    15.1. Chapter 15 Problems and Solutions 187

    15.2. Additional Problems for Chapter 15 198

CHAPTER 16
Introduction to Biomolecules   201

    16.1. Chapter 16 Problems and Solutions 201

    16.2. Additional Problems for Chapter 16 210

CHAPTER 17
Solutions to Additional Problems   213

Preface

This book provides solutions to the problems from *Organic Chemistry: A Two-Semester Course of Essential Organic Chemistry* by Viktor Zhdankin and Peter Grundt. The text of original problems is included in this manual, so it can be used independently from the textbook. Problem solutions provide detailed explanation with reference to the related sections of the main textbook. Sets of additional problems are included in each chapter with the solutions grouped separately at the end of the manual.

While this manual is primarily intended as a supplement to the original textbook, it can be also used as a source of additional problems with any basic organic chemistry text. The problems included in this manual cover all essential material within the requirements outlined by the American Chemical Society (ACS). This book provides excellent preparation for standardized ACS exams, MCAT, PCAT, Chemistry GRE, and other professional proficiency exams.

Covalent Bonding and Structure of Molecules

1.1. Chapter 1 Problems and Solutions

Problem 1.1. Which elements have the following electronic configurations?

a) $1s^2\, 2s^2\, 2p_x^{\,2}\, 2p_y^{\,2}\, 2p_z^{\,2}$

b) $1s^2\, 2s^2\, 2p_x^{\,1}\, 2p_y^{\,0}\, 2p_z^{\,0}$

c) $1s^2\, 2s^2\, 2p_x^{\,1}\, 2p_y^{\,1}\, 2p_z^{\,1}$

d) $[Ne]\, 3s^2\, 3p_x^{\,1}\, 3p_y^{\,1}\, 3p_z^{\,0}$

Solution:
See Table 1.1 in the textbook and the Periodic Table for solution.

a) neon   b) boron   c) nitrogen   d) silicon

Problem 1.2. How many valence electrons do the following elements have?

a) phosphorus   b) magnesium   c) sodium   d) silicon   e) nitrogen

Solution:
Number of valence electrons of an element corresponds to the group number in the Periodic Table.

a) 5   b) 2   c) 1   d) 4   e) 5

Problem 1.3. Use $\delta+$ and $\delta-$ to indicate the polarity of the following bonds:

a) C–F   b) S–O   c) Li–C

Solution:

The more electronegative element in each pair has a partial negative charge which is indicated as δ−. See Table 1.2 in the textbook for electronegativity values of elements.

a)
δ+   δ−
C——F

b)
δ+   δ−
S——O

c)
δ+   δ−
Li——C

Problem 1.4. Which of the following pairs of elements will form an ionic compound? Which pair will form a nonpolar covalent bond?

a) H and C   b) Br and Cl   c) Cl and Cl   d) Mg and F

Solution:

The polar covalent bond is generally formed by any two elements in which the difference in the electronegativity values is 1.9 or lower. The ionic compounds are generally formed from elements with a significant difference in electronegativity of more than 1.9. See Table 1.2 in the textbook for electronegativity values of elements.

a) polar covalent   b) polar covalent   c) nonpolar covalent   d) ionic

Problem 1.5. Draw Lewis structures of two compounds with molecular formula C_2H_7N.

Solution:

Figure 1.4 in the textbook shows typical bonding patterns for atoms of C, N, and H. Two Lewis structures can be assembled for C_2H_7N by using these patterns:

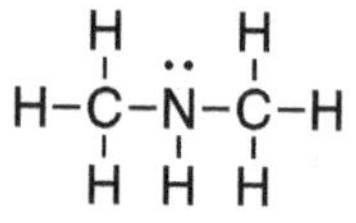

dimethylamine
(a 2° amine)

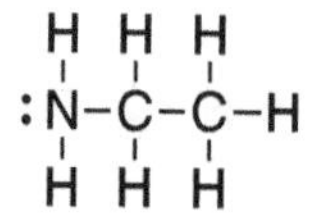

ethylamine
(a 1° amine)

Problem 1.6. The molecules shown below are wrong Lewis structures violating the octet rule and formal charges. Correct these structures by moving electron pairs from bonded to nonbonded positions, showing formal charges if needed.

a)

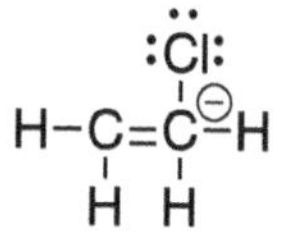

b)

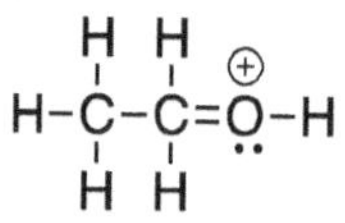

c)

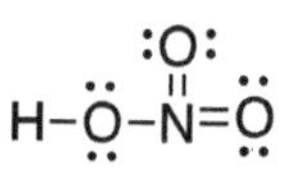

Solution:

This problem can be solved by using Figures 1.4 and 1.7 in the textbook.

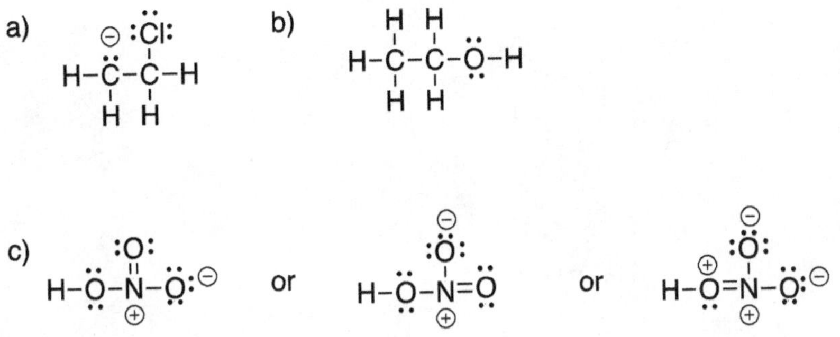

a)

⊖ :C̈l:
|
H–C̈–C–H
| |
H H

b)

H H
| |
H–C–C–Ö–H
| |
H H

c)

:O:
‖
H–Ö–N–Ö:⊖   or   H–Ö–N=Ö   or   H–Ö=N–Ö:⊖
      ⊕   ⊕   ⊕

Problem 1.7. For each condensed structure shown, draw the corresponding line–angle structure.

a) $(CH_3)_2CH(CH_2)_3CH_3$

b) $CH_3CONHCH_2CH_3$

c) $CH_3CH_2CH(CH_3)CH(CH_3)_2$

d) $(CH_3)_3COCH_3$

Solution:

This problem can be solved by converting condensed structures to Lewis structures and then removing symbols of C with attached hydrogens and showing only the chain of bonds between carbon atoms:

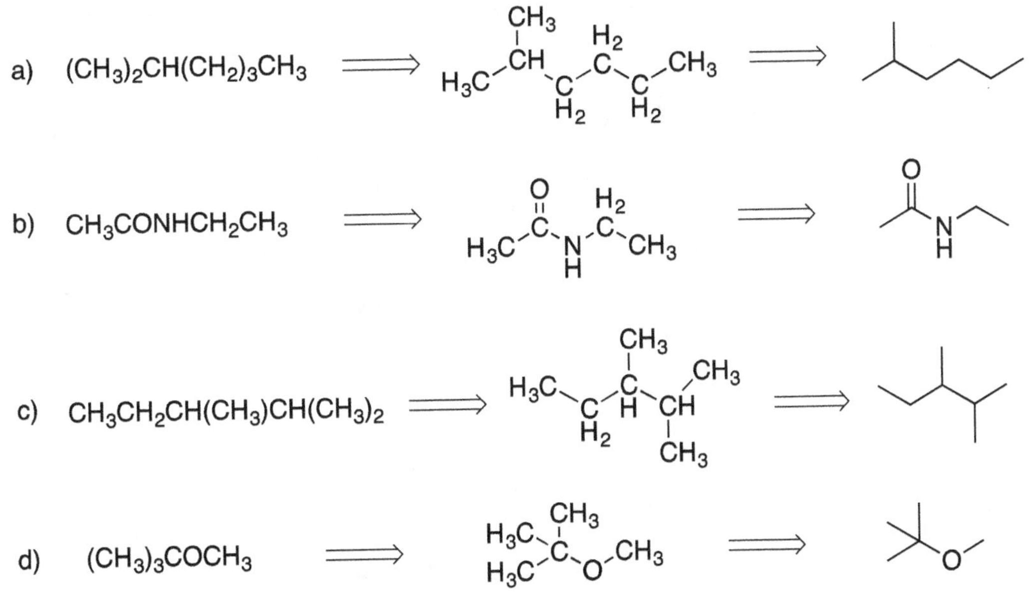

a) $(CH_3)_2CH(CH_2)_3CH_3$ ⟹ ⟹

b) $CH_3CONHCH_2CH_3$ ⟹ ⟹

c) $CH_3CH_2CH(CH_3)CH(CH_3)_2$ ⟹ ⟹

d) $(CH_3)_3COCH_3$ ⟹ ⟹

Problem 1.8. All structures shown below depict the correct number of nonbonding electrons and bonds. What is the formal charge on the indicated atoms?

a) 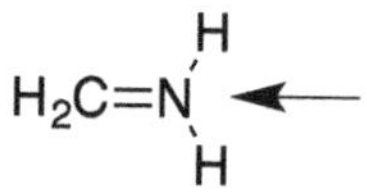 $H_2C=\overset{\overset{\displaystyle H}{|}}{N}\underset{\displaystyle H}{}$ ←

b) 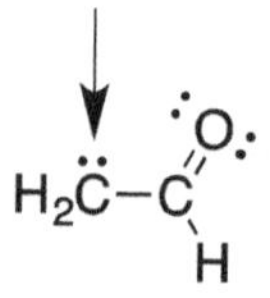 ↓ $H_2\ddot{C}-C\overset{\ddot{O}\text{:}}{\underset{\displaystyle H}{}}$

c) $H_2C=\overset{\text{..}}{\underset{\displaystyle H}{O}}$ ←

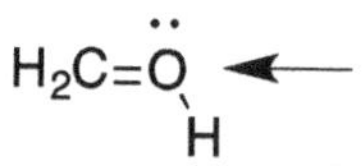

d) 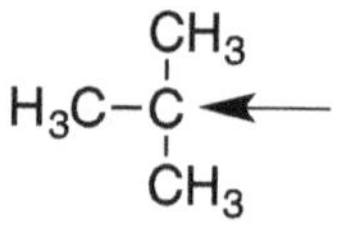 $H_3C-\overset{\overset{\displaystyle CH_3}{|}}{\underset{\displaystyle CH_3}{C}}$ ←

Solution:

This problem can be solved by using Figure 1.7 in the textbook.

a) +1   b) –1   c) +1   d) +1

Problem 1.9. For each of the molecules below, convert the condensed structure into a line structure and name the major functional group present in each molecule.

a) CH$_3$CH$_2$CHO

b) (CH$_3$)$_3$CCN

c) (CH$_3$)$_3$COCH$_3$

d) (CH$_3$)$_3$CCOOCH$_2$CH$_3$

Solution:

See Table 1.3 in the textbook for common functional groups.

a)

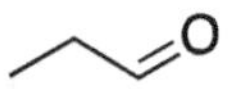

aldehyde

b)

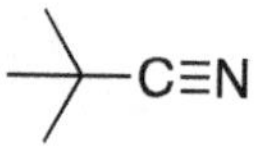

nitrile or cyano

c)

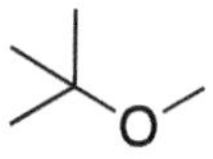

ether

d)

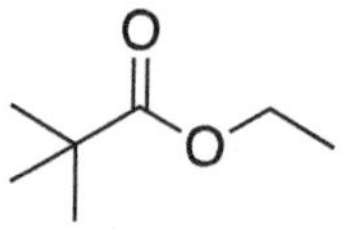

carboxylic acid ester

Problem 1.10. Below are ingredients of some personal care products that may be found in your home. Based on the suffix of the name, what functional groups are present in these molecules?

a) menthol

b) acetone

c) benzyl benzoate

d) cyclohexene

Solution:

a) The name contains the suffix -ol, therefore an alcohol functional group is present in the molecule.

Structure of menthol:

b) The name contains the suffix -one, therefore a ketone functional group is present in the molecule.

Structure of acetone:

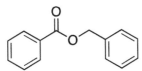

c) The name contains the suffix -oate, therefore a carboxylic acid ester is present in the molecule (see Table 1.3 in the textbook for the functional group of the carboxylic ester).

Structure of benzyl benzoate:

d) The name contains the suffix -ene, therefore an alkene functional group is present in the molecule.

Structure of cyclohexene:

Problem 1.11. Identify the functional groups indicated by numbers in the molecule shown below.

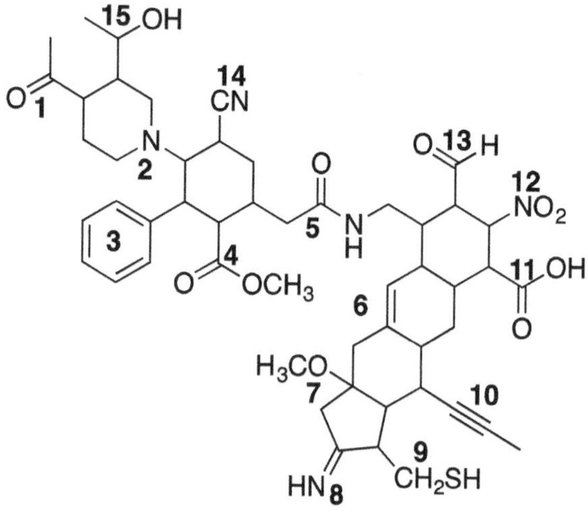

Solution:

Use Table 1.3 in the textbook for naming common functional groups.

1 ketone; **2** amine (or 3° amine); **3** arene (phenyl); **4** carboxylic ester; **5** carboxylic amide; **6** alkene; **7** ether; **8** imine; **9** thiol; **10** alkyne; **11** carboxylic acid; **12** nitro group; **13** aldehyde

Problem 1.12. Ignoring any bond between carbon and hydrogen, indicate the shortest bond in the molecules shown below.

a) $CH_3CCCH_2CH_3$ b) $CH_3COCH_2CH_2CHCH_2$

Solution:

a) The molecule contains a carbon–carbon triple bond, which, while ignoring any bond between carbon and hydrogen, is the shortest bond in this molecule:

$$H_3C-C\equiv C-CH_2$$
$$\qquad\qquad\quad CH_3$$

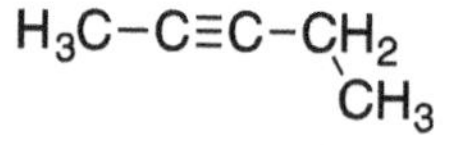

b) The molecule contains a carbon–oxygen double bond, which, while ignoring any bond between carbon and hydrogen, is the shortest bond in this molecule (see Figure 1.13 in the textbook for typical bond lengths):

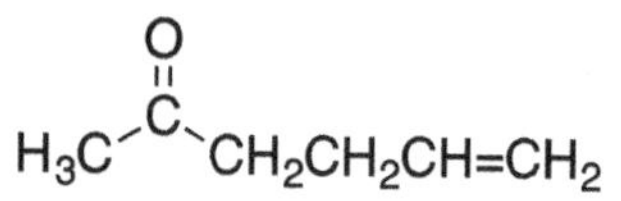

Problem 1.13. What is the approximate chlorine-carbon-carbon bond angle in vinyl chloride ($CH_2=CHCl$)?

Solution:
The approximate chlorine-carbon-carbon bond angle is 120°. See Figure 1.11 in the textbook for the trigonal planar geometry.

Problem 1.14. Cyclopropane is a cyclic compound with the molecular formula C_3H_6. Explain why the carbon-carbon-carbon bond angle in cyclopropane is significantly smaller than 109°.

Solution:
The Lewis structure of cyclopropane is shown below. The three carbon atoms in cyclopropane form a triangle (see the line structure below). Therefore, the carbon-carbon-carbon bond angle has to be 60°.

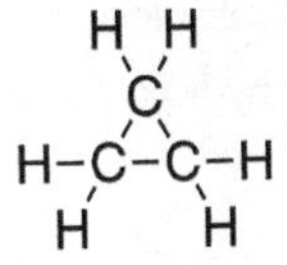

Problem 1.15. For each series of compounds, indicate the one with a molecular dipole moment of $\mu = 0$.

a)

b) $Cl-C\equiv C-Br$

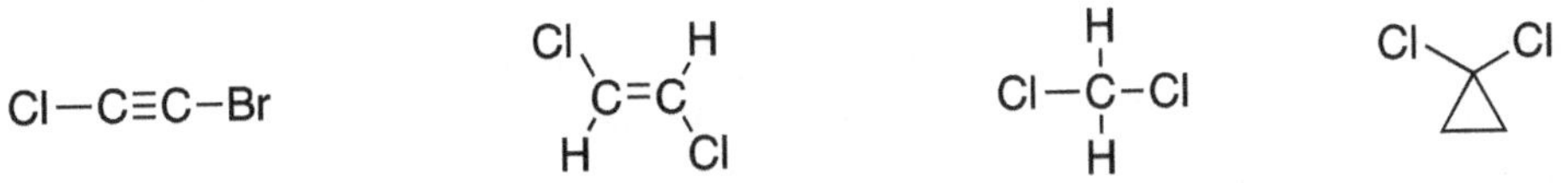

Solution:
Dipole moment μ is defined as a vector sum of the individual bond dipoles within the molecule. For a nonpolar molecule ($\mu = 0$), dipole moments of bonds are pointing in exactly opposite directions and canceling each other (see Figure 1.14 of the textbook).

a)

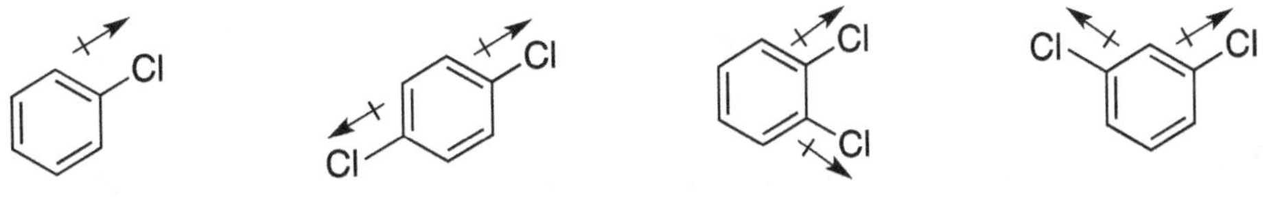

$\mu > 0 D$ $\mu = 0 D$ $\mu > 0 D$ $\mu > 0 D$

b) $Cl-C\equiv C-Br$

$\mu > 0 D$ $\mu = 0 D$ $\mu > 0 D$ $\mu > 0 D$

Problem 1.16. Sort the following compounds by increasing boiling point.

a) HO⌒⌒⌒   ⌒⌒⌒   HO⌒⌒⌒OH

b)

OH
|
⊥ (tert-butanol)   HO⌒⌒ (propanol)   OH on branched structure

Solution:

a) All compounds have a similar molecular mass, but differ by the number of alcohol (hydroxyl) functional groups present in the molecule. The hydroxyl groups have the ability to interact with each other via intramolecular dipole–dipole attraction (hydrogen bonding) resulting in increase of the boiling point. The more hydroxyl groups are present the higher the boiling point is:

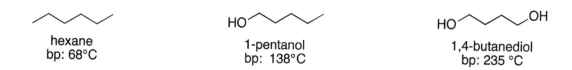

hexane	1-pentanol	1,4-butanediol
bp: 68°C	bp: 138°C	bp: 235 °C

b) All compounds have the same molecular mass, but differ by the way the atoms are connected. They are constitutional isomers. As explained above, hydroxyl groups have the ability to interact with each other via intramolecular dipole–dipole interaction resulting in increase of the boiling point. However, for a tertiary alcohol the hydroxyl is sterically more hindered than in primary and secondary alcohols. While in a secondary alcohol the hydroxyl group is sterically more hindered than in a primary alcohol. Therefore, the order of boiling points is as followed:

OH
|
⊥

OH
|
⋋

HO⌒⌒

tert-butanol
bp: 81 °C

2-butanol
bp: 99 °C

1-butanol
bp: 118 °C

Problem 1.17. Draw the most important resonance form for each of the species below.

a)
$\overset{\ominus}{H_2C}-N\equiv\overset{\oplus}{N}:$

b)
$\overset{\oplus}{N}H_2$
$\|$
$H_3C-\overset{\|}{C}-\overset{\ominus}{\ddot{O}}:$

c)
CH_3
$|$
$H_3C-\overset{\oplus}{C}-\overset{..}{\underset{..}{S}}-CH_3$

Solution:

The most important resonance contributors satisfy the following requirements: a) a formal negative formal charge in the contributing structure should stay on the most electronegative atom, b) the contributor should have the largest number of covalent bonds and the smallest number of atoms with formal charges, and c) the contributor should have completely filled valence shells for all atoms (octets of electrons).

a)

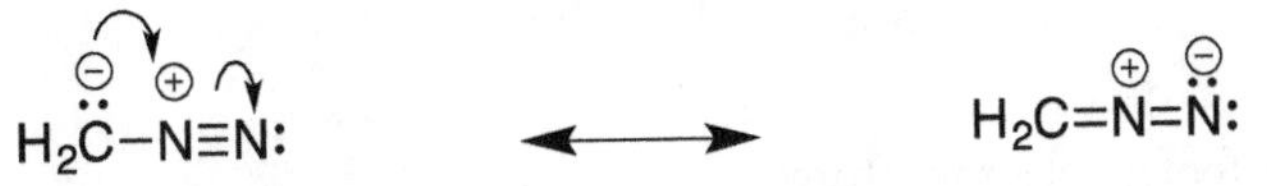

b)

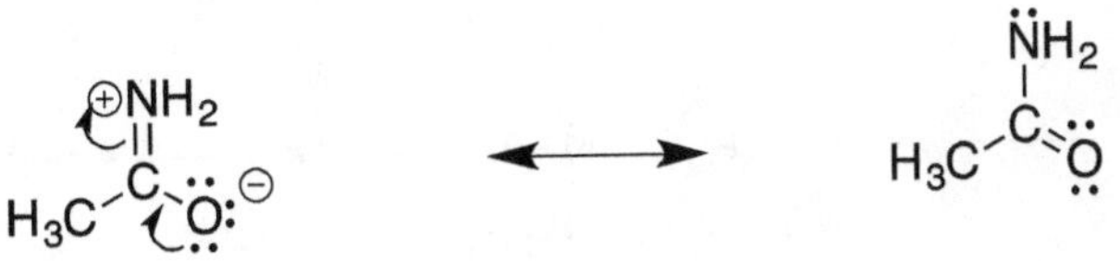

c)

Problem 1.18. Draw the contributing structures of the molecules below, as indicated by the curved arrows.

a)

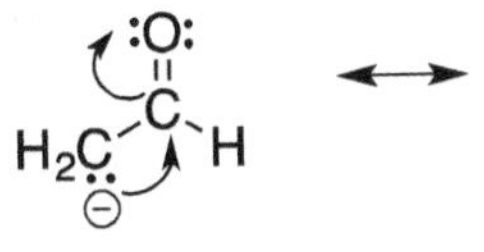

b)

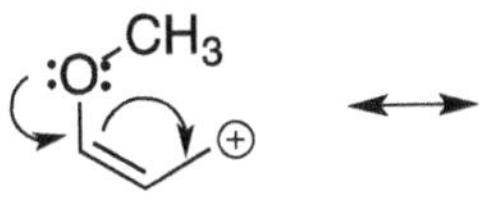

Solution:

a)

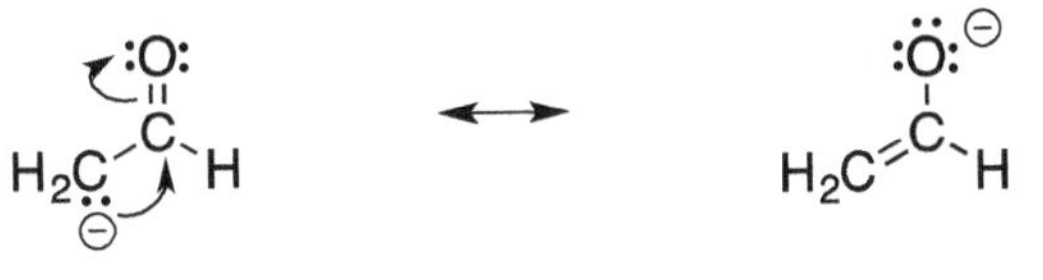

b)

Problem 1.19. Complete the resonance forms of the conjugate base of nitromethane ($^-$:CH$_2$NO$_2$) by adding the missing charges.

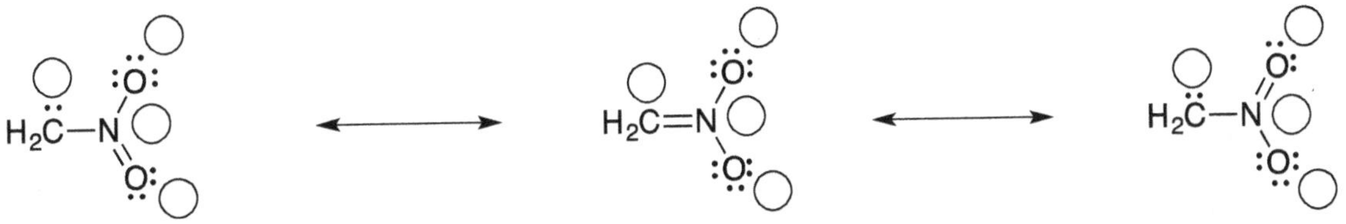

Solution:
See Figure 1.7 in the textbook for typical formal charges.

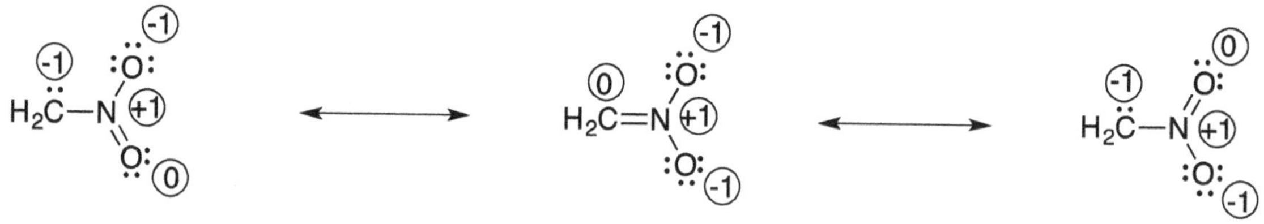

Problem 1.20. Which of the following pairs of structures depict resonance contributors?

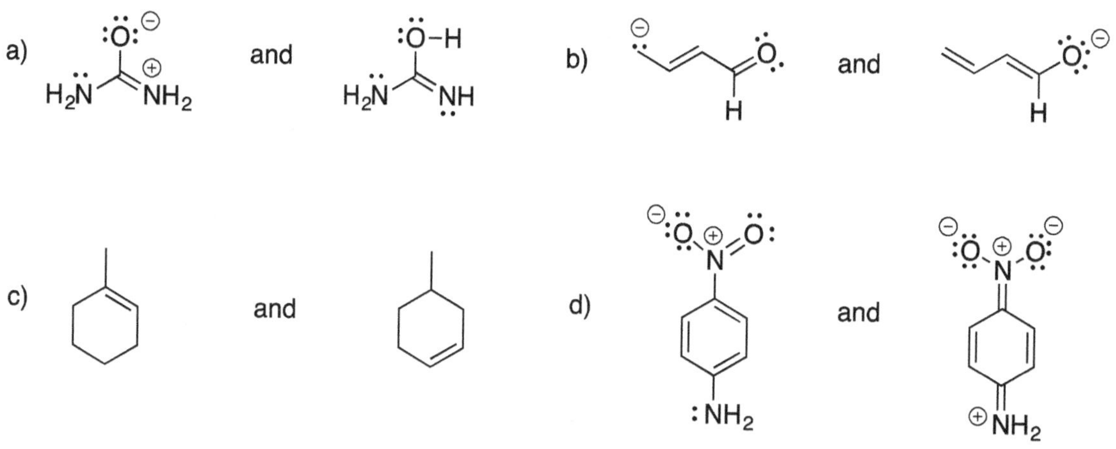

a)

and

b)

and

c)

and

d)

and

Solution:

a) constitutional isomers (hydrogen atom is moved from N to O)

b) resonance structures (all atoms stay in the same position, electrons move)

c) constitutional isomers (hydrogen atoms changed their position)

d) resonance structures (all atoms stay in the same position, electrons move)

Problem 1.21. Which atomic orbitals overlap to form the carbon–carbon bond of acetonitrile (CH_3CN)?

Solution:

The carbon atom of the methyl group (CH_3) is sp³ hybridized, in order to accommodate four sigma bonds. The carbon atom of the cyano group (CN) forms two sigma bonds and two pi bonds. Therefore, the carbon–carbon bond in acetonitrile is formed by overlap of an sp³ orbital and an sp orbital.

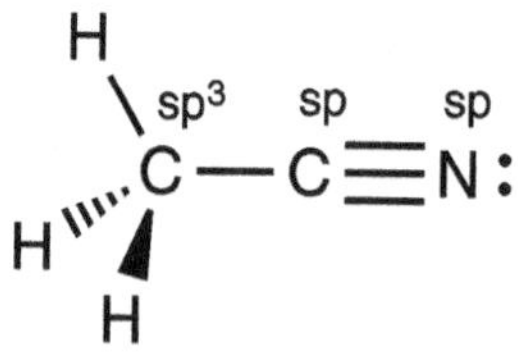

Problem 1.22. Why is the center carbon atom of an allene molecule ($H_2C=C=CH_2$) sp hybridized?

Solution:
The center carbon atom in allene forms two sigma bonds and two pi bonds. The only way for this atom to adopt this bonding pattern is an sp hybridization.

Problem 1.23. Consider the molecule in the box and answer the corresponding questions.

a) How many σ bonds are formed by the overlap of the two sp orbitals?
b) How many σ bonds are formed by the overlap of the sp and sp^2 orbitals?
c) How many σ bonds are formed by the overlap of the sp and sp^3 orbitals?
d) How many σ bonds are formed by the overlap of the sp^2 and sp^2 orbitals?
e) How many σ bonds are formed by the overlap of the sp^3 and sp^3 orbitals?
f) How many σ bonds are formed by the overlap of the s and sp orbitals?
g) How many σ bonds are formed by the overlap of the s and sp^2 orbitals?
h) How many σ bonds are formed by the overlap of the s and sp^3 orbitals?
i) How many σ bonds are formed by the overlap of the s and s orbitals?
j) What is the total number of π bonds in the whole molecule?

Solution:
   a) 1   b) 1   c) 0   d) 2   e) 1   f) 1   g) 4   h) 4   i) 0   j) 4

1.2. Additional Problems for Chapter 1 (for answers see Ch 17)

Problem 1.24. Determine if S–F bond is ionic, polar covalent, or nonpolar covalent. Indicate the direction of polarity in the S–F bond using the symbols δ+ and δ- on appropriate atoms.

Problem 1.25. Draw Lewis structures for the following molecules.

   a) HCN   b) a ketone with molecular formula C_3H_6O

Problem 1.26. Draw the resonance contributing structure indicated by the curved arrows:

Problem 1.27. Determine the direction of molecular dipole moment in the following molecule.

Problem 1.28. Identify and name all the functional groups in the following molecule.

Problem 1.29. Determine the molecular formula for the structure in problem 1.28.

Proton Transfer Reactions in Organic Chemistry

2.1. Chapter 2 Problems and Solutions

Problem 2.1. For each of the following compounds, draw the structures of its conjugate base and its conjugate acid:

    a) $H_2C=CH_2$ b) CH_3CH_2OH c) NH_3 d) HF

Solution:

A conjugate base is formed by removal of proton (H^+) from the molecule. When several hydrogens of different type are present in the molecule, the most acidic hydrogen is removed first (see Table 2.1 of the textbook). Conjugate bases:

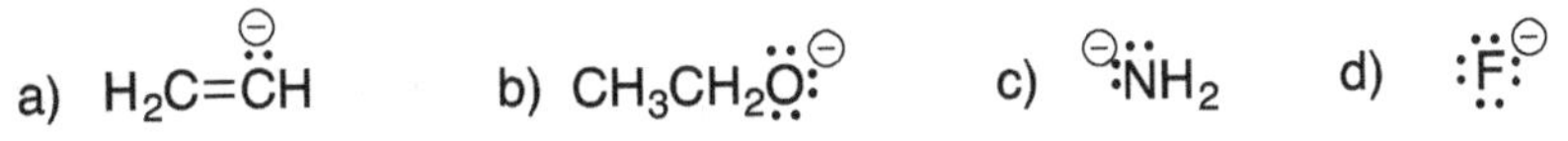

    a) $H_2C=\overset{\ominus}{\ddot{C}}H$ b) $CH_3CH_2\overset{\ominus}{\ddot{\underset{\cdot\cdot}{O}}}$ c) $^{\ominus}\!\ddot{N}H_2$ d) $:\!\overset{\ominus}{\ddot{F}}\!$

Conjugate acids are formed by addition of protons to the molecules:

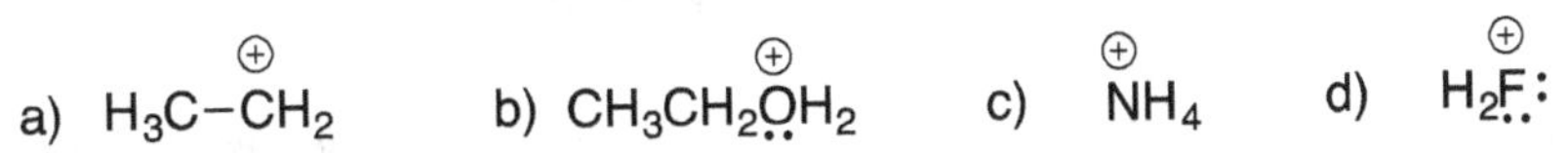

    a) $H_3C-\overset{\oplus}{C}H_2$ b) $CH_3CH_2\overset{\oplus}{\underset{\cdot\cdot}{O}}H_2$ c) $\overset{\oplus}{N}H_4$ d) $H_2\overset{\oplus}{\ddot{F}}\!:$

Problem 2.2. Use Table 2.1 to identify the stronger base within each pair.

    a) $^-\!:\!CH_3$ and $^-\!:\!C\equiv CH$ b) $CH_3CH_2O^-$ and $CH_3CO_2^-$
    c) F^- and I^- d) $^-\!:\!CH_3$ and $^-\!:\!NH_2$

Solution:

Basicity of a molecule is measured by the pK_a value of its conjugate acid. A higher pK_a value of a conjugate acid corresponds to a stronger base.

    a) $^-$:CH$_3$ is a stronger base than $^-$:C≡CH   b) CH$_3$CH$_2$O$^-$ is a stronger base than CH$_3$CO$_2^-$
    c) F$^-$ is a stronger base than I$^-$ d) $^-$:CH$_3$ is a stronger base than $^-$:NH$_2$

Problem 2.3. For each reaction, identify the strongest base, the strongest acid, the weakest acid, and the weakest base; indicate the side of equilibrium.

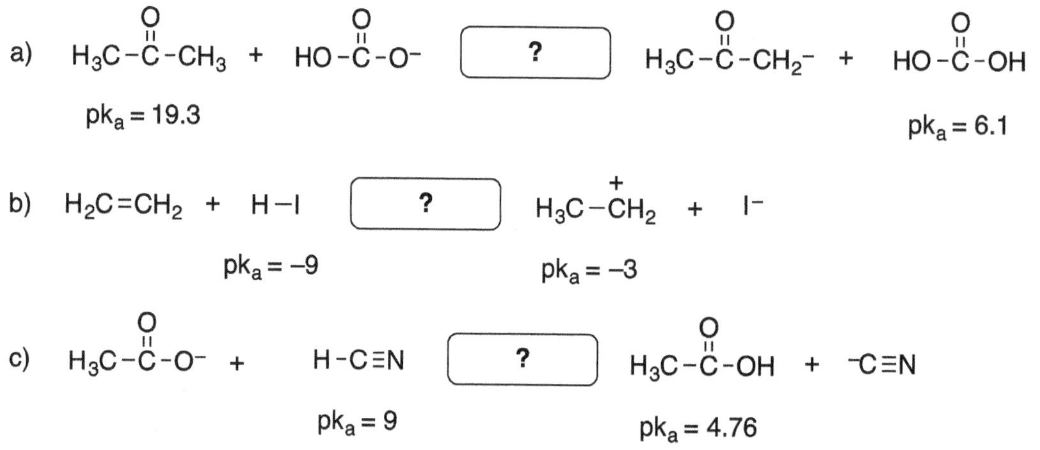

a)   H$_3$C–C(=O)–CH$_3$ + HO–C(=O)–O$^-$ [?]   H$_3$C–C(=O)–CH$_2^-$ + HO–C(=O)–OH

      pk_a = 19.3   pk_a = 6.1

b)   H$_2$C=CH$_2$ + H–I   [?]   H$_3$C–$\overset{+}{C}$H$_2$ + I$^-$

                  pk_a = –9   pk_a = –3

c)   H$_3$C–C(=O)–O$^-$ + H–C≡N   [?]   H$_3$C–C(=O)–OH + $^-$C≡N

                      pk_a = 9   pk_a = 4.76

Solution:

When comparing the relative strength of two acids, the acid with the smaller pK_a value is the stronger acid. The position of equilibrium is always shifted toward the weaker acid.

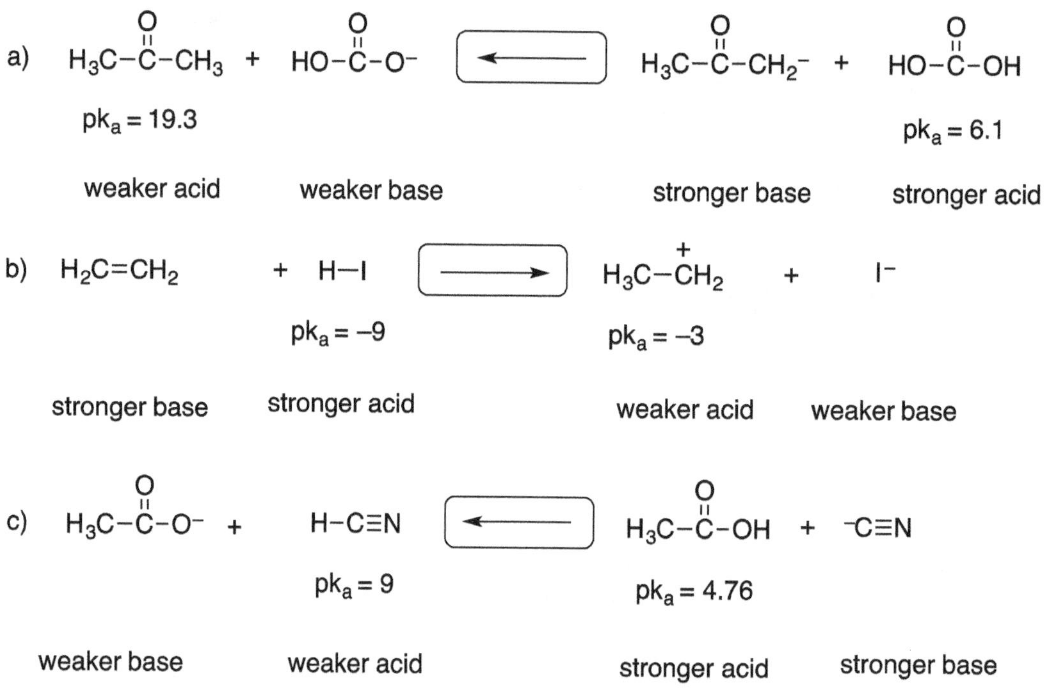

a)   H$_3$C–C(=O)–CH$_3$ + HO–C(=O)–O$^-$ [⟵]   H$_3$C–C(=O)–CH$_2^-$ + HO–C(=O)–OH

      pk_a = 19.3   pk_a = 6.1

      weaker acid   weaker base   stronger base   stronger acid

b)   H$_2$C=CH$_2$ + H–I   [⟶]   H$_3$C–$\overset{+}{C}$H$_2$ +   I$^-$

                  pk_a = –9   pk_a = –3

     stronger base   stronger acid   weaker acid   weaker base

c)   H$_3$C–C(=O)–O$^-$ + H–C≡N   [⟵]   H$_3$C–C(=O)–OH + $^-$C≡N

                      pk_a = 9   pk_a = 4.76

     weaker base   weaker acid   stronger acid   stronger base

Problem 2.4. Sort each set of compounds according to increasing relative acidity (least acidic to most acidic).

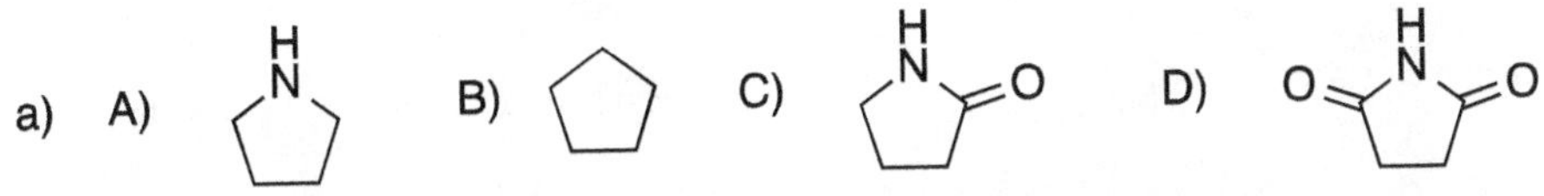

a) A)   B)   C)   D)

b) A) CH_3CH_3 B) $(CH_3)_3COH$ C) CF_3OH D) CH_3OH

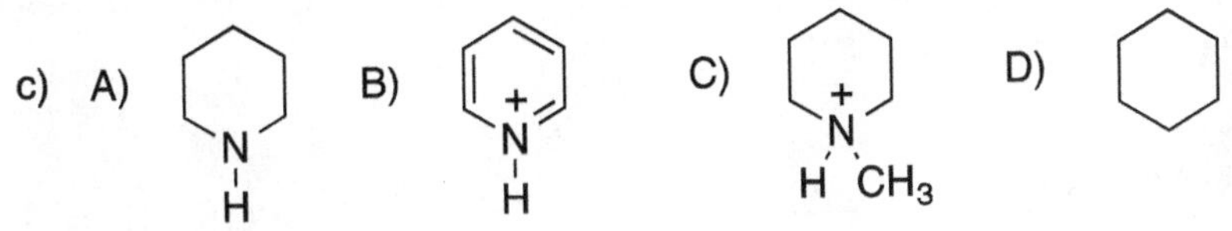

c) A)   B)   C)   D)

Solution:

When evaluating the acidity of a compound H–X, first check the position of the element X in the Periodic Table (see Figure 2.5 in the textbook). At the next step, check any additional factors leading to stabilization of the conjugate base :X⁻. The most important factors are hybridization of element X in compound H–X and resonance delocalization of change in :X⁻. Finally, check if the inductive effect of a remote substituent can additionally influence acidity of compounds H–X derived from the same element X (see Figure 2.6 in the textbook). For example, the explanations for the set of molecules c: Compound D has C–H bonds with the weakest acidity (pK_a about 50). Compound A is an amine with N–H bond (pK_a about 38, close to NH_3) while C is a conjugate acid of amine (pK_a about 10, close to NH_4^+), so C is much more acidic than A. Compound B has sp^2 hybridized nitrogen so it is more acidic than C.

a) B < A < C < D (most acidic)   b) A < B < D < C   c) D < A < C < B

Problem 2.5. Sort the following set of compounds according to increasing relative basicity (least basic to most basic):

A) CH_3S^- B) $CH_3CH_2^-$ C) $(CH_3)_2N^-$ D) CH_3O^-

Solution:

Basicity of a molecule is measured by the acidity of conjugate acid. A higher pK_a value of a conjugate acid corresponds to a stronger base. In order to solve this problem, acidity of the conjugate acids $CH_3S–H$, $CH_3CH_2–H$, $(CH_3)_2N–H$, and $CH_3O–H$ should be evaluated based on the element's position in the Periodic Table (see Figure 2.5 in the textbook).

A < D < C < B (strongest base)

Problem 2.6. All acid–base reactions proceed as written. For each reaction indicate the strongest base, the strongest acid, the weakest base, and the weakest acid. Use curved arrows to indicate the flow of electrons.

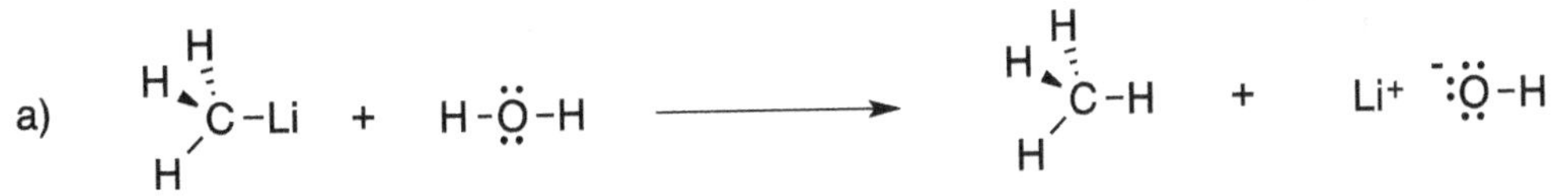

a)

b)

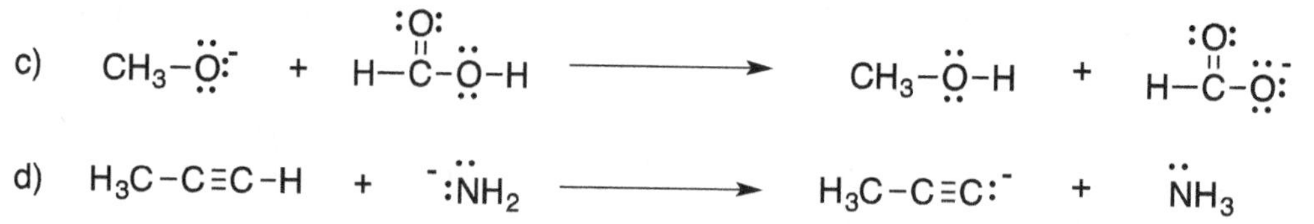

c) $CH_3-\overset{\cdot\cdot}{\underset{\cdot\cdot}{O}}:^-$ + $H-\overset{:O:}{\overset{\|}{C}}-\overset{\cdot\cdot}{\underset{\cdot\cdot}{O}}-H$ $\longrightarrow$ $CH_3-\overset{\cdot\cdot}{\underset{\cdot\cdot}{O}}-H$ + $H-\overset{:O:}{\overset{\|}{C}}-\overset{\cdot\cdot}{\underset{\cdot\cdot}{O}}:^-$

d) $H_3C-C\equiv C-H$ + $^-:\overset{\cdot\cdot}{N}H_2$ $\longrightarrow$ $H_3C-C\equiv C:^-$ + $\overset{\cdot\cdot}{N}H_3$

Solution:

Acid–base reactions always proceed from the stronger acid to the weaker acid. The stronger base corresponds to a conjugate acid with weaker acidity.

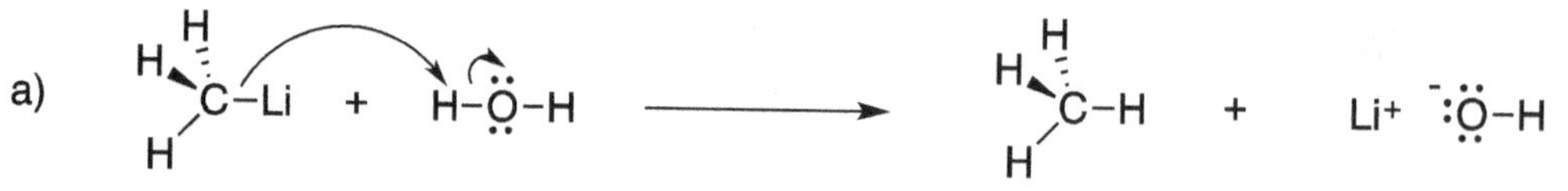

a)

stronger base · · · · stronger acid · · · · · · · · · · · · weaker acid · · · · · · weaker base

b)

stronger base · · · · stronger acid · · · · · · · · · · · · weaker acid · · · · · · weaker base

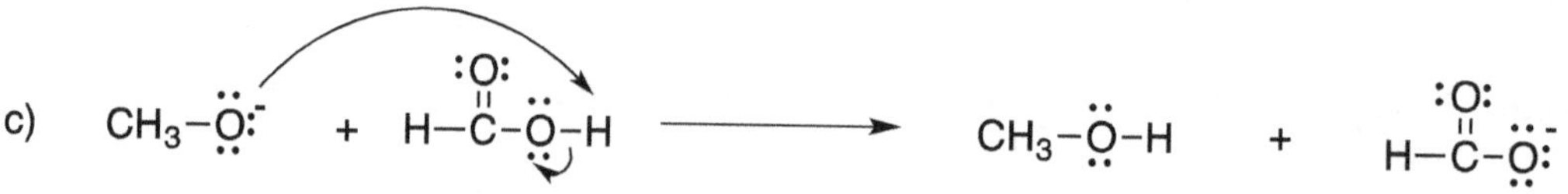

c)

stronger base · · · · stronger acid · · · · · · · · · · · · weaker acid · · · · · · weaker base

d) $H_3C-C\equiv C-H$ + $^-:\overset{\cdot\cdot}{N}H_2$ $\longrightarrow$ $H_3C-C\equiv C:^-$ + $\overset{\cdot\cdot}{N}H_3$

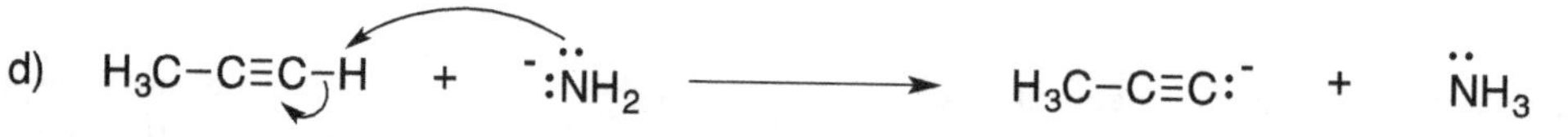

stronger acid · · · · stronger base · · · · · · · · · · · · weaker base · · · · · · weaker acid

Problem 2.7. For each compound, indicate the most acidic proton or group of protons.

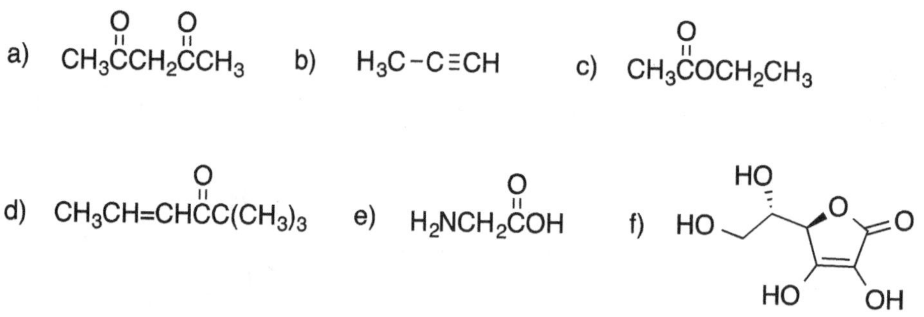

a) $CH_3\overset{O}{\overset{\|}{C}}CH_2\overset{O}{\overset{\|}{C}}CH_3$ b) $H_3C-C\equiv CH$ c) $CH_3\overset{O}{\overset{\|}{C}}OCH_2CH_3$

d) $CH_3CH=CH\overset{O}{\overset{\|}{C}}C(CH_3)_3$ e) $H_2NCH_2\overset{O}{\overset{\|}{C}}OH$ f)

Solution:

The most acidic protons are highlighted in boldface. In order to answer questions a–d and f, resonance stabilization of all possible conjugate bases should be compared.

a) $CH_3\overset{O}{\underset{}{C}}CH_2\overset{O}{\underset{}{C}}CH_3$

b) $H_3C-C\equiv CH$

c) $CH_3\overset{O}{\underset{}{C}}OCH_2CH_3$

d) $CH_3CH=CH\overset{O}{\underset{}{C}}C(CH_3)_3$

e) $H_2NCH_2\overset{O}{\underset{}{C}}OH$

f)

Problem 2.8. Indicate the most basic site in each of the following molecules:

a) $H_2\overset{..}{N}-CH_2CH_2-\overset{..}{\underset{..}{O}}-H$

b)

c)

d)

Solution:

The most basic sites are highlighted in boldface. In order to answer questions b and d, resonance stabilization of all possible conjugate acids should be compared.

a) $H_2\mathbf{\overset{..}{N}}-CH_2CH_2-\overset{..}{\underset{..}{O}}-H$

b)

c)

d)

2.2. Additional Problems for Chapter 2 (for answers see Ch 17)

Problem 2.9. For each pair, identify the first species as an acid or base and the second species as its conjugate acid or conjugate base.

a) CH_3S^- and CH_3SH b) $H_2PO_4^-$ and HPO_4^{2-}

Problem 2.10. For the following reaction, label each reactant and each product as acid, base, conjugate acid, or conjugate base below each structure.

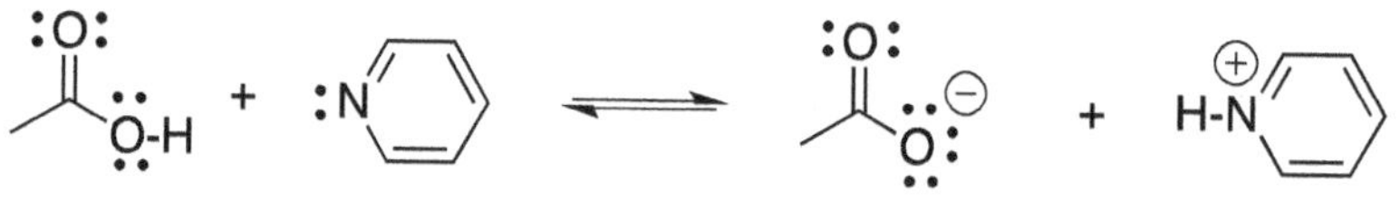

Problem 2.11. Provide the reaction of CH_3CH_2OH as a Bronsted–Lowry base with H-Cl using the curved arrow formalism.

Problem 2.12. Select the strongest acid in each set:

a) CH_3CH_3 CH_3NH_2 CH_3OH
b) CH_3CH_3 $CH_2=CH_2$ $HC\equiv CH$
c) CH_3CH_2OH CF_3CH_2OH FCH_2CH_2OH

Problem 2.13. Provide structures of the two possible cationic intermediates in the following reactions:

a)

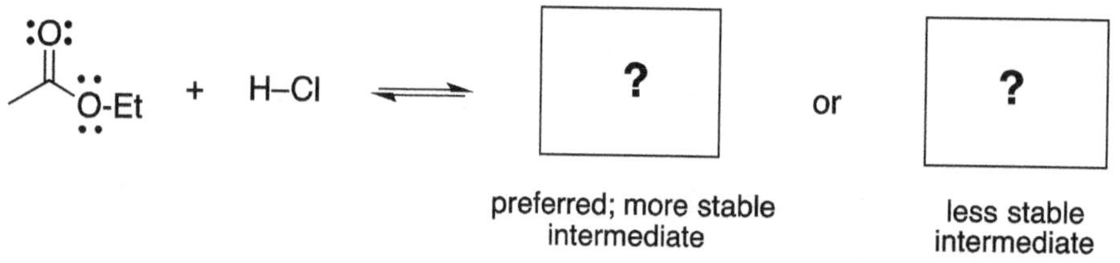

preferred; more stable intermediate	less stable intermediate

b)

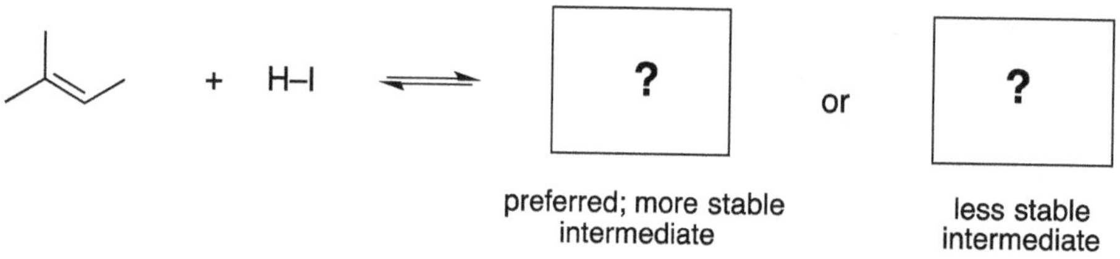

preferred; more stable intermediate	less stable intermediate

Problem 2.14. Given pK_a (acetylene) = 25 and pK_a (H_2) = 35, predict whether the direction and position of equilibrium in the following reaction will lie to the right (favors the forward reaction) or to the left (favors the backward reaction).

$$HC\equiv CH \quad + \quad Na^+H^- \quad \rightleftharpoons \quad HC\equiv C^-Na^+ \quad + \quad H_2$$

acetylene

Alkanes and Cycloalkanes

3.1. Chapter 3 Problems and Solutions

Problem 3.1. Write condensed and line structures for isomeric hexanes and heptanes. Identify types of carbon and hydrogen atoms in each molecule.

Solution:

Isomeric hexanes (C_6H_{14}):

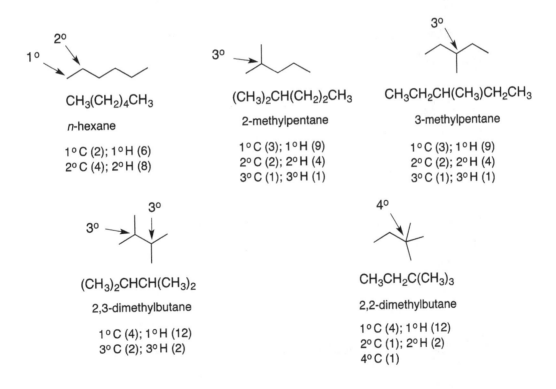

$CH_3(CH_2)_4CH_3$

n-hexane

1° C (2); 1° H (6)
2° C (4); 2° H (8)

$(CH_3)_2CH(CH_2)_2CH_3$

2-methylpentane

1° C (3); 1° H (9)
2° C (2); 2° H (4)
3° C (1); 3° H (1)

$CH_3CH_2CH(CH_3)CH_2CH_3$

3-methylpentane

1° C (3); 1° H (9)
2° C (2); 2° H (4)
3° C (1); 3° H (1)

$(CH_3)_2CHCH(CH_3)_2$

2,3-dimethylbutane

1° C (4); 1° H (12)
3° C (2); 3° H (2)

$CH_3CH_2C(CH_3)_3$

2,2-dimethylbutane

1° C (4); 1° H (12)
2° C (1); 2° H (2)
4° C (1)

19

Isomeric heptanes (C_7H_{16}):

$CH_3(CH_2)_5CH_3$

n-heptane

1° C (2); 1° H (6)
2° C (5); 2° H (10)

$(CH_3)_2CH(CH_2)_3CH_3$

2-methylhexane

1° C (3); 1° H (9)
2° C (3); 2° H (6)
3° C (1); 3° H (1)

$CH_3CH_2CH(CH_3)CH_2CH_2CH_3$

3-methylhexane

1° C (3); 1° H (9)
2° C (3); 2° H (6)
3° C (1); 3° H (1)

$(CH_3)_2CHCH(CH_3)CH_2CH_3$

2,3-dimethylpentane

1° C (4); 1° H (12)
2° C (1); 2° H (2)
3° C (2); 3° H (2)

$(CH_3)_2CHCH_2CH(CH_3)_2$

2,4-dimethylpentane

1° C (4); 1° H (12)
2° C (1); 2° H (2)
3° C (2); 3° H (2)

$CH_3CH_2C(CH_3)_3$

2,2-dimethylpentane

1° C (4); 1° H (12)
2° C (2); 2° H (4)
4° C (1)

$CH_3CH_2CH(CH_2CH_3)CH_2CH_3$

3-ethylpentane

1° C (3); 1° H (9)
2° C (3); 2° H (6)
3° C (1); 3° H (1)

$CH_3CH_2C(CH_3)_2CH_2CH_3$

3,3-dimethylpentane

1° C (4); 1° H (12)
2° C (2); 2° H (4)
4° C (1)

$(CH_3)_2CHC(CH_3)_3$

2,2,3-trimethylbutane

1° C (5); 1° H (15)
3° C (1); 3° H (1)
4° C (1)

Problem 3.2. A molecule of isooctane has five primary, one secondary, one tertiary, and one quaternary carbon atom. Draw the line structure of isooctane.

Solution:

Two structures can satisfy this requirement; 2,2,4-trimethylpentane is known as isooctane.

$(CH_3)_2CHCH_2C(CH_3)_3$

isooctane
(2,2,4-trimethylpentane)

$(CH_3)_2CHC(CH_3)_2CH_2CH_3$

2,3,3-trimethylpentane
(also has five 1°, one 2°, one 3°, and one 4° carbon)

Problem 3.3. Provide the IUPAC name for each of the following compounds:

a)

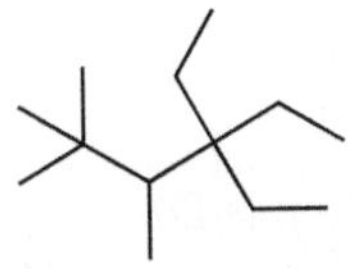

b) $(CH_3)_2CH(CH_2)_3CH_3$

c)

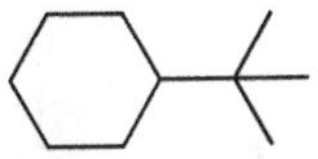

Solution:

a)

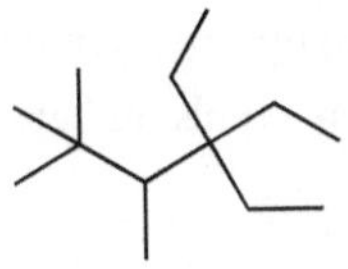

4,4-diethyl-2,2,3-trimethylhexane

b) $(CH_3)_2CH(CH_2)_3CH_3$

2-methylhexane

c)

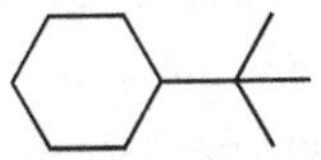

tert-butylcyclohexane

Problem 3.4. Convert the Newman projections into a line–angle structure and provide the IUPAC name of each compound:

a)

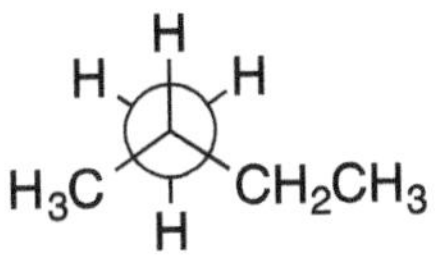

b)

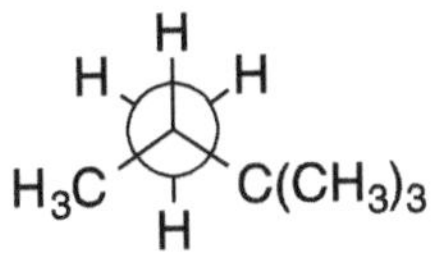

c)

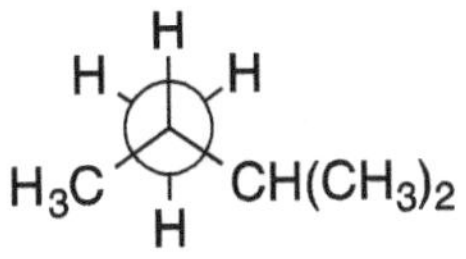

Solution:

a) 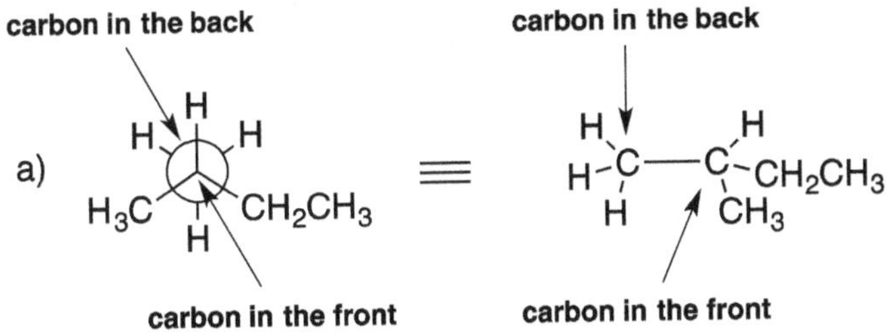 carbon in the back

carbon in the front

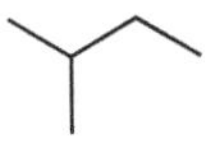

2-methylbutane

b)

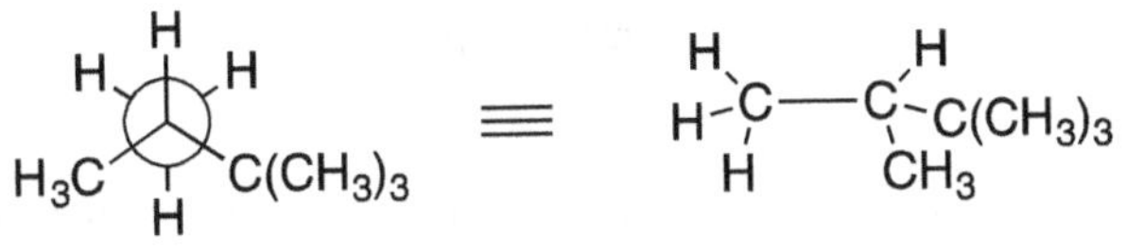

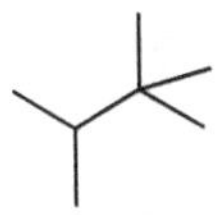

2,2,3-trimethylbutane

c)

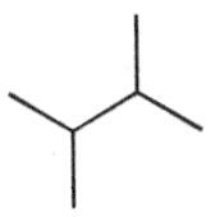

2,3-dimethylbutane

Problem 3.5. Which of the following Newman projections depicts the least stable conformer of 1-bromo-2-methyl-propane?

A)   B)   C)   D)

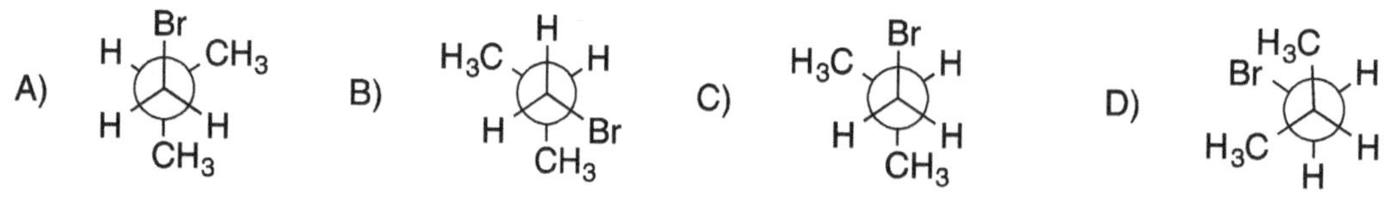

Solution:

Newman projection D corresponds to the least stable conformer of 1-bromo-2-methyl-propane. In this conformation, all three substituents (Br and two CH_3) are in close proximity to each other and the repulsion between these bulky groups results in increased steric strain.

Problem 3.6. Draw chair representations of each of the following compounds. Which compound contains a quaternary (4°) carbon atom?

a) cyclohexane

b) methylcyclohexane

c) 1, 1-dimethylcyclohexane

d) *trans*-1, 3-dimethyl cyclohexane

Solution:

a)

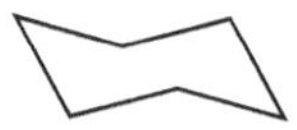

cyclohexane

b)

methylcyclohexane

4° carbon

c)

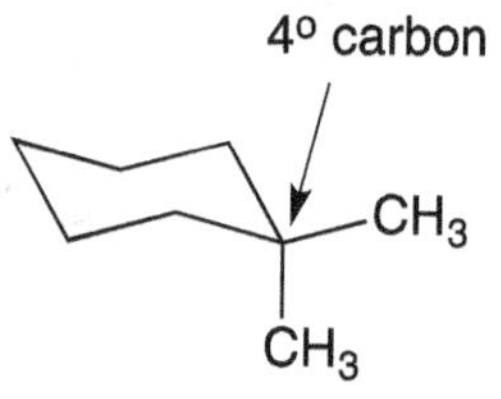

1,1-dimethylcyclohexane

d)

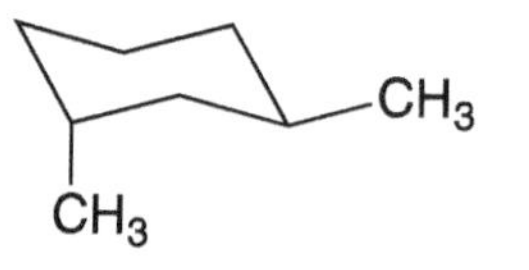

1,3-dimethylcyclohexane

Problem 3.7. Sort the following structures by increasing stability (least stable to most stable):

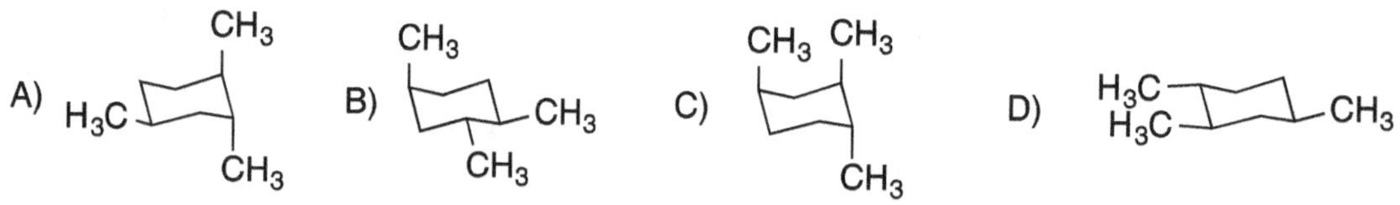

A)   B)   C)   D)

Solution:
The chair conformation with all methyl groups in axial positions has the lowest stability because of significant diaxial interactions. Increasing number of methyl groups in equatorial positions leads to increased stability of the structure.

C)	A)	B)	D)
least stable structure (three methyl groups in axial position)	(two methyl groups in axial position)	(one methyl group in axial position)	**most stable structure** (all methyl groups are in equatorial position)

C) < A) < B) < D)

Problem 3.8. Consider the following pairs of structures and determine if they are in all respects identical, *cis/trans* isomers, conformational isomers, or constitutional isomers.

a)

b)

c)

d)

e)

f)

Solution:

a)   **identical**

cis-1,4-dichlorocyclohexane   *cis*-1,4-dichlorocyclohexane

b)   **conformers**

trans-1,4-difluorocyclohexane   *trans*-1,4-difluorocyclohexane

c) **constitutional isomers**

trans-1,4-diiodocyclohexane

                               cis-1,3-diiodocyclohexane

d) 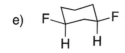 **conformers**

cis-1,3-difluorocyclohexane

                               cis-1,3-difluorocyclohexane

e) **cis/trans isomers**

cis-1,3-difluorocyclohexane

                               trans-1,3-difluorocyclohexane

f) **cis/trans isomers**

trans-1,4-dichlorocyclohexane

                               cis-1,4-dichlorocyclohexane

Problem 3.9. Sort the following set of radicals according to increasing relative stability:

A) 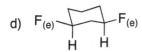   B)   C)

Solution:

A)   <   C)   <   B)

least stable
(1° radical)

                                                     most stable
                                                    (3° radical)

Problem 3.10. Provide major products in each of the radical reactions below. Propose a mechanism for each reaction.

a) 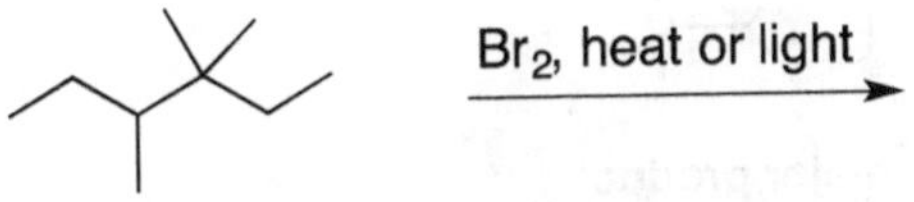   Br$_2$, heat or light

b)    Cl$_2$, light

Solution:

a) 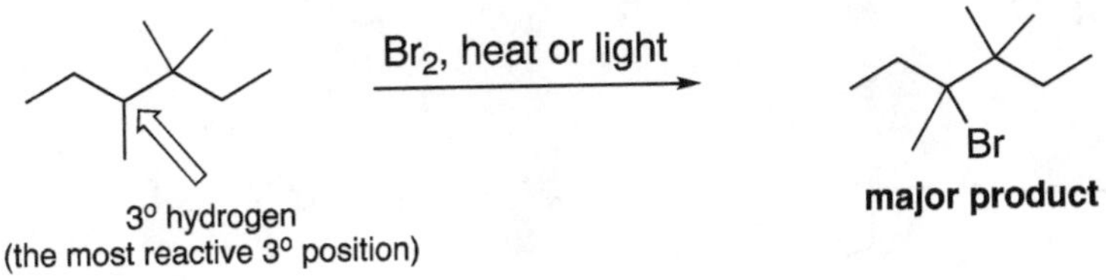   Br$_2$, heat or light

3° hydrogen
(the most reactive 3° position)

major product

Initiation: Br—Br $\xrightarrow{\text{heat or light}}$ Br• + •Br

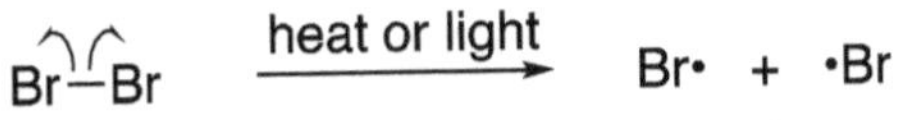

Chain Propagation:

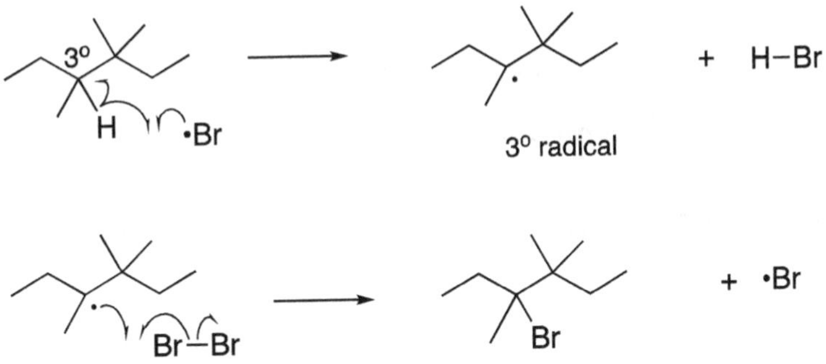

3°   H   •Br   →   + H—Br

3° radical

Br—Br   →   + •Br

Br

Chain Termination: R• •R   ⟶   R—R

(recombination of any two radicals participating in chain propagation)

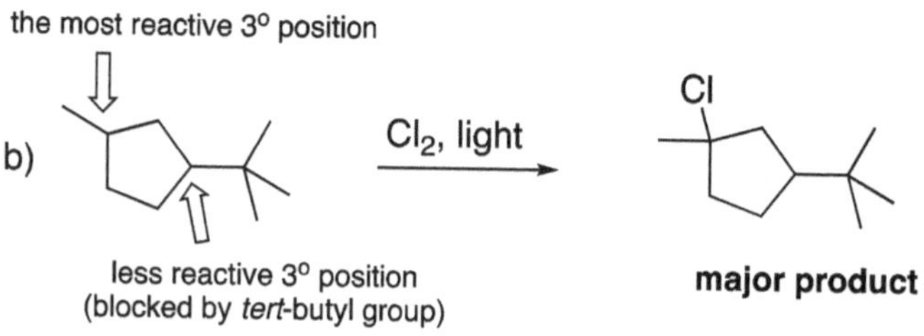

the most reactive 3° position

b)

Cl$_2$, light

major product

less reactive 3° position
(blocked by *tert*-butyl group)

Initiation:

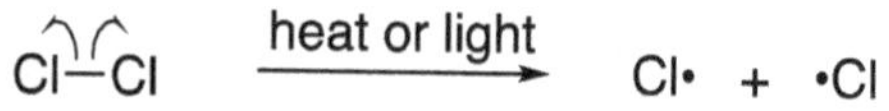

Cl—Cl $\xrightarrow{\text{heat or light}}$ Cl• + •Cl

Chain Propagation:

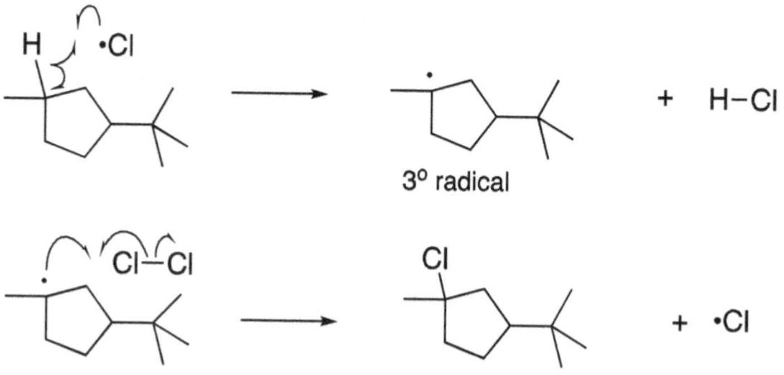

H •Cl

$\longrightarrow$

3° radical

+ H—Cl

Cl—Cl

$\longrightarrow$

Cl

+ •Cl

Chain Termination: R• •R $\longrightarrow$ R—R

(recombination of any two radicals participating in chain propagation)

3.2. Additional Problems for Chapter 3 (for answers see Ch 17)

Problem 3.11. Provide the IUPAC name for each structure below.

a)

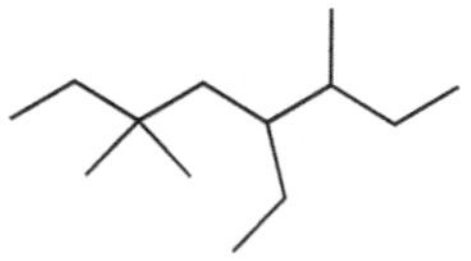

b)

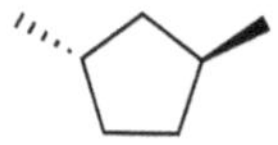

Problem 3.12. a) Draw the alternative chair conformation of bromocyclohexane (after the ring-flip).

ring-flip

?

A   B

b) Label Br as axial (a) or equatorial (e) in structures A and B. Which conformation is lower in energy?

Problem 3.13. Draw Newman projections for all staggered and eclipsed conformations of 1-chloropropane [Cl-CH$_2$-CH$_2$-CH$_3$] formed by rotation of groups about C1–C2 from 0° to 360° as indicated. Label each conformation A–E as anti, gauche, or eclipsed.

$\xrightarrow[\text{rotation}]{60°}$ A $\xrightarrow[\text{rotation}]{60°}$ B $\xrightarrow[\text{rotation}]{60°}$ C $\xrightarrow[\text{rotation}]{60°}$ D $\xrightarrow[\text{rotation}]{60°}$ E

360° rotation

Problem 3.14. Draw (a) planar conformation and (b) nonplanar (chair) conformation of *trans*-1,4-dimethylcyclohexane.

Problem 3.15. Draw the most stable chair conformation corresponding to the following planar structure:

Problem 3.16. Identify the substituents in the chair conformations of *trans*-1,3-dimethylcyclohexane as axial or equatorial.

Problem 3.17. Which chair conformation of *cis*- or *trans*-1,3-dimethylcyclohexanes is more stable? Explain briefly.

Stereochemistry

4.1. Chapter 4 Problems and Solutions

Problem 4.1. Determine if the following compounds are chiral or achiral:

A)

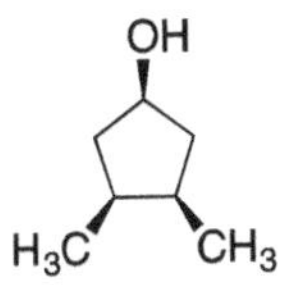

B)

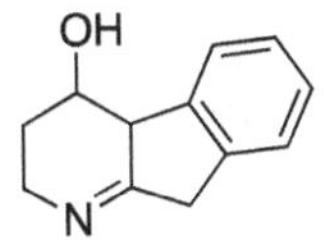

C)

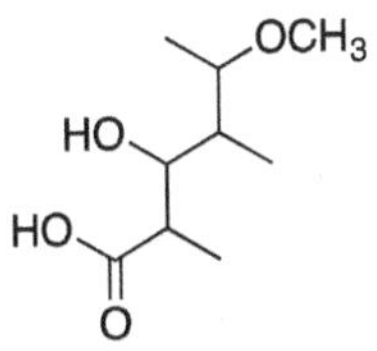

D)

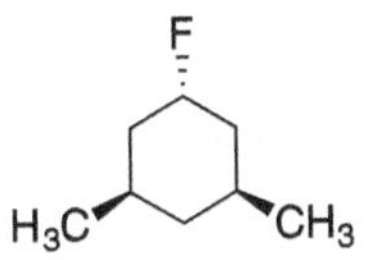

Solution:

All achiral objects are characterized by the presence of a plane of symmetry cutting the object in two halves that are related to each other as mirror images.

A) 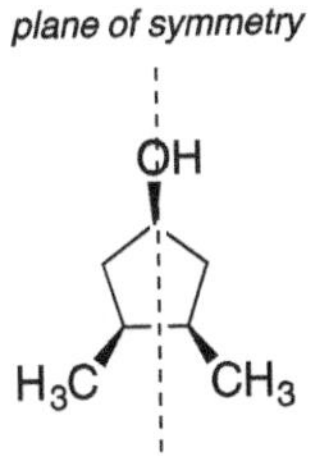 *plane of symmetry*

achiral

B)

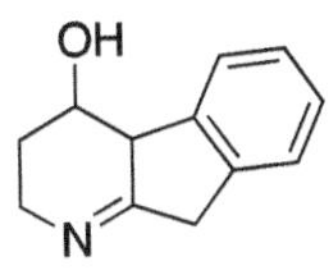

chiral

C)

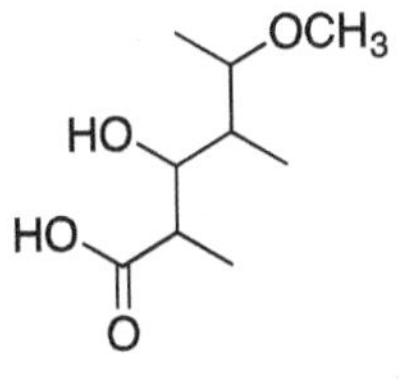

chiral

D) 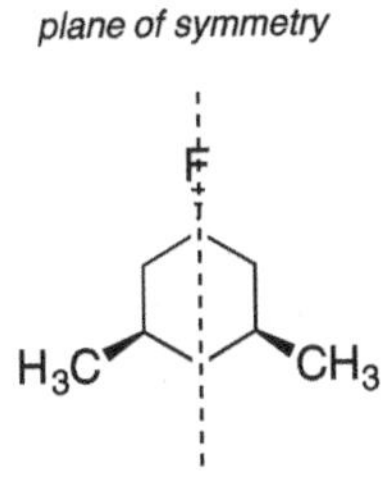 *plane of symmetry*

achiral

29

Problem 4.2. How many chiral centers do each of these compounds have?

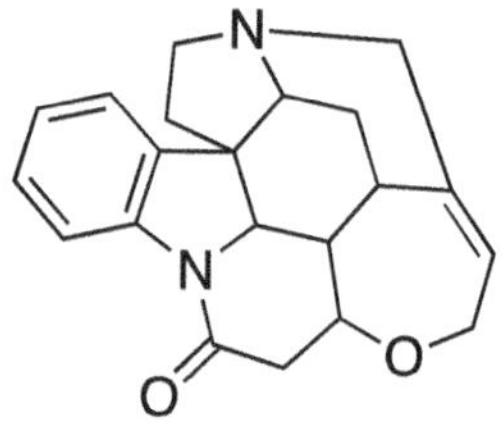

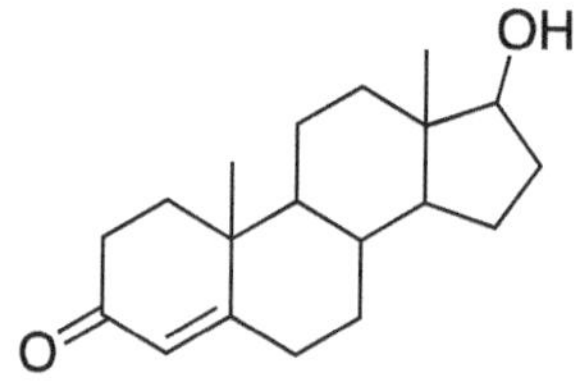

Solution:

A chiral center is a tetrahedral carbon atom with four different substituents. Chiral carbon atoms are marked in the structures below with asterisks:

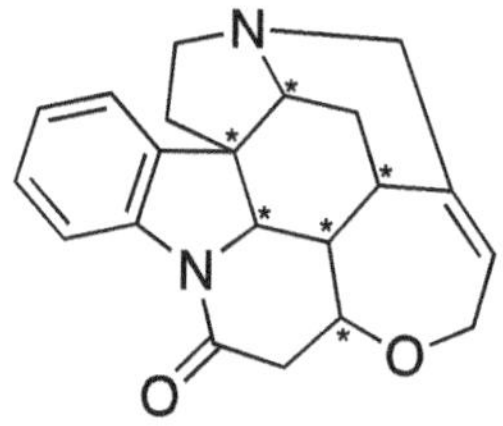

6 chiral centers 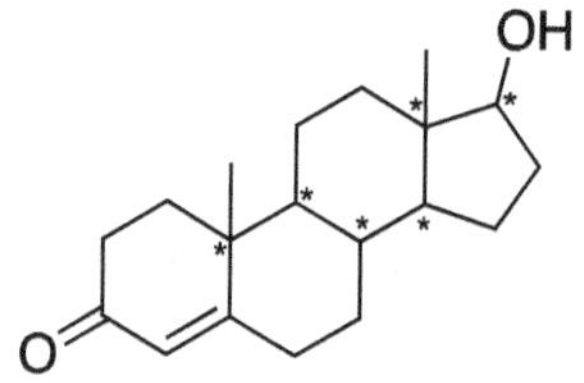   6 chiral centers

Problem 4.3. Assign priorities to the following sets of substituents:

a) –H, -CH(CH₃)₂, -B(OCH₃)₂, -CH₂CH₂OCH₃
b) –CO₂H, -CH₂SH, -CH=CH₂, -OH
c) –CN, -CH₂NH₂, -CONH₂, -CON(CH₃)₂
d) –Br, -CH₂CH₂Br, -C(CH₃)₃, -CH₂Cl

Solution:

The priority numbers are shown under each substituent (see Section 4.2 for priority rules):

a) –H, -CH(CH₃)₂, -B(OCH₃)₂, -CH₂CH₂OCH₃
   4   1   3   2
b) –CO₂H, -CH₂SH, -CH=CH₂, -OH
   3   2   4   1
c) –CN, -CH₂NH₂, -CONH₂, -CON(CH₃)₂
   3   4   2   1
d) –Br, -CH₂CH₂Br, -C(CH₃)₃, -CH₂Cl
   1   4   3   2

Problem 4.4. Consider each of the following orders of priority (highest to lowest within each order). Which order is incorrect?

I) -OH > -CH$_2$OH > -CH$_3$ > -H

II) -CH=CH$_2$ > -CH$_2$COOH > -CH$_2$CH=CH$_2$ > -CH$_3$

III) -NH$_3$$^+$ > -COO$^-$ > -CH$_3$ > -H

IV) -NH$_3$$^+$ > -CHO > -CH$_2$SH > -CH$_3$

Solution:

Order IV is incorrect (-CHO and CH$_2$SH should be switched.)

Problem 4.5. In each of the following compounds, assign the R/S configurations to each chiral center. Which are enantiomers, which are diastereomers?

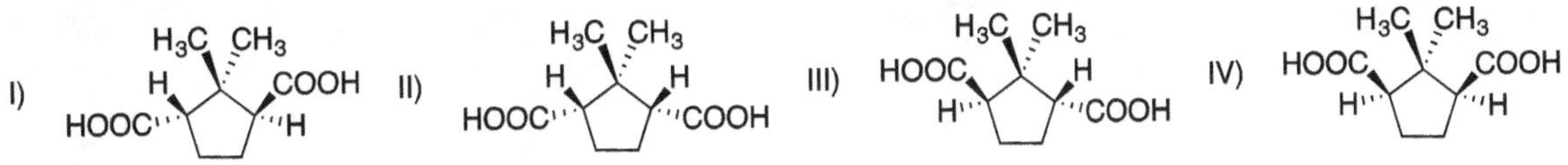

Solution:

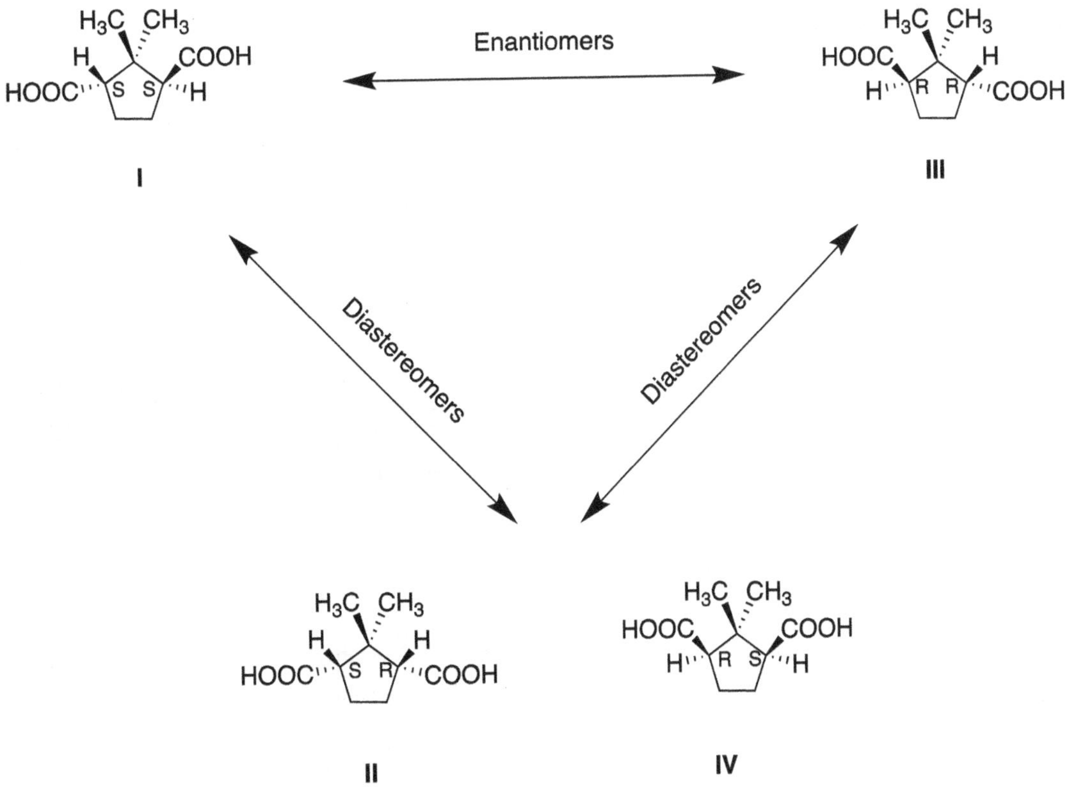

Due to the plane of symmetry, structures **II** and **IV** depict the same stereoisomer. This is an example for a meso compound.

Problem 4.6. In which of the following structures are both chiral centers in R configuration?

I)

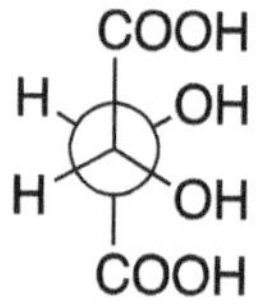

H—C—OH (COOH top, with OH and OH, COOH bottom)
H—C—OH

II) 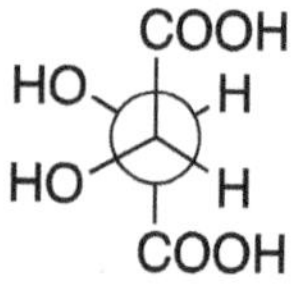
HO—C—H (COOH top)
HO—C—H (COOH bottom)

III) 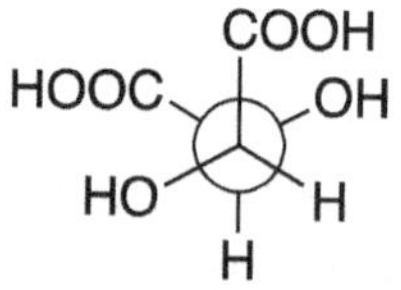
HOOC—C—OH (COOH top)
HO—C—H (H bottom)

IV) 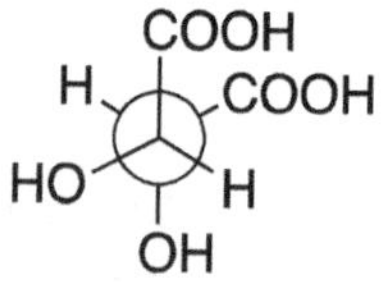
H—C—COOH (COOH top)
HO—C—H (OH bottom)

Solution:

In order to solve this problem, the Newman projections should be converted to Fischer projections shown below:

I)
```
      COOH
   H——|——OH
  HO——|——H
      COOH
```

II)
```
      COOH
  HO——|——H
   H——|——OH
      COOH
```

III)
```
      COOH
  HO——|——H
  HO——|——H
      COOH
```

IV)
```
      COOH
  HO——|——H
   H——|——OH
      COOH
```

I) 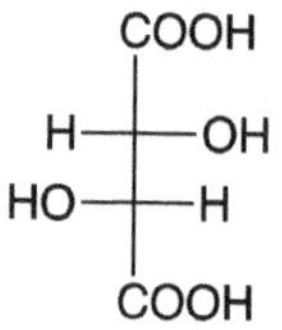 RR   II) 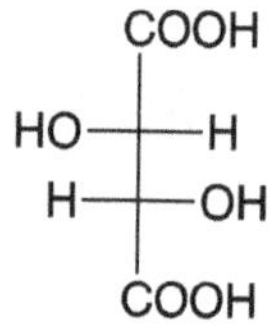 SS   III) 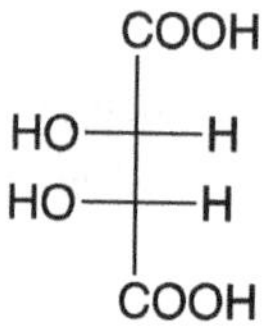 SR   IV) 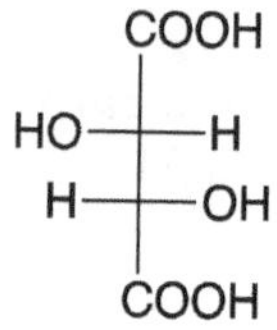 SS

Problem 4.7. Determine the configuration (R or S) at carbon atoms 2 and 3 in each compound.

a) 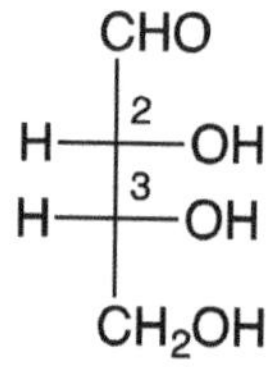
```
      CHO
   H——|2——OH
   H——|3——OH
      CH2OH
```

b) 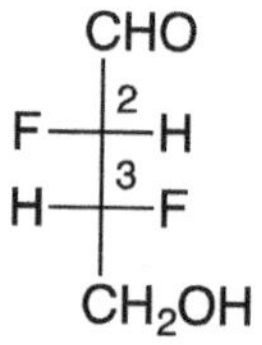
```
      CHO
   F——|2——H
   H——|3——F
      CH2OH
```

c) 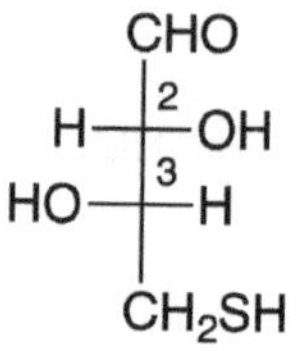
```
      CHO
   H——|2——OH
  HO——|3——H
      CH2SH
```

Solution:

a) 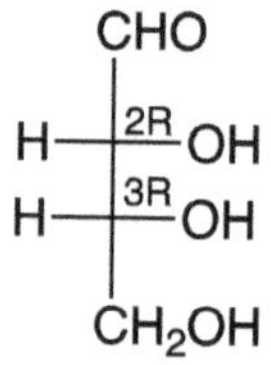
```
      CHO
   H——|2R—OH
   H——|3R—OH
      CH2OH
```

b) 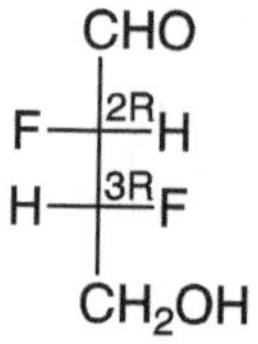
```
      CHO
   F——|2R—H
   H——|3R—F
      CH2OH
```

c) 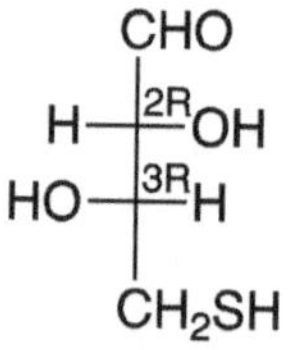
```
      CHO
   H——|2R—OH
  HO——|3R—H
      CH2SH
```

Problem 4.8. Which of the following are meso compounds?

I) *cis*-1,3-dimethylcyclohexane   II) (1R,2R)-1,2-dimethylcylcohexane
III) (3R,4S)-3,4-dimethylhexane   IV) *cis*-1,4-dimethylcyclohexane

Solution:

IUPAC definition of a meso compound: "A term for the achiral member(s) of a set of diastereoisomers which also includes one or more chiral members." In other words, it is an achiral molecule which has two or more chiral centers.

cis-1,3-dimethylcyclohexane

(achiral and a meso compound)

(1*R*,2*R*)-1,2-dimethylcyclohexane

(chiral)

(3*R*,4*S*)-3,4-dimethylhexane

(achiral and a meso compound)

cis-1,4-dimethylcyclohexane

(achiral but NOT a meso compound)

this molecule does not have chiral carbons
(in other words, it is impossible to assign
R or S configuration to carbons 1 and 4)

4.2. Additional Problems for Chapter 4 (for answers see Ch 17)

Problem 4.9. How many stereoisomers are possible for the following molecule?

Problem 4.10. Which of the following compounds is/are chiral?

Problem 4.11. Fill in appropriate groups in the templates so that each structure represents the specified stereoisomer:

a) (S)-2-butanol

b) (R)-2-bromobutane

Problem 4.12. Which of the following structures represent the same stereoisomer?

Problem 4.13. Identify the relationship between the following pairs of structures as enantiomers, diastereomers, constitutional isomers, or identical molecules.

a)

and

b)

and

Problem 4.14. Chiral molecules interact with plane polarized light and rotate the plane of polarization of that light by a certain angle. The angle of rotation (α) of polarized light can be measured with a polarimeter. However, specific rotation ($[\alpha]$) is used as a basis for comparing the optical activity of stereoisomers. **Specific rotation** is defined as the observed rotation of the plane of polarized light for a sample in a tube 1 dm in length and the concentration of the solution of 1 g/100 mL.

$$\text{Specific Rotation}[\alpha] = \frac{\text{Observed Rotation in degrees}, \alpha}{[\text{Sample Length in dm}] \bullet [\text{Concentration of solution in g/ml}]}$$

A solution containing 0.2 g/mL of a pure R enantiomer in a 1 dm polarimeter rotates plane polarized light by +3°. What is the specific rotation of the R isomer?
What will be the specific rotation of its S isomer?

Nucleophilic Substitution and β-Elimination Reactions

5.1. Chapter 5 Problems and Solutions

Problem 5.1. Draw the products of nucleophilic substitution in the reactions below. Identify the substrate, leaving group, and nucleophile, and use curved arrows to show the movement of electrons in each reaction.

a)  [structure with Br] →(NaSH / ethanol)

b) CH_3CH_2I + Ph_3P →(pentane)

c) 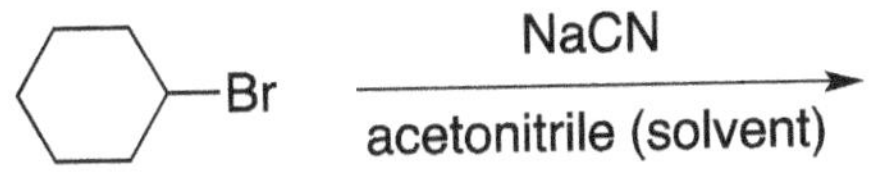 [cyclohexyl]—Br →(NaCN / acetonitrile (solvent))

Solution:

a) 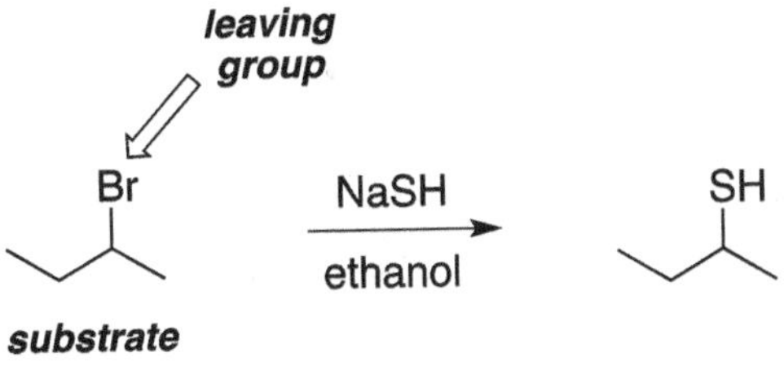 [structure] →(NaSH / ethanol) [product SH]
leaving group / substrate

[mechanism structures] :SH + Br⁻
nucleophile

35

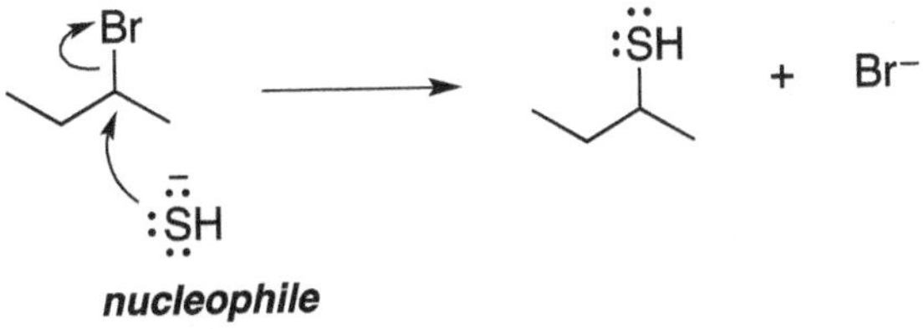

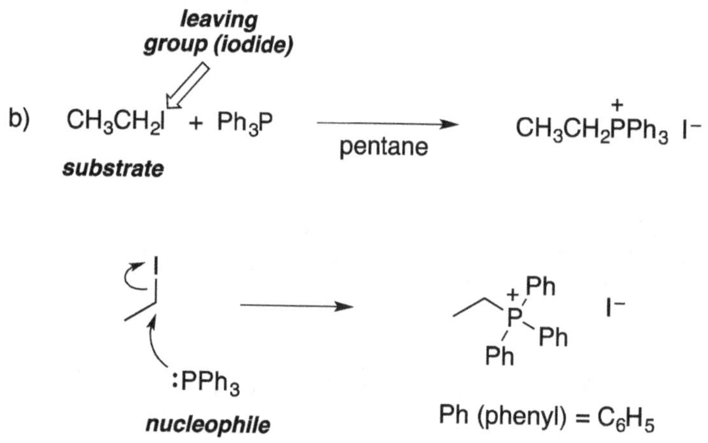

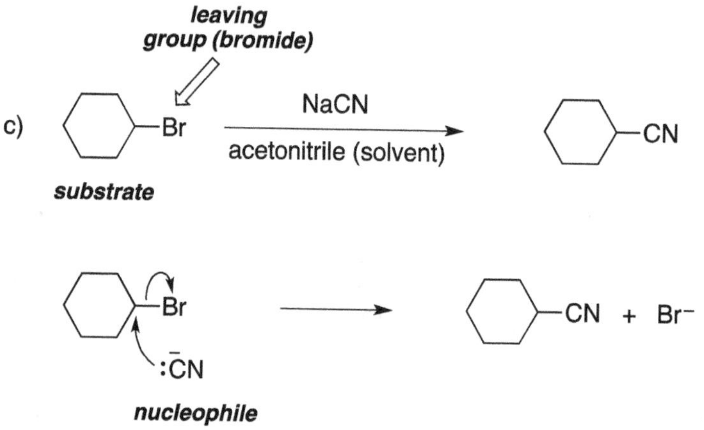

b)   CH₃CH₂I + Ph₃P $\xrightarrow{\text{pentane}}$ CH₃CH₂P⁺Ph₃ I⁻

leaving group (iodide)

substrate

:PPh₃
nucleophile

Ph (phenyl) = C₆H₅

leaving group (bromide)

c) —Br $\xrightarrow[\text{acetonitrile (solvent)}]{\text{NaCN}}$ —CN

substrate

—Br ⟶ —CN + Br⁻

:C̄N
nucleophile

Problem 5.2. Draw the products of elimination in the reactions below. Identify the substrate, leaving group, and base, and use curved arrows to show the movement of electrons in each reaction.

a) —Cl $\xrightarrow[\text{EtOH}]{\text{EtONa}}$ b) Br $\xrightarrow[\text{t-BuOH}]{\text{t-BuOK}}$

Solution:

leaving group (chloride)

a) —Cl $\xrightarrow[\text{EtOH}]{\text{EtONa}}$

substrate

⟶ + HOCH₂CH₃ + Cl⁻

α —Cl
β
H
—OCH₂CH₃
base

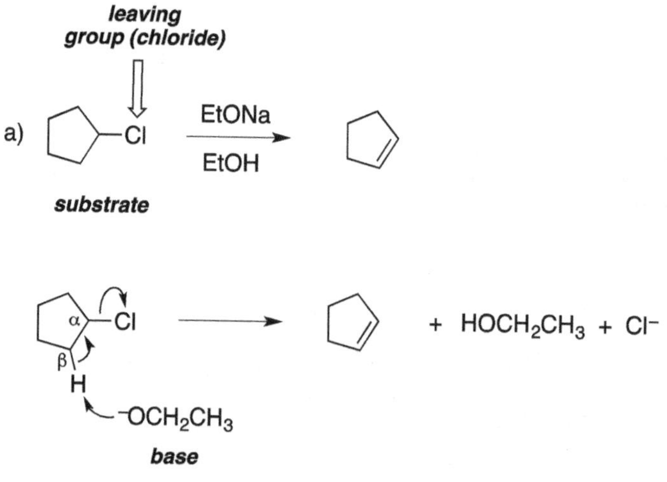

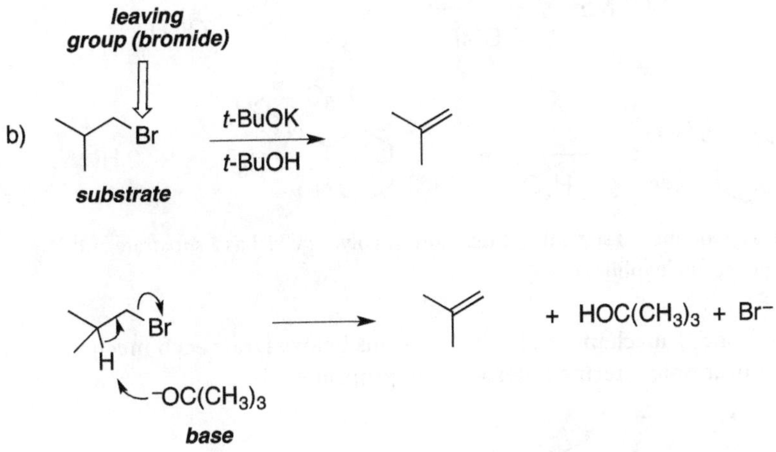

b)

leaving
group (bromide)

$$\Downarrow$$

$\overset{\displaystyle}{\underset{\text{substrate}}{\diagdown}}$Br $\xrightarrow[\text{$t$-BuOH}]{\text{$t$-BuOK}}$ $\diagup\!\!\!=$

+ HOC(CH₃)₃ + Br⁻

base

Problem 5.3. Provide the products of the following reactions:

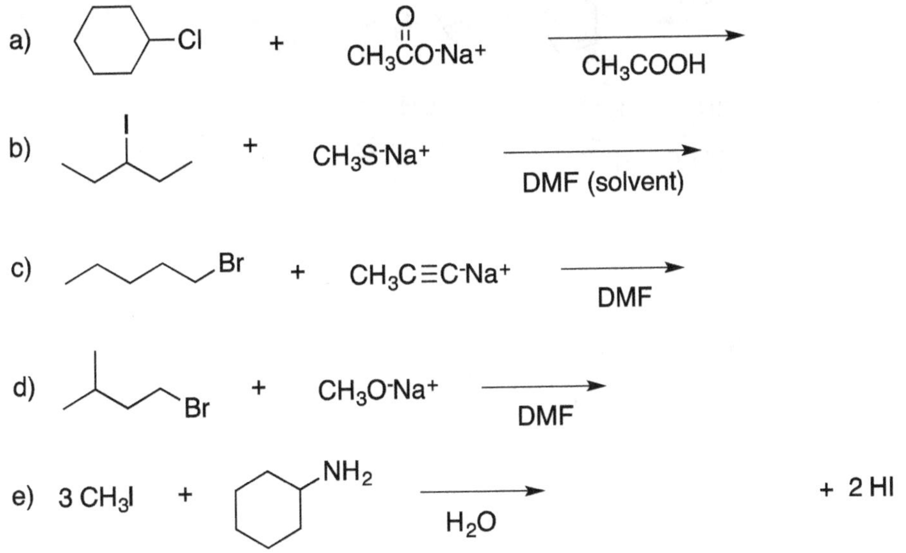

a) ⬡—Cl + $\underset{\displaystyle CH_3\overset{\textstyle O}{\overset{\|}{C}}O^-Na^+}{}$ $\xrightarrow{\text{CH}_3\text{COOH}}$

b) (sec-pentyl iodide) + CH₃S⁻Na⁺ $\xrightarrow{\text{DMF (solvent)}}$

c) ⁀⁀⁀Br + CH₃C≡C⁻Na⁺ $\xrightarrow{\text{DMF}}$

d) ⤳Br + CH₃O⁻Na⁺ $\xrightarrow{\text{DMF}}$

e) 3 CH₃I + ⬡—NH₂ $\xrightarrow{\text{H}_2\text{O}}$ + 2 HI

Solution:

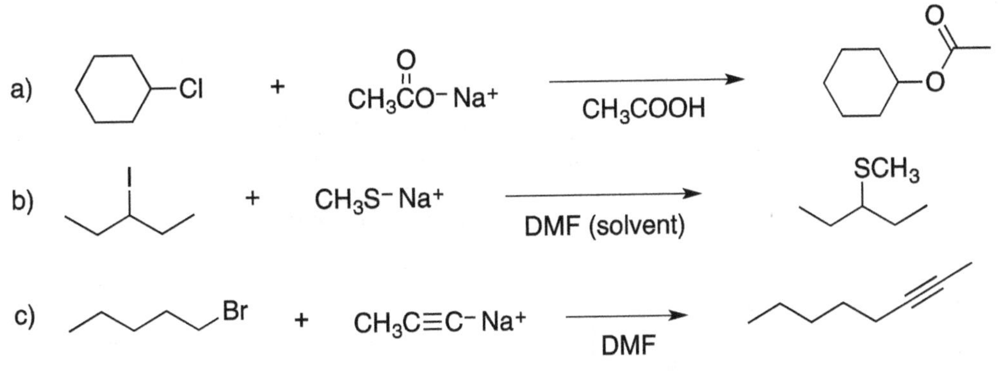

a) ⬡—Cl + $CH_3\overset{O}{\overset{\|}{C}}O^- Na^+$ $\xrightarrow{\text{CH}_3\text{COOH}}$ (cyclohexyl acetate)

b) (sec-pentyl iodide) + CH₃S⁻ Na⁺ $\xrightarrow{\text{DMF (solvent)}}$ (sec-pentyl methyl sulfide, SCH₃)

c) ⁀⁀⁀Br + CH₃C≡C⁻ Na⁺ $\xrightarrow{\text{DMF}}$ (2-octyne)

d) $+$ CH₃O⁻Na⁺ $\xrightarrow{\text{DMF}}$

e) 3 CH₃I $+$ $\xrightarrow{\text{H}_2\text{O}}$ $+$ 2 HI

(this reaction is a sequence of several S_N2 reactions involving CH₃I as a substrate and 1°, 2°, and 3° amines as nucleophiles)

Problem 5.4. Identify the S_N2 or S_N1 mechanisms in the reactions below. Draw each mechanism with curved arrows and show carbocationic intermediates when appropriate.

a) $\xrightarrow[\text{acetone}]{\text{NaI}}$

b) $\xrightarrow{\text{C}_2\text{H}_5\text{OH}}$

c) $\xrightarrow[\text{CH}_3\text{CO}_2\text{H}]{\text{CH}_3\text{CO}_2\text{Na}}$

Solution:

a) $\xrightarrow[\text{acetone}]{\text{NaI}}$

S_N2 mechanism: $\longrightarrow$ $+$ Br⁻

b) $\xrightarrow{\text{C}_2\text{H}_5\text{OH}}$

S_N1 mechanism: $\xrightarrow{\text{1st step}}$ $\longleftrightarrow$

allylic carbocation
has resonance stabilization

$\xrightarrow{\text{2nd step}}$ $\underset{\substack{\text{proton}\\\text{transfer}}}{\overset{\text{EtOH}}{\rightleftharpoons}}$

oxonium cation

c)

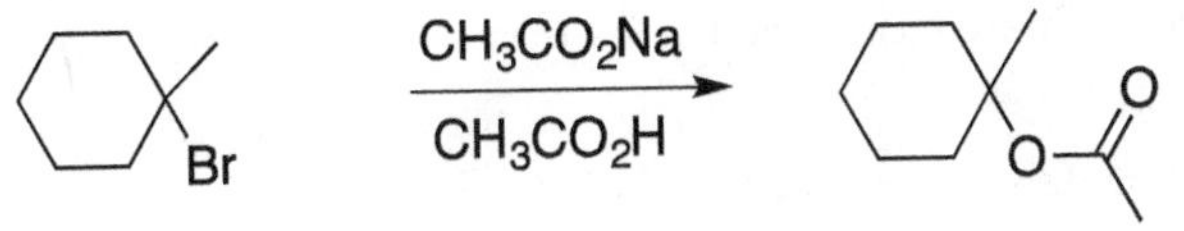

S_N1 mechanism:

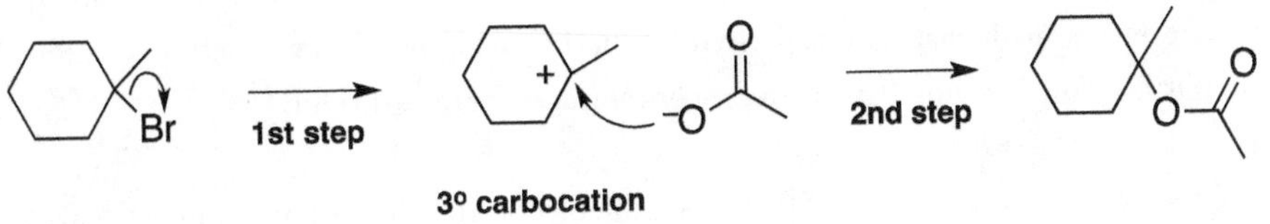

3° carbocation

Problem 5.5. The reaction of 1-bromopropane ($CH_3CH_2CH_2Br$) with the azide ion is a typical S_N2 reaction. Answer the following questions about the rate of this reaction:

a) What happens to the rate of the reaction if the concentration of 1-bromopropane is doubled, while the concentration of the azide ion stays the same?

b) What happens to the rate of the reaction if the concentration of the azide ion is doubled, while the concentration of 1-bromopropane stays the same?

c) What happens to the rate of the reaction if the concentration of 1-bromopropane is halved, while the concentration of the azide ion is doubled?

d) What happens to the rate of the reaction if the concentration of both 1-bromopropane and the azide ion is doubled?

Solution:

The overall rate of this S_N2 reaction depends on the concentrations of both the participating reactants and is mathematically expressed by the following second-order kinetics equation:

$$Rate = k\left[CH_3CH_2CH_2Br\right]\left[N_3^-\right].$$

a) The rate of the reaction will increase twice if $\left[CH_3CH_2CH_2Br\right]$ is doubled, while the concentration of the azide ion ($\left[N_3^-\right]$) stays the same.

b) The rate of the reaction will increase twice if $\left[N_3^-\right]$ is doubled, while $\left[CH_3CH_2CH_2Br\right]$ stays the same.

c) The rate of the reaction will stay unchanged if $\left[CH_3CH_2CH_2Br\right]$ is halved, while $\left[N_3^-\right]$ is doubled.

d) The reaction will be four times faster if $\left[CH_3CH_2CH_2Br\right]$ is doubled and $\left[N_3^-\right]$ is doubled.

Problem 5.6. The reaction of *tert*-butylbromide ($(CH_3)_3CBr$) with the azide ion (N_3^-) in methanol is a typical S_N1 reaction. Answer the following questions about the rate of this reaction:

a) What happens to the rate of the reaction if the concentration of *tert*-butylbromide is doubled, while the concentration of the azide ion stays the same?

b) What happens to the rate of the reaction if the concentration of the azide ion is doubled, while the concentration of *tert*-butylbromide stays the same?

c) What happens to the rate of the reaction if the concentration of *tert*-butylbromide is halved, while the concentration of the azide ion is doubled?

d) What happens to the rate of the reaction if the concentration of both *tert*-butylbromide and the azide ion is doubled?

Solution:

The overall rate of this S_N1 reaction is predetermined by the rate of the first step which involves only molecules of $(CH_3)_3CBr$, and therefore it is mathematically expressed by the following first order kinetics equation: Rate = k $[t\text{-BuBr}]$. The rate of this reaction does not depend on the concentration of the azide ion $([N_3^-])$.

a) The rate of the reaction will increase twice if $[t\text{-BuBr}]$ is doubled, while the concentration of the azide ion $([N_3^-])$ stays the same.

b) The rate of the reaction will stay unchanged if $[N_3^-]$ is doubled, while $[t\text{-BuBr}]$ stays the same.

c) The reaction will be twice slower if $[t\text{-BuBr}]$ is halved, while $[N_3^-]$ is doubled.

d) The reaction will be two times faster if $[t\text{-BuBr}]$ is doubled and $[N_3^-]$ is doubled.

Problem 5.7. Sort the following compounds from least reactive to most reactive according to their relative reactivity in a nucleophilic substitution reaction via an S_N1 mechanism:

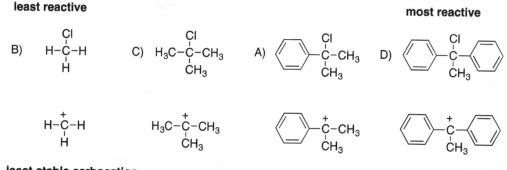

Solution:

The substrates producing stabilized carbocations in the first step of the S_N1 mechanism have higher reactivity in this reaction. Carbocations with resonance stabilization (e.g., benzylic and allylic cations) have the highest stability. See Figure 5.8 in Chapter 5 of the textbook for relative stability of carbocations. Substrate D is the most reactive substrate, because two phenyl groups are involved in the resonance delocalization of positive charge in the 3° carbocation. Substrate A produces a less stable 3° benzylic cation stabilized by one phenyl group. Substrate C forms a relatively less stable 3° alkyl cation. Finally, chloromethane B is the least reactive substrate in S_N1 reactions because of the low stability of the methyl cation.

Relative reactivity: B (least reactive) < C < A < D (most reactive)

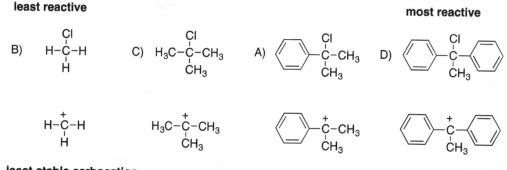

Problem 5.8. Suggest the product(s) of carbocationic rearrangements in the reactions below. Provide a mechanistic explanation for the formation of each product.

a) $\xrightarrow{H_2O}$

b) $\xrightarrow{CH_3OH}$

c) $\xrightarrow{H_2O}$

Solution:

a) $\xrightarrow{H_2O}$

normal S$_N$1 product   +   **product of rearrangement (1,2-hydride shift)**

Mechanism of rearrangement:

2° carbocation $\xrightarrow{\text{1,2-hydride shift}}$ **benzylic carbocation (has resonance stabilization)**

$\xrightarrow[\substack{(nucleophilic\ addition \\ and\ proton\ transfer)}]{H_2O}$

b) $\xrightarrow{CH_3OH}$

normal S$_N$1 product   +   **product of rearrangement (1,2-hydride shift)**

Mechanism of rearrangement:

2° carbocation $\xrightarrow{\text{1,2-hydride shift}}$ 3° carbocation

$\xrightarrow[\substack{(nucleophilic\ addition \\ and\ proton\ transfer)}]{CH_3OH}$

c)

normal S_N1 product   product of rearrangement
(1,2-hydride shift)

Mechanism of rearrangement:

2° carbocation

1,2-hydride shift

3° carbocation

$$\xrightarrow[\text{\textit{(nucleophilic addition and proton transfer)}}]{\text{H}_2\text{O}}$$

Problem 5.9. Draw three-dimensional structures of product(s) for the reactions below. Assign (R) or (S) configuration to each stereocenter. Provide a mechanistic explanation for the formation of each product.

a)
$$\xrightarrow[\text{acetonitrile}]{\text{NaN}_3}$$

b)
$$\xrightarrow[\text{DMSO}]{\text{KF}}$$

c)
$$\xrightarrow[\text{water}]{\text{H}_2\text{O}}$$

d)
$$\xrightarrow[\text{DMSO}]{\text{NaSCH}_3}$$

e)
$$\xrightarrow[\text{DMSO}]{\text{NaN}_3}$$

Solution:

a)
$$\xrightarrow[\text{acetonitrile}]{\text{NaN}_3}$$

(S_N2 reaction with inversion of configuration)

b)
$$\xrightarrow[\text{DMSO}]{\text{KF}}$$

(S_N2 reaction with inversion of configuration)

c)

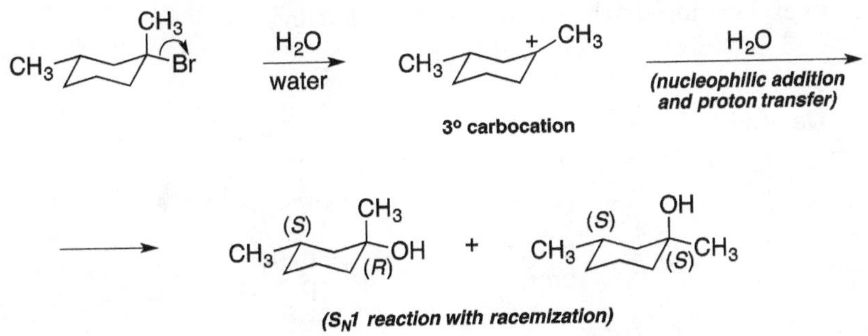
H_2O
water
H_2O
(nucleophilic addition and proton transfer)
3° carbocation
(S)
(R)
(S)
(S)
(S_N1 reaction with racemization)

d)

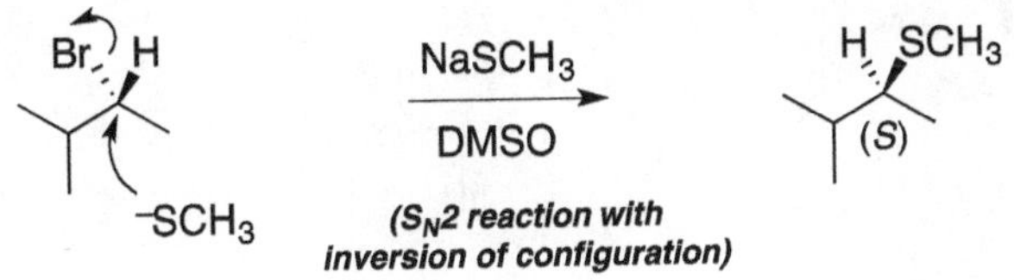
$NaSCH_3$
DMSO
(S_N2 reaction with inversion of configuration)
(S)

e)

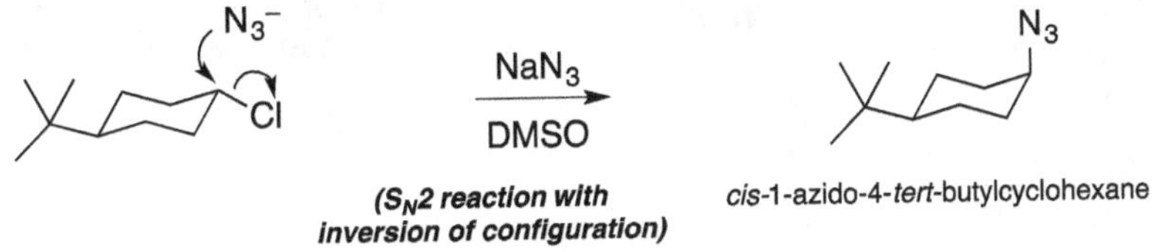
NaN_3
DMSO
(S_N2 reaction with inversion of configuration)
cis-1-azido-4-*tert*-butylcyclohexane

Problem 5.10. Suggest a mechanism explaining formation of the product in the following reaction:

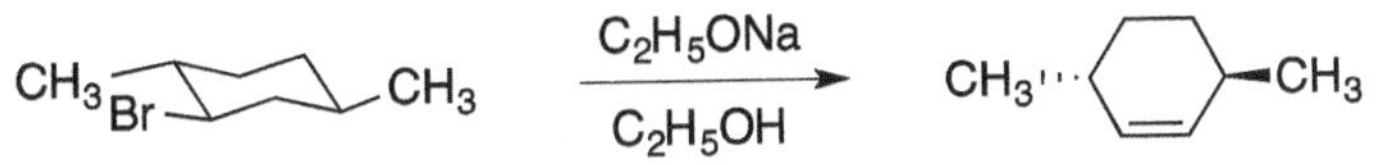
C_2H_5ONa
C_2H_5OH

Solution:

This is an E2-β-elimination reaction requiring anti-coplanar arrangement of the initial system of atoms H–C–C–Br. The required anti-coplanar arrangement of the H–C–C–Br system can be achieved only when the leaving group Br and the hydrogen at the β-carbon are in the axial positions as shown below:

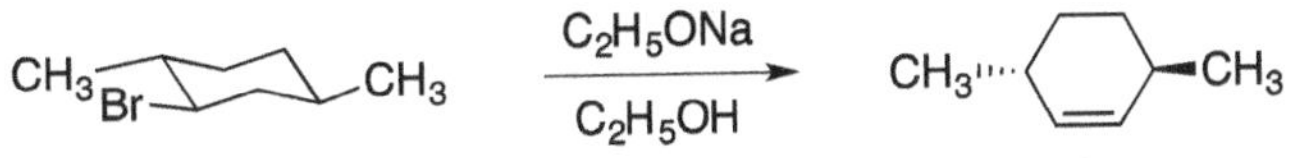
C_2H_5ONa
C_2H_5OH

E2-β-elimination mechanism:

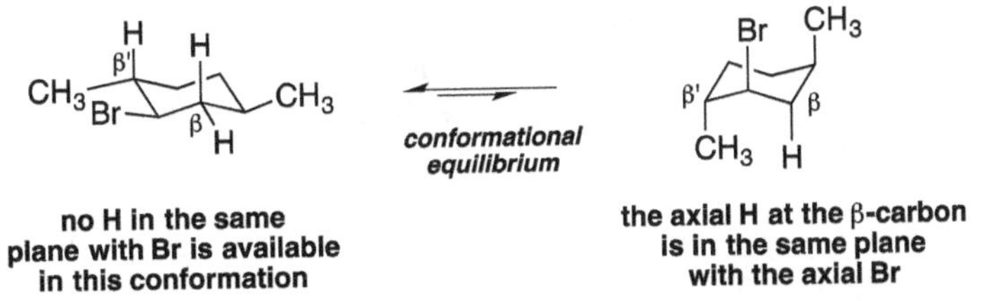
conformational equilibrium
no H in the same plane with Br is available in this conformation
the axial H at the β-carbon is in the same plane with the axial Br

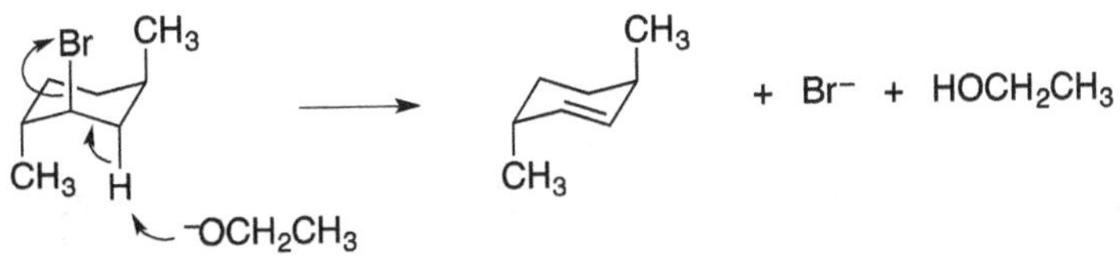
+ Br^- + $HOCH_2CH_3$

Problem 5.11. Provide an explanation for the outcome of the following reactions:

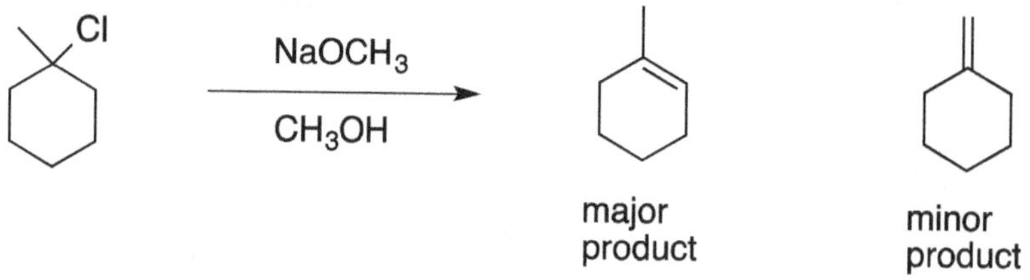

NaOCH₃ / **CH₃OH**

major product   minor product

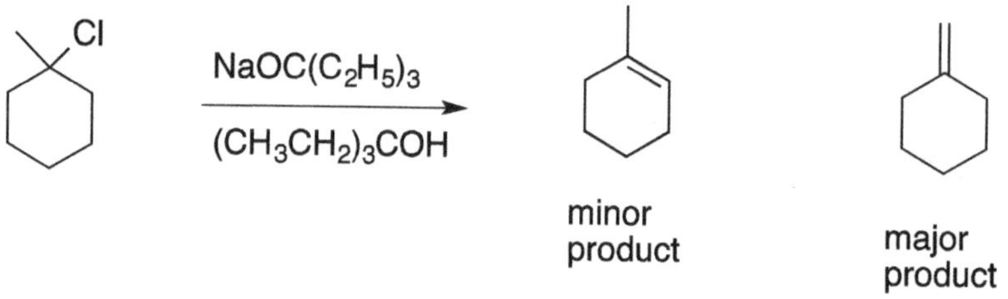

NaOC(C₂H₅)₃ / **(CH₃CH₂)₃COH**

minor product   major product

Solution:

This E2-β-elimination reaction yields the expected more highly substituted alkene in the reaction with $NaOCH_3$ as the base. The reaction of the bulkier base, $NaOC(CH_2CH_3)_3$, forms the less highly substituted alkene as the major product because of the deprotonation of the less sterically hindered 1° hydrogen at the β' carbon as explained below:

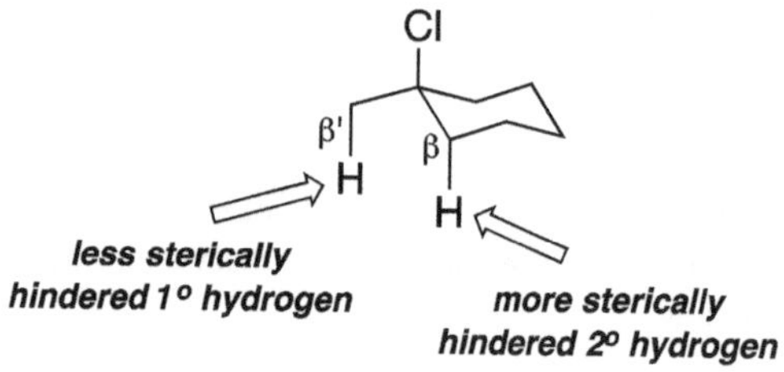

less sterically hindered 1° hydrogen

more sterically hindered 2° hydrogen

$^-OC(C_2H_5)_3$ **is a bulkier base compared to** $^-OCH_3$ **and more likely will deprotonate the less sterically hindered 1° hydrogen at the β' carbon**

major product (less higly substituted alkene)

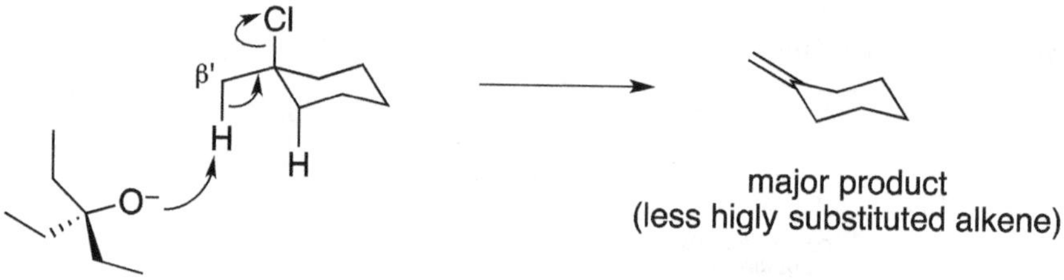

Problem 5.12. Assume an E2-elimination mechanism. Which of the following will react faster: *trans-1-tert*-butyl-4-chlorocyclohexane or *cis-1-tert*-butyl-4-chlorocyclohexane?

The reaction of *trans-1-tert*-butyl-4-chlorocyclohexane will require initial flipping of the chair in order to achieve the required anti-coplanar arrangement of the H–C–C–Cl system with axial Cl (see solution to the problem 5.10). This flipping will also bring the *tert*-butyl group to the axial conformation (see the picture below). For a bulky substituent such as the *tert*-butyl group, the axial conformation is so high in energy that the more stable equatorial conformation almost completely dominates at the equilibrium (see Section 3.4 of the textbook). As a result, the reaction of *trans*-1-*tert*-butyl-4-chlorocyclohexane will proceed extremely slowly. In contrast, the major conformation of *cis*-1-*tert*-butyl-4-chlorocyclohexane has the *tert*-butyl group in equatorial conformation and chlorine in axial conformation, perfectly arranged for the anti-coplanar elimination. Note that because of the conformational requirements, these two reactions will result in the regioisomeric products (3-*tert*-butylcyclohexene and 1-*tert*-butylcyclohexene):

trans-1-*tert*-butyl-4-chlorocyclohexane
major conformation

conformational
equilibrium

**a very minor conformer
because of the axial position
of the bulky *tert*-butyl group**

3-*tert*-butylcyclohexene

*a very slow reaction because of the extremely low
concentration of the required conformation*

1-*tert*-butylcyclohexene

cis-1-*tert*-butyl-4-chlorocyclohexane
major conformation

*fast reaction because the required anti-coplanar
arrangement exists in the major conformer*

Problem 5.13. For each of reactions provide the major product:

a)

NaOCH₃
⟶
(E2-elimination)

b)

NaOCH₃
⟶
(E2-elimination)

Solution:

Both substrates initially must achieve the required anti-coplanar arrangement of the H–C–C–Br system by rotation about the C–C bond as shown below:

a)

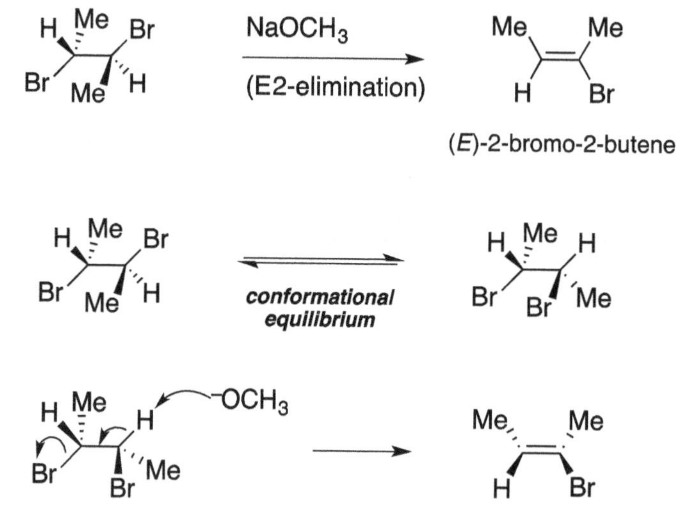
NaOCH$_3$
(E2-elimination)
(*E*)-2-bromo-2-butene
conformational equilibrium

b)

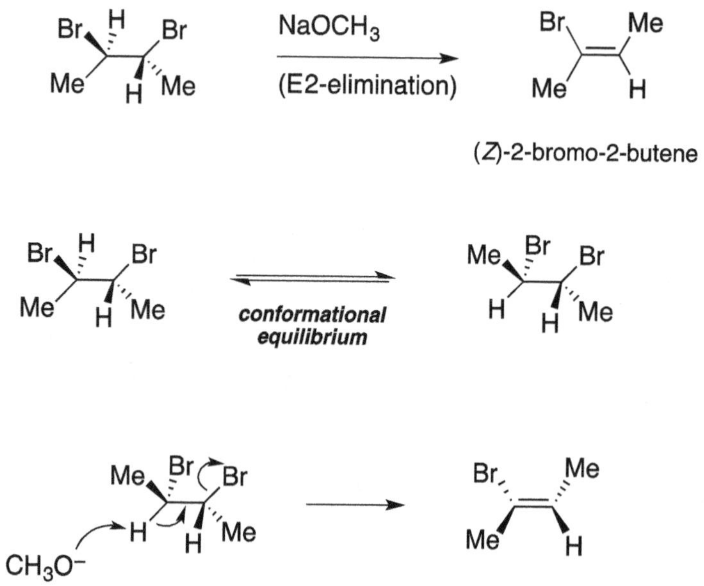
NaOCH$_3$
(E2-elimination)
(*Z*)-2-bromo-2-butene
conformational equilibrium

Problem 5.14. Regardless of mechanism, which of the following would only give a single alkene as the product of an elimination reaction?

a) 3-chloro-3-ethylpentane

b) 2-chloro-2-methylpentane

c) 3-chloro-3-methylpentane

d) 2-chloro-4-methylpentane

Solution:

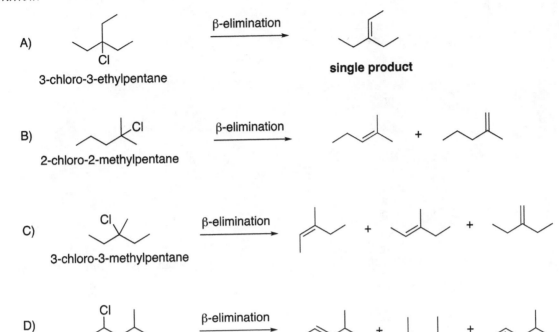

A) 3-chloro-3-ethylpentane → β-elimination → **single product**

B) 2-chloro-2-methylpentane → β-elimination → +

C) 3-chloro-3-methylpentane → β-elimination → + +

D) 2-chloro-4-methylpentane → β-elimination → + +

5.2. Additional Problems for Chapter 5 (for answers see Ch 17)

Problem 5.15. Select the stronger nucleophile from each pair:

a) NH_3 or $^-NH_2$

b) CH_3OCH_3 or CH_3SCH_3

c) F^- or I^- in CH_3OH

d) F^- or I^- in DMF

Problem 5.16. From each pair, select the halide that undergoes S_N1 solvolysis in CH_3OH more rapidly.

a)   [structure with Cl]   or   [structure with Cl]

b)   [structure with Br]   or   [structure with Br]

c)   [structure with Cl]   or   [structure with Cl]

d)   [structure with I]   or   [structure with I]

Problem 5.17. From each pair, select the halide that undergoes S_N2 reaction with NaN_3 in acetone more rapidly.

a) ~~~Cl   or   ~~~Cl

b) (cyclohexene with Br)   or   (cyclohexane with Br)

c) ~~~Cl   or   (tert-butyl-CH2-Cl)

d) ~~~Cl   or   ~~~I

Problem 5.18. Provide the structure of major organic product formed in these β-elimination reactions.

a) (2-bromo-2-methylbutane) $\dfrac{NaOCH_3}{CH_3OH}$

b) (2-bromo-2-methylbutane) $\dfrac{KOt\text{-}Bu}{t\text{-}BuOH}$

c) (1-chloro-1-methylcyclohexane) $\dfrac{NaOEt}{EtOH}$

CHAPTER 6

Alkenes

6.1. Chapter 6 Problems and Solutions

Problem 6.1. Provide the IUPAC name for each of the following compounds:

a) 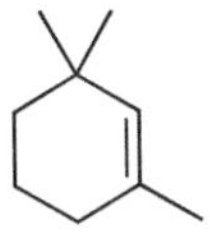

b) 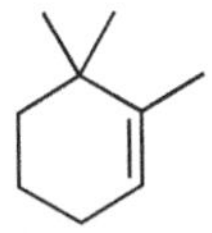

c) 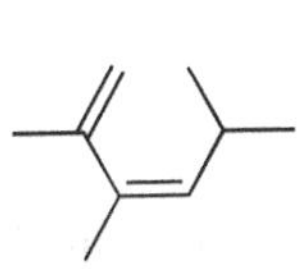

d) 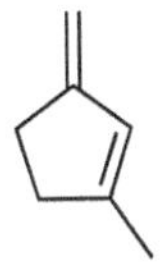

e) 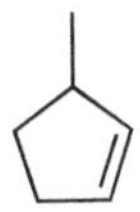

f) 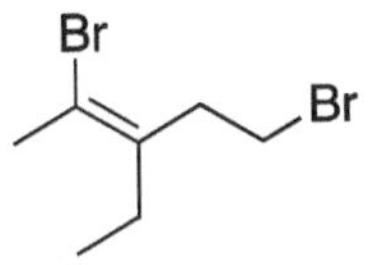

g) 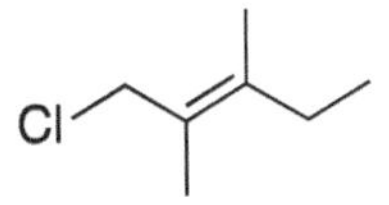

h) 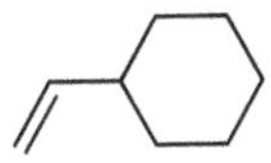

Solution:

a) 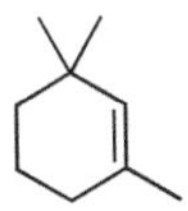

1,3,3-trimethylcyclohexene

b) 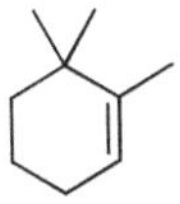

1,6,6-trimethylcyclohexene

c) 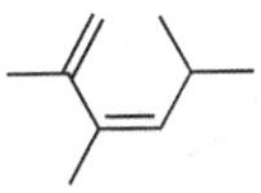

(*Z*)-2,3,5-trimethyl-1,3-hexadiene

d) 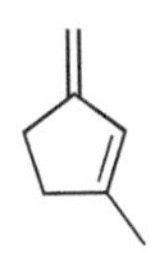

1-methyl-3-methylenecyclopentene

e) 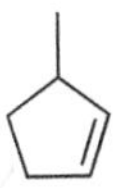

3-methylcyclopentene

f) 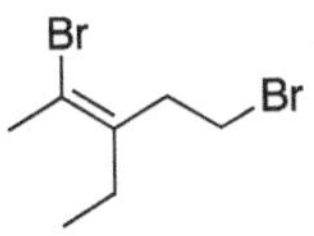

(*Z*)-2,5-dibromo-3-ethyl-2-pentene

g) 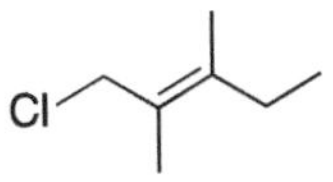

(*E*)-1-chloro-2,3-dimethyl-2-pentene

h) 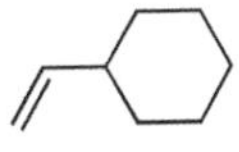

vinylcyclohexane

Problem 6.2. Draw structural formulas for the following alkenes:

a) 1-methyl-1-vinyl-cyclohexane

b) vinyl chloride

c) allyl bromide

d) methylenecyclohexane

Solution:

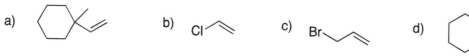

a) 1-methyl-1-vinyl-cyclohexane

b) vinyl chloride

c) allyl bromide

d) methylenecyclohexane

Problem 6.3. Draw the structures for the following alkenes and determine how many stereoisomers are possible (ignore any conformers):

a) 1-bromo-3-methyl-2-butene

b) 4-chloro-2-pentene

c) 2-iodo-3-methyl-2-pentene

Solution:

a) Only one stereoisomer is possible for 1-bromo-3-methyl-2-butene:

b) The four stereoisomers of 4-chloro-2-pentene are shown below:

(R,E)-4-chloro-2-pentene

(S,E)-4-chloro-2-pentene

(R,Z)-4-chloro-2-pentene

(S,Z)-4-chloro-2-pentene

c) E and Z stereoisomers are possible for 2-iodo-3-methyl-2-pentene:

(Z)-2-iodo-3-methyl-2-pentene

(E)-2-iodo-3-methyl-2-pentene

Problem 6.4. Determine the configuration of the double bond in the following alkenes:

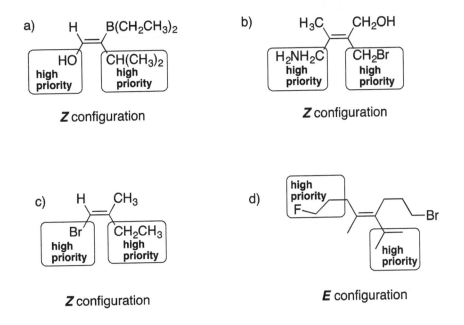

Solution:

Alkenes with Z configuration have the high-priority substituents on the same side of the double bond. For the assignment of priority of the substituents, see Section 4.2 of the textbook.

Problem 6.5. Determine the index of hydrogen deficiency (see Section 1.3) for the following molecules:

a) C_6H_8 b) $H_2C=CHCH_2NH_2$

c) [structure: chlorocyclopentene]

d) [structure: pyrrole]

e) [structure: bicyclic alkene]

Solution:

a) The index of hydrogen deficiency (also called the degree of unsaturation) is defined as the number of hydrogen molecules (H_2) that should be added to the molecule in order to produce a saturated hydrocarbon. The saturated hydrocarbon C_6H_{14} can be produced by adding $3H_2$ to C_6H_8, and therefore this molecule has three units of unsaturation (the index of hydrogen deficiency = 3).

b) This molecule has one carbon–carbon double bond which corresponds to one unit of unsaturation (the index of hydrogen deficiency = 1).

c) This molecule has one carbon–carbon double bond and one cycle, which corresponds to two units of unsaturation (the index of hydrogen deficiency = 2).

d) This molecule has two carbon–carbon double bonds and one cycle, which corresponds to three units of unsaturation (the index of hydrogen deficiency = 3).

e) This molecule has one carbon–carbon double bond and two cycles, which corresponds to three units of unsaturation (the index of hydrogen deficiency = 3).

Problem 6.6. Using curved arrows and showing reaction intermediates, write detailed mechanisms for the reactions shown in Figure 6.8.

Solution:

Figure 6.8, Reaction 1:

3° carbocation   oxonium ion   (proton transfer, see Figure 5.7 in Section 5.2.2)

Figure 6.8, Reaction 2:

benzylic carbocation
(has resonance stabilization, see Figure 5.8 in Section 5.2.2)

oxonium ion

(proton transfer)

Figure 6.8, Reaction 3:

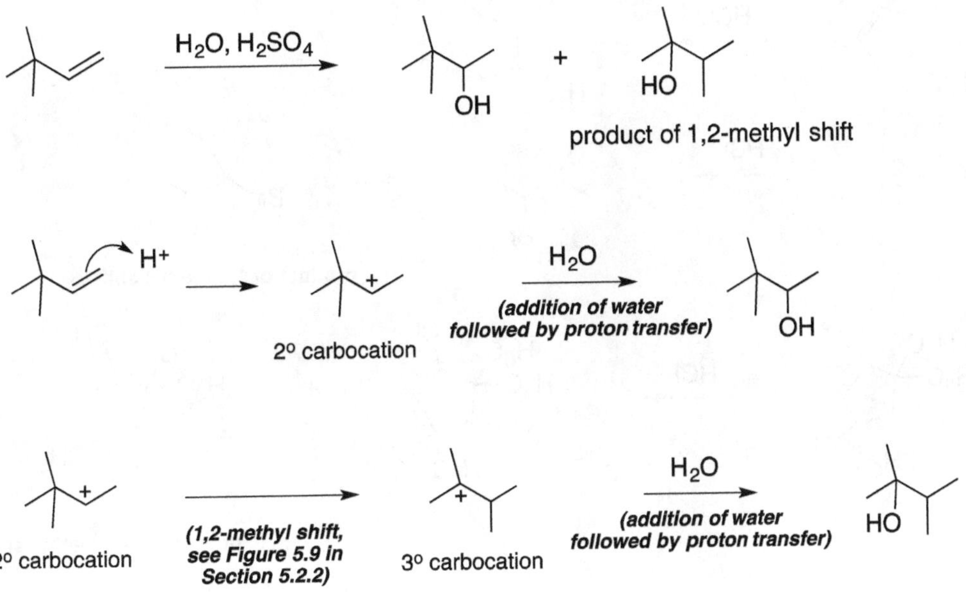

H₂O, H₂SO₄

+

product of 1,2-methyl shift

H⁺

2° carbocation

H₂O

(addition of water followed by proton transfer)

2° carbocation

(1,2-methyl shift, see Figure 5.9 in Section 5.2.2)

3° carbocation

H₂O

(addition of water followed by proton transfer)

Problem 6.7. Provide the products of electrophilic addition of HCl or HBr. In addition, give structures of the rearranged products when 1,2-hydride shift or 1,2-alkyl shift is possible.

a)

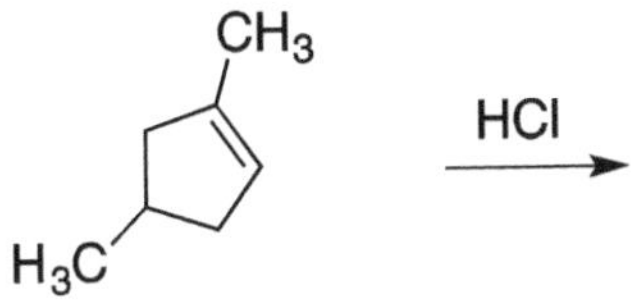

CH₃

H₃C

HCl

b)

HBr

c)

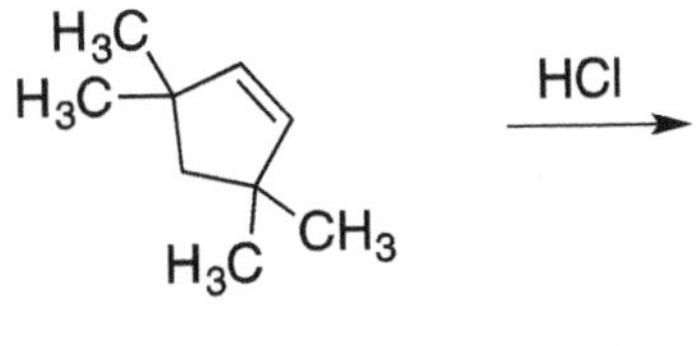

H₃C
H₃C

H₃C CH₃

HCl

Solution:

a)

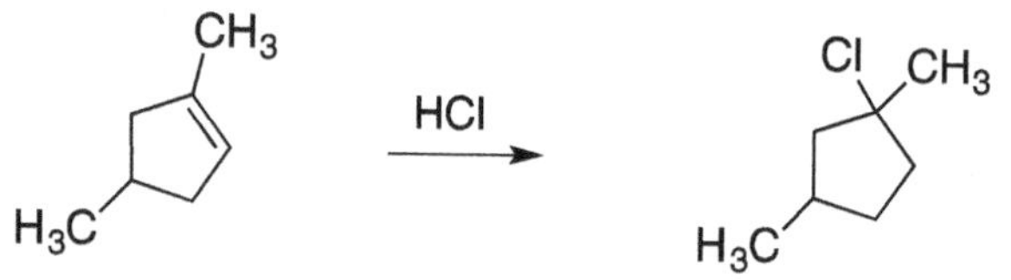

b)

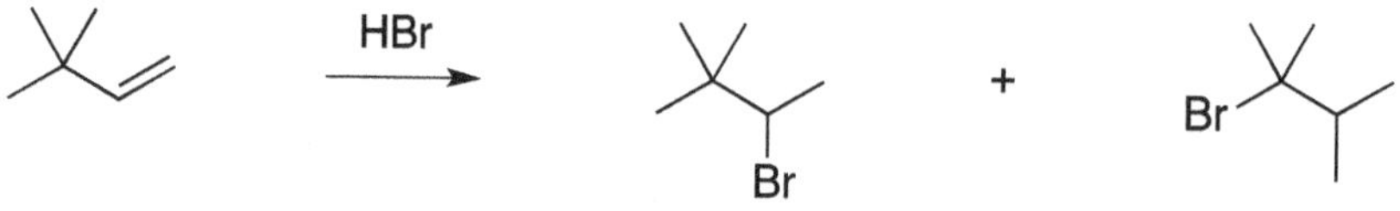

product of 1,2-methyl shift

c)

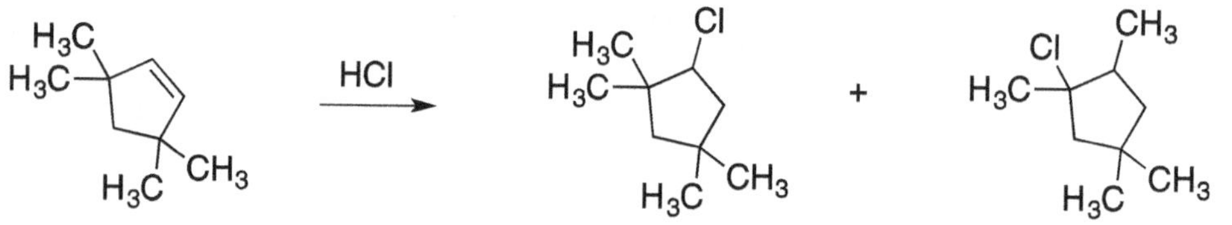

product of 1,2-methyl shift

Problem 6.8. Provide the products of acid-catalyzed hydration in the reactions below. In addition, give structures of the rearranged products when a 1,2-hydride shift or 1,2-alkyl shift is possible.

a) 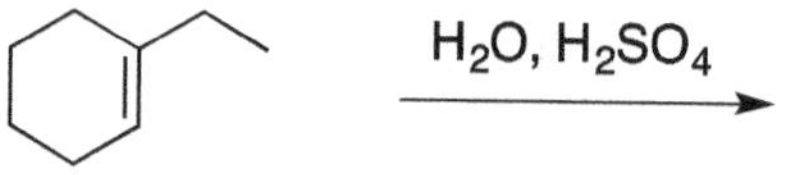
H_2O, H_2SO_4

b) 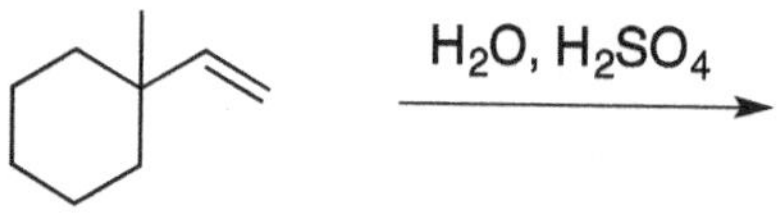
H_2O, H_2SO_4

c) 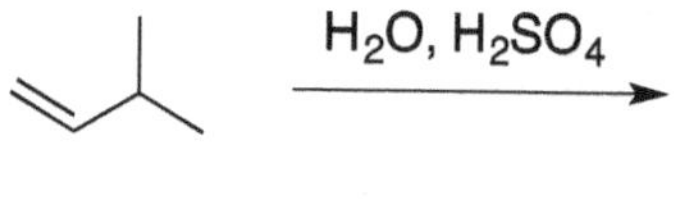
H_2O, H_2SO_4

Solution:

a) 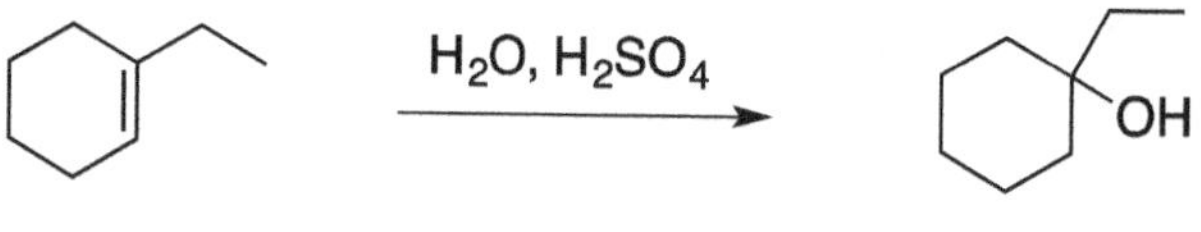
H_2O, H_2SO_4

b) 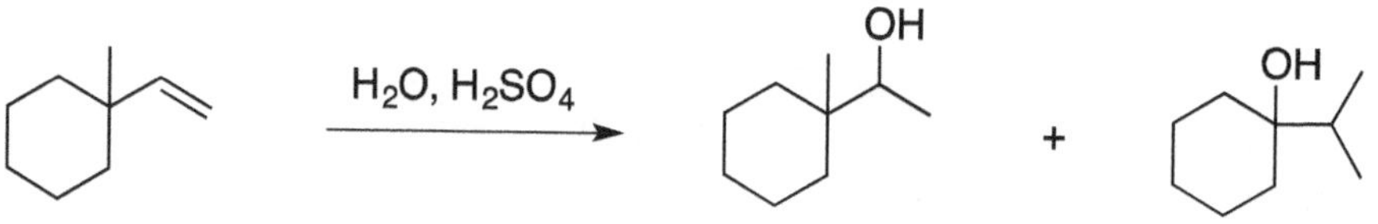
H_2O, H_2SO_4

product of 1,2-methyl shift

c)

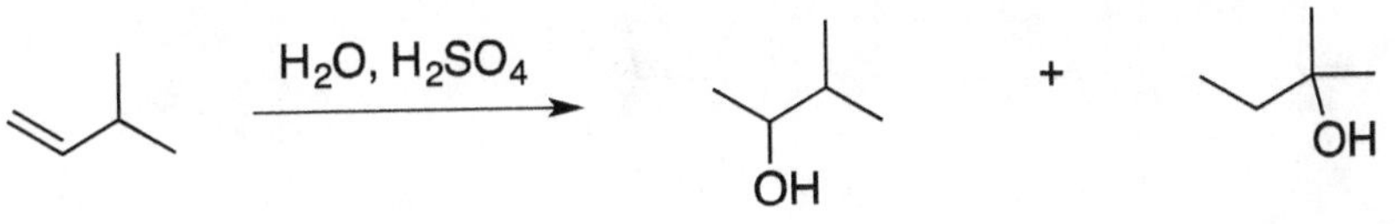

$$H_2O, H_2SO_4$$

+

product of 1,2-hydride shift

Problem 6.9. Draw three-dimensional structures of the products from the following stereoselective reactions:

a)

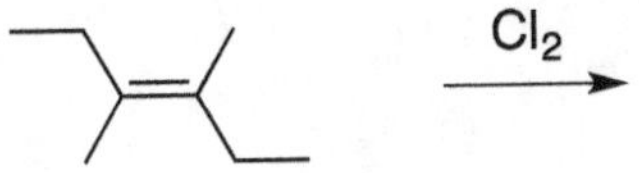

$\xrightarrow{Cl_2}$

b)

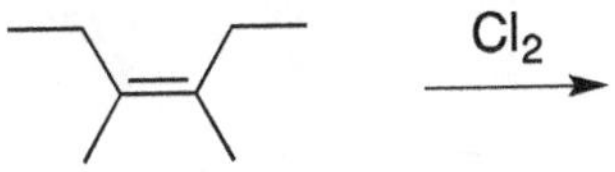

$\xrightarrow{Cl_2}$

c)

$\xrightarrow{Br_2/H_2O}$

d)

$\xrightarrow{Br_2/H_2O}$

e)

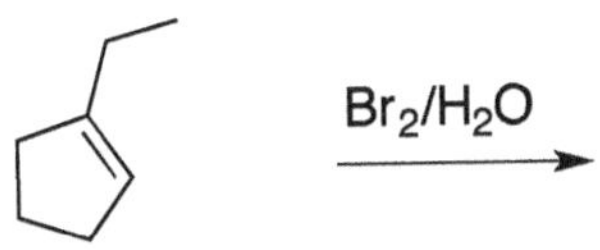

$\xrightarrow{Br_2/H_2O}$

Solution:

All these reactions proceed as *anti* stereoselective addition via initial formation of a cyclic chloronium or bromonium intermediate. In the case of Br_2 addition in water to a nonsymmetrical alkene (reaction e), the reaction proceeds as a regioselective addition with the nucleophile (H_2O) adding to the more highly substituted carbon of the double bond. All chiral products are formed as a racemic mixture of two enantiomers (only one enantiomer is shown for each reaction below).

a) 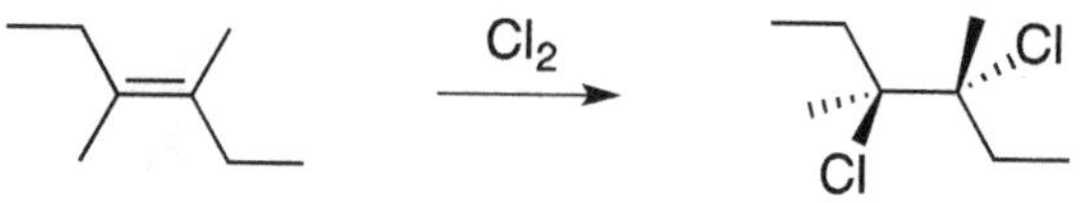 Cl₂ →

a) Cl_2

b) 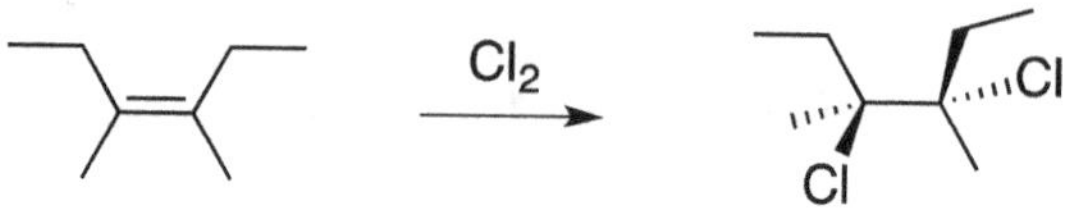 Cl_2

c) 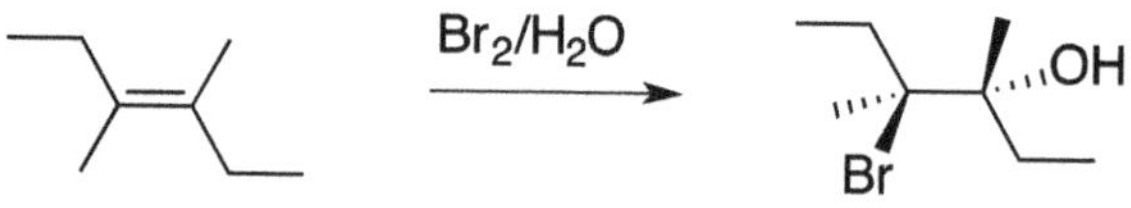 Br_2/H_2O

d) 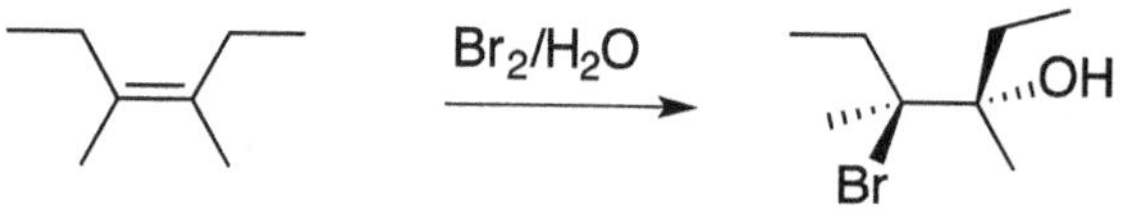 Br_2/H_2O

e) 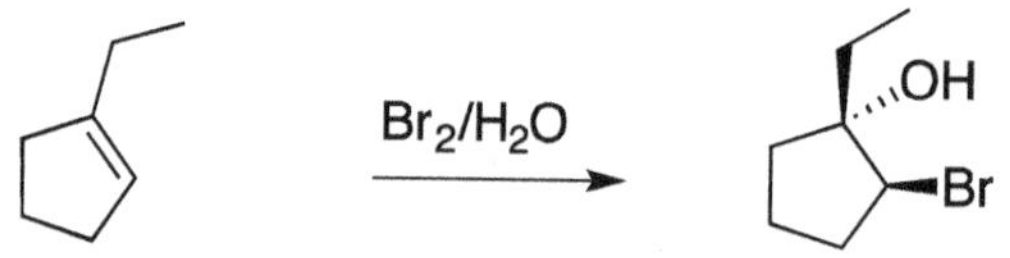 Br_2/H_2O

Problem 6.10. Draw three-dimensional structures of the products in the following stereoselective reactions:

a) 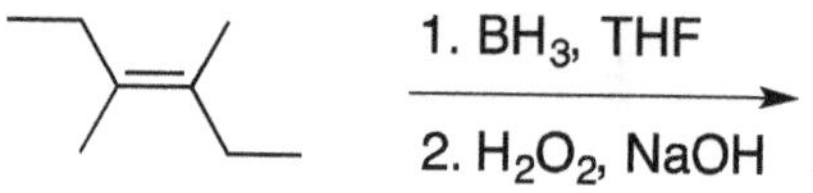 1. BH_3, THF
   2. H_2O_2, NaOH

b) 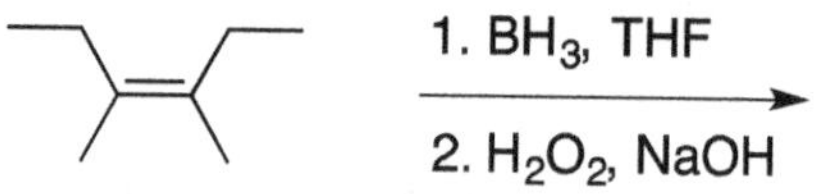 1. BH_3, THF
   2. H_2O_2, NaOH

c) 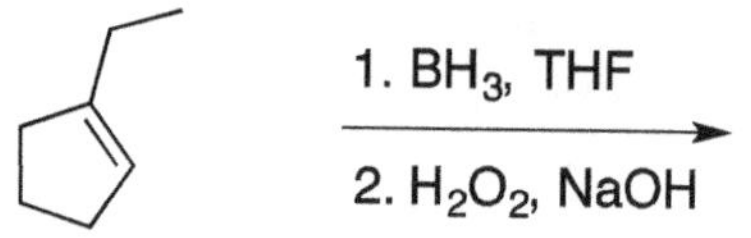 1. BH_3, THF
   2. H_2O_2, NaOH

Solution:

These hydroboration–oxidation reactions proceed as *syn* stereoselective addition. In the reaction of a nonsymmetrical alkene (reaction c), the reaction proceeds as a regioselective addition with the nucleophile (hydride anion) adding to the more highly substituted carbon of the double bond. All chiral products are formed as a racemic mixture of two enantiomers (only one enantiomer is shown for each reaction below).

a)

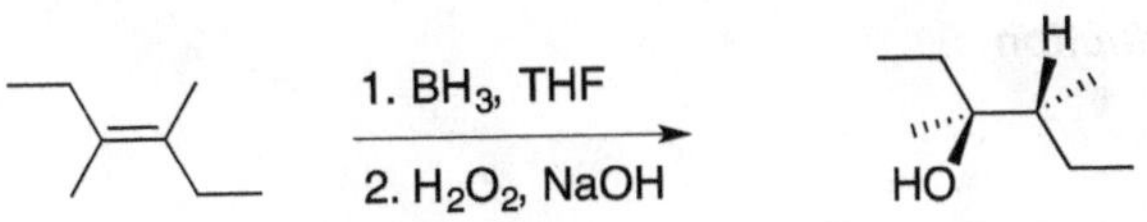

1. BH_3, THF
2. H_2O_2, NaOH
H
HO

b)

1. BH_3, THF
2. H_2O_2, NaOH
HO
H

c)

1. BH_3, THF
2. H_2O_2, NaOH
H
OH

Problem 6.11. Determine which of the following transformations are oxidation reactions, reduction reactions, or neither oxidation nor reduction:

Br

O
OH
O
H

2
O
OCH3
H3C
OCH3
O
O

O
OH

+
O
Cl
COCH3

O
N
N
O
N
N
O
+ CO2

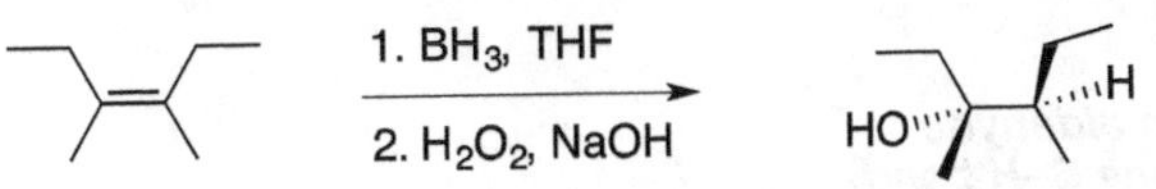

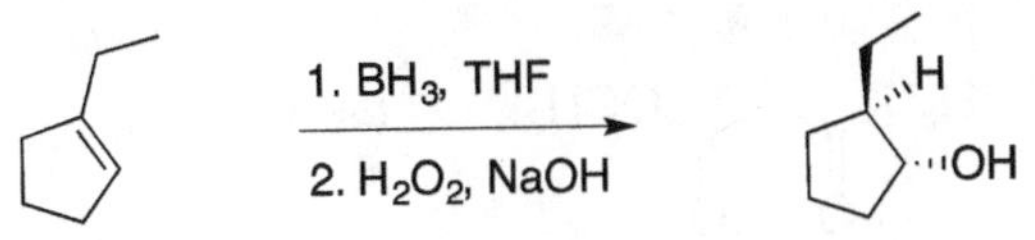

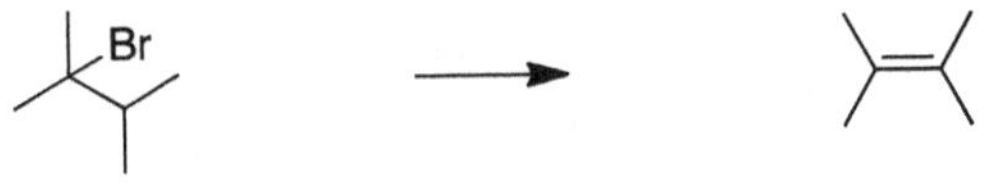

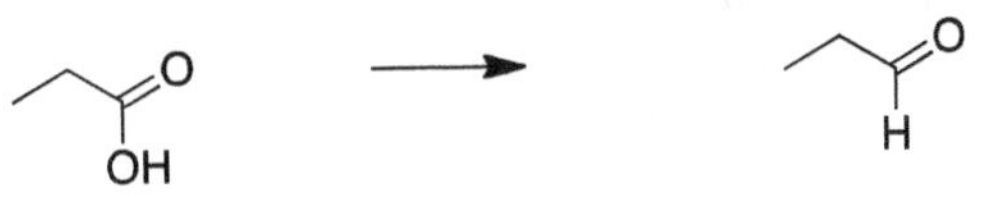

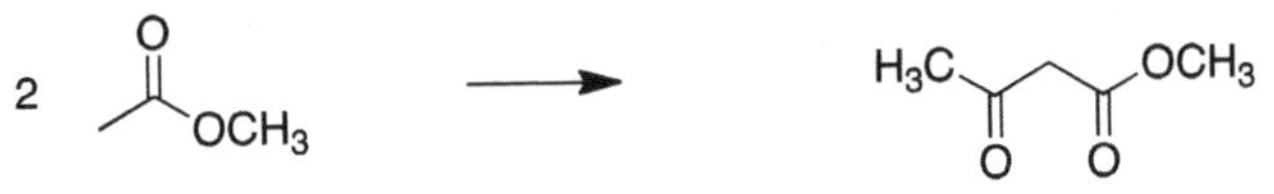

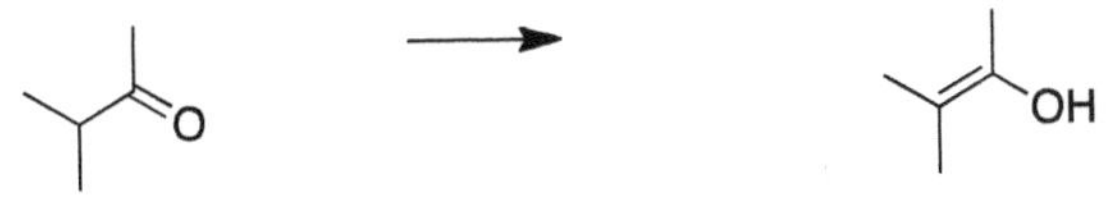

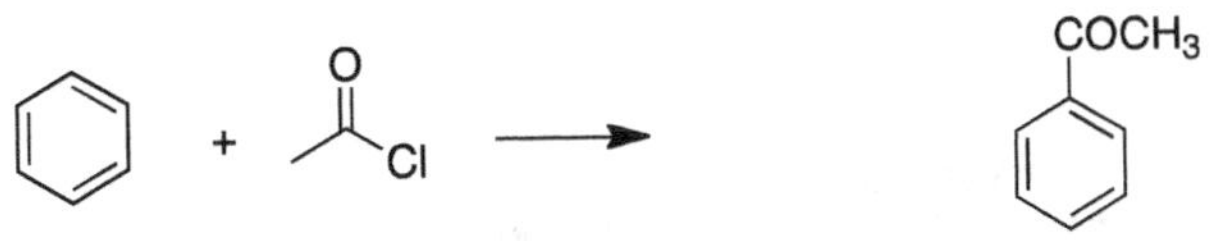

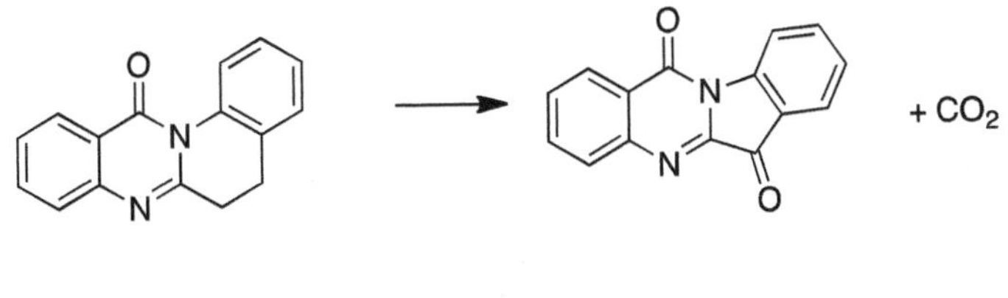

Solution:

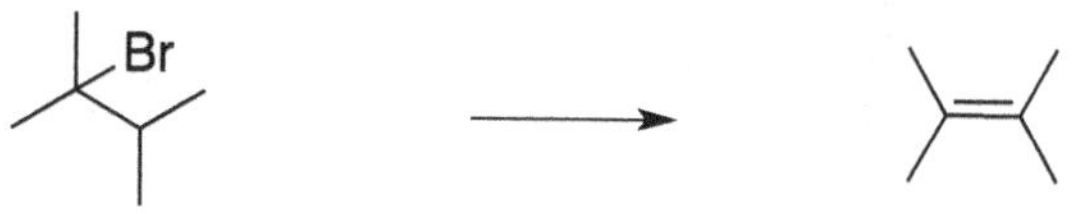

this is neither oxidation nor reduction
(elimination of HBr)

reduction of carboxylic acid to aldehyde
(one C–O bond is replaced with one C–H bond)

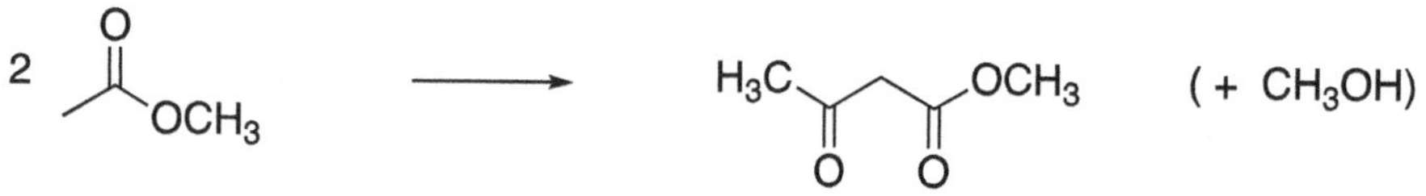

this is neither oxidation nor reduction
(two molecules of ester combine together with elimination of CH_3OH;
the overall number of C–O and C–H bonds stays unchanged)

this is neither oxidation nor reduction
(one C–O bond and one C–H bond are removed)

this is neither oxidation nor reduction
(the overall number of C–O and C–H bonds stays unchanged)

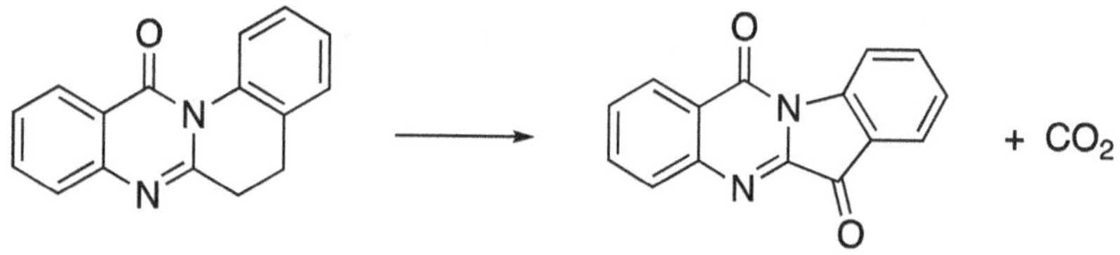

this is an oxidation reaction
(C–O bonds are added and C–H bonds are removed)

Problem 6.12. Rank the following compounds by relative stability/heat of hydrogenation:

a) 1-hexene

b) *cis*-3-hexene

c) *trans*-3-hexene

d) 2,3-dimethyl-2-butene

e) (*E*)-3-methyl-2-pentene

Solution:

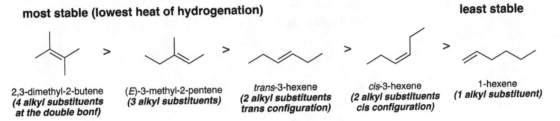

most stable (lowest heat of hydrogenation)   least stable

2,3-dimethyl-2-butene   (*E*)-3-methyl-2-pentene   trans-3-hexene   cis-3-hexene   1-hexene
(4 alkyl substituents   **(3 alkyl substituents)**   **(2 alkyl substituents**   **(2 alkyl substituents**   **(1 alkyl substituent)**
at the double bonf)   **trans configuration)**   **cis configuration)**

Problem 6.13. Draw three-dimensional structures of the products from the following stereoselective reactions:

a)
1. OsO₄
2. NaHSO₃, H₂O

b)
1. OsO₄
2. NaHSO₃, H₂O

c)
1. OsO₄
2. NaHSO₃, H₂O

d)
H₂
Pd (catalyst)

e)
H₂
Pd (catalyst)

Solution:

All these reactions proceed as *syn* stereoselective additions. The chiral products are formed as a racemic mixture of two enantiomers (only one enantiomer is shown for each reaction below).

a)

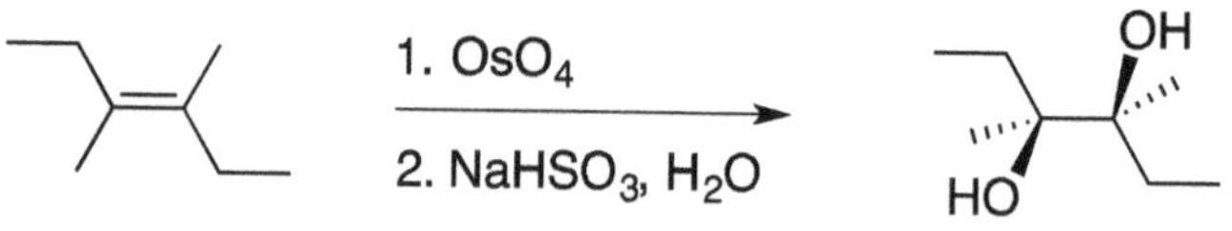

1. OsO$_4$

2. NaHSO$_3$, H$_2$O

b)

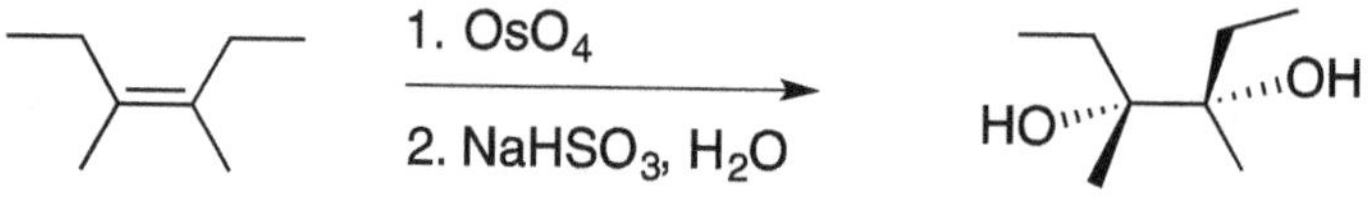

1. OsO$_4$

2. NaHSO$_3$, H$_2$O

c)

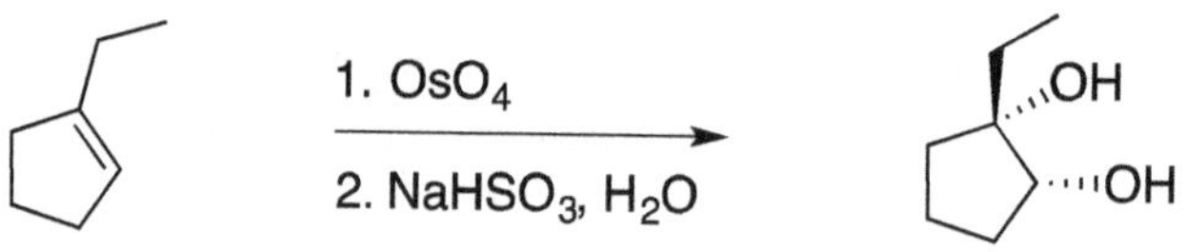

1. OsO$_4$

2. NaHSO$_3$, H$_2$O

d)

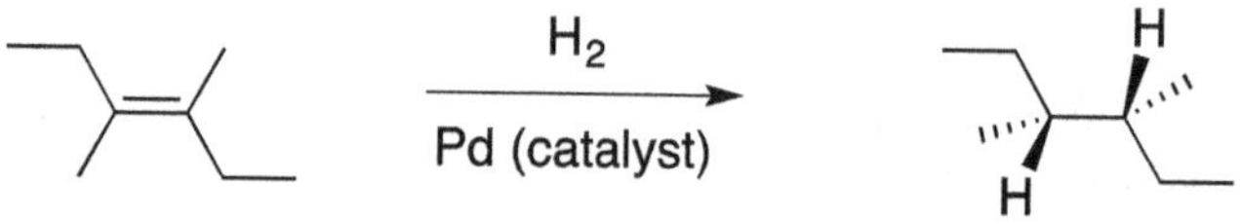

H$_2$

Pd (catalyst)

e)

H$_2$

Pd (catalyst)

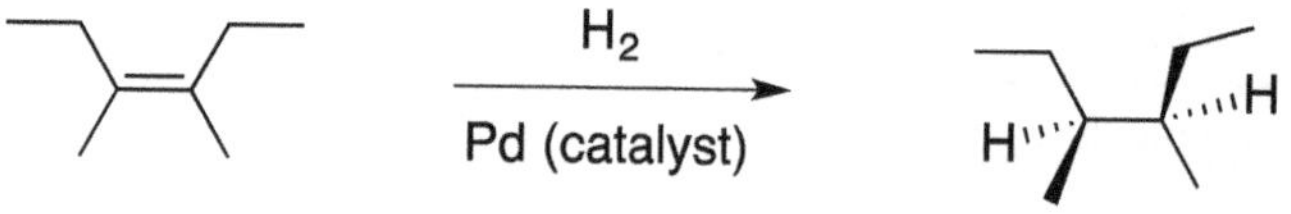

Problem 6.14. Draw the structure of the product in the following ozonolysis reaction:

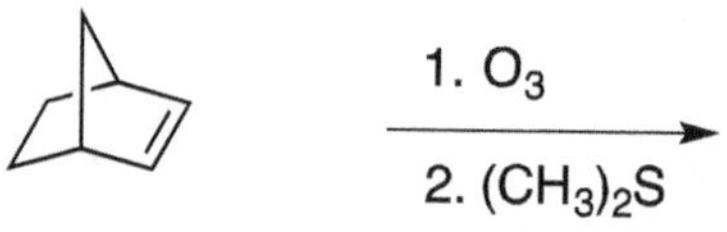

1. O$_3$

2. (CH$_3$)$_2$S

Solution:

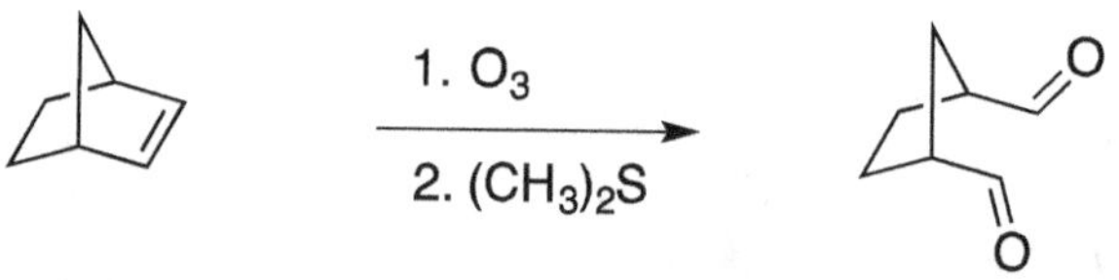

1. O$_3$

2. (CH$_3$)$_2$S

Problem 6.15. Provide the products in the following reactions:

a)

NBS, hv
—————→
CCl₄

b)

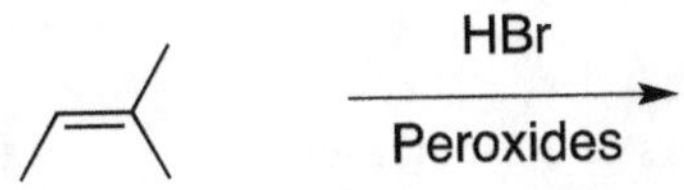

HBr
—————→
Peroxides

c)

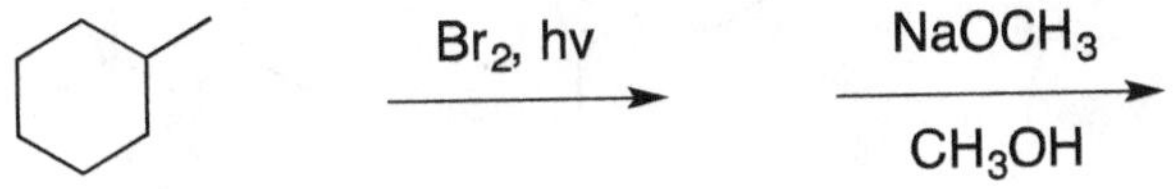

Br₂, hv
—————→

NaOCH₃
—————→
CH₃OH

Solution:

a)

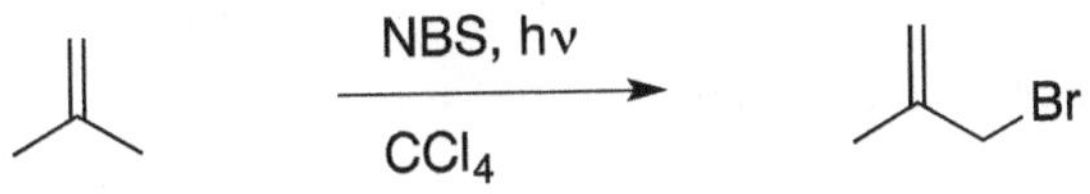

NBS, hv
—————→
CCl₄

b)

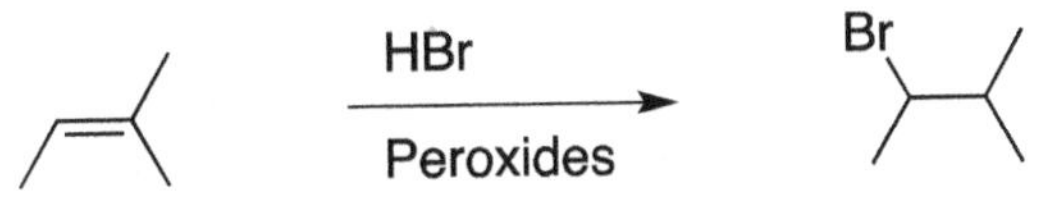

HBr
—————→
Peroxides

c)

Br₂, hv
—————→

NaOCH₃, CH₃OH
—————→
*(E2 elimination,
Section 5.4)*

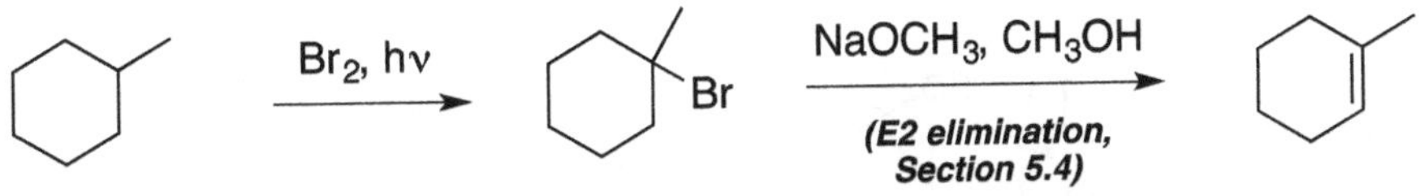

6.2. Additional Problems for Chapter 6 (for answers see Ch 17)

Problem 6.16. Calculate the index of hydrogen deficiency (IHD) of compounds with the following molecular formulas:

a) $C_6H_{12}N_2$ b) C_5H_9Br c) C_8H_8O

Problem 6.17. What is the IHD value of aspartame (shown below)?

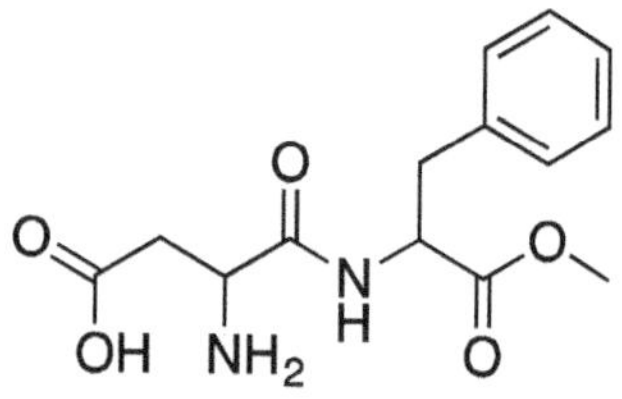

Problem 6.18. Provide the structures of all *cis/trans* isomers of 2,5-octadiene.

Problem 6.19. Select all structure(s) that will exhibit *cis–trans* isomerism.

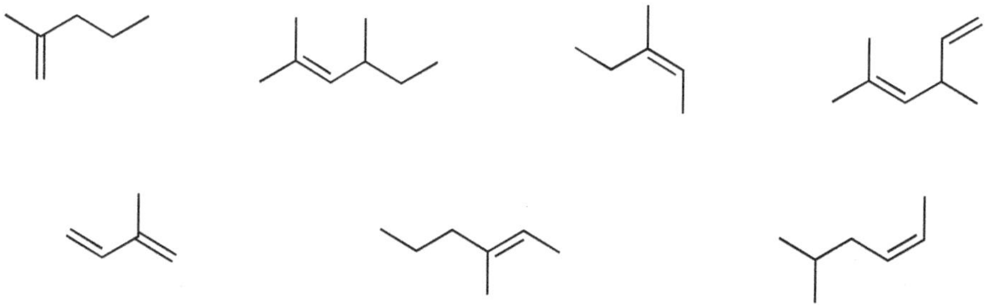

Problem 6.20. Select the most stable alkene from each set:

a)

b)

Problem 6.21. Give reagent(s) on each arrow (one reagent per box) that can be used to convert the reactant to the indicated product in high yield.

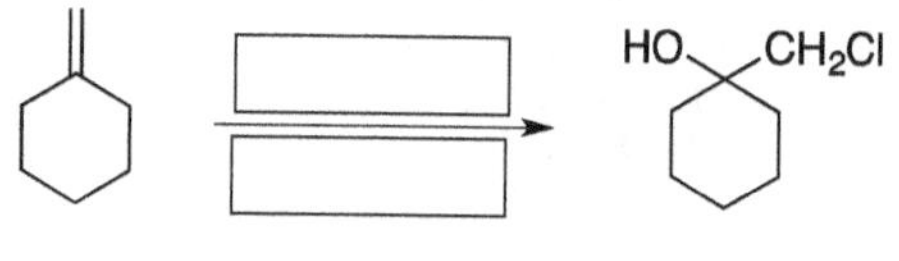

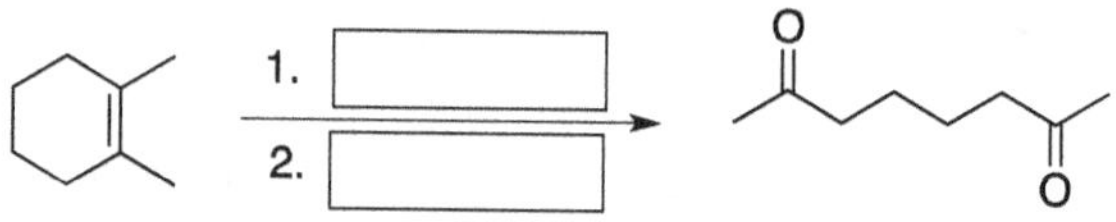

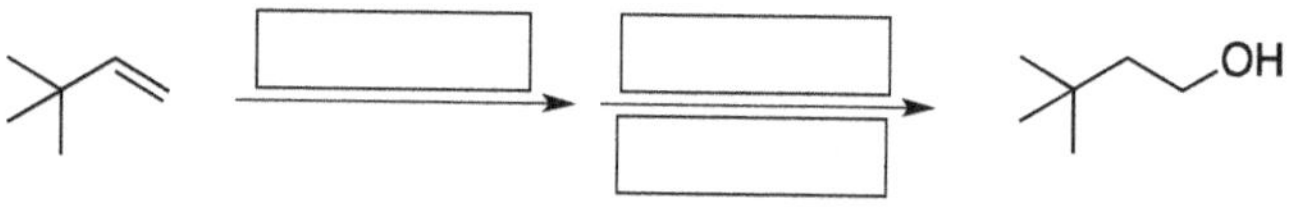

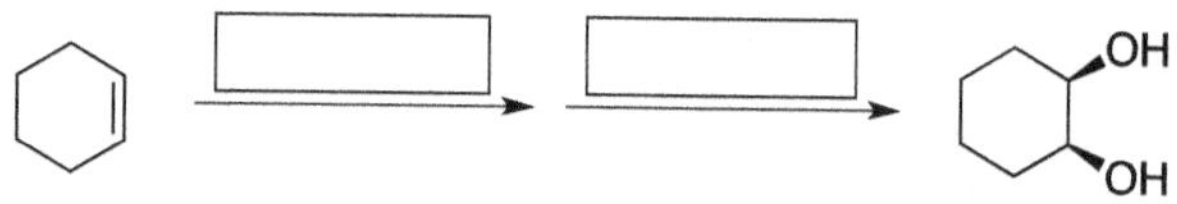

Alkynes

7.1. Chapter 7 Problems and Solutions

Problem 7.1. Provide the IUPAC name for each of the following compounds.

a) 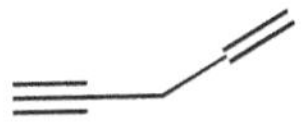
b) 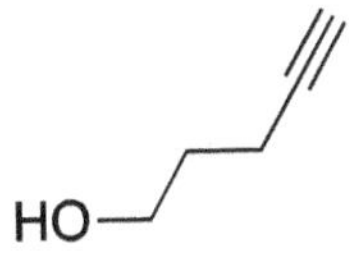
c)

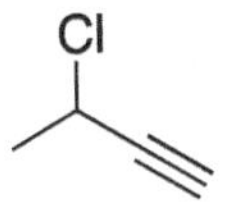

Solution:

a)

1-penten-4-yne

b)

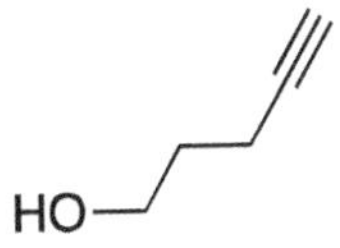

4-pentyn-1-ol

c)

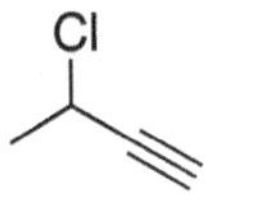

3-chloro-1-butyne

Problem 7.2. Draw structural formulas for the following alkynes.

a) 2,5-dimethyl-3-heptyne   b) 3-ethynyl-1-cyclopentene   c) 3-butyn-2-ol

Solution:

a)

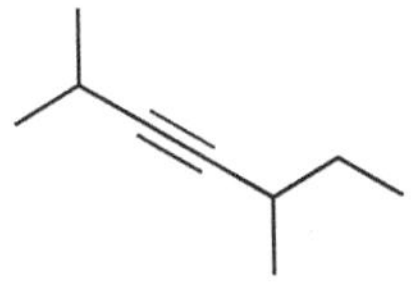

2,5-dimethyl-3-heptyne

b)

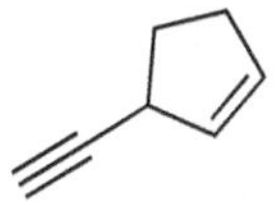

3-ethynyl-1-cyclopentene

c)

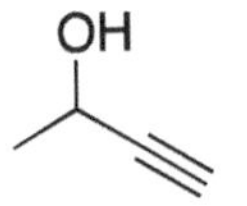

3-butyn-2-ol

Problem 7.3. Write detailed mechanisms for the reactions shown in Figures 7.3 and 7.4.

Solution:

Reaction shown in Figure 7.3:

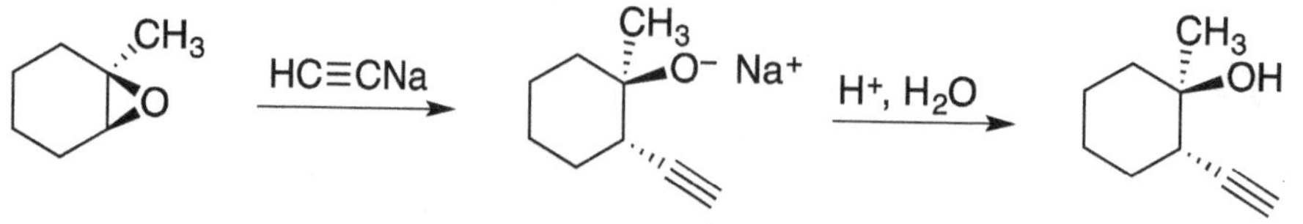

Mechanism:

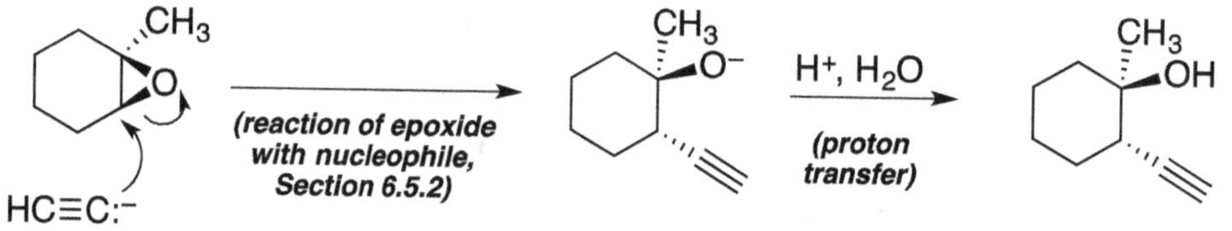

Figure 7.4, reaction 1:

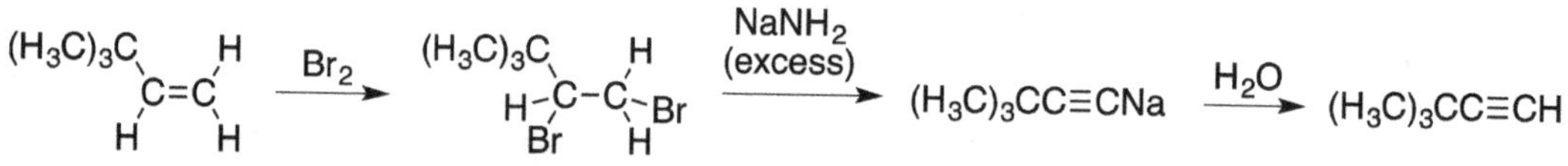

Mechanism:

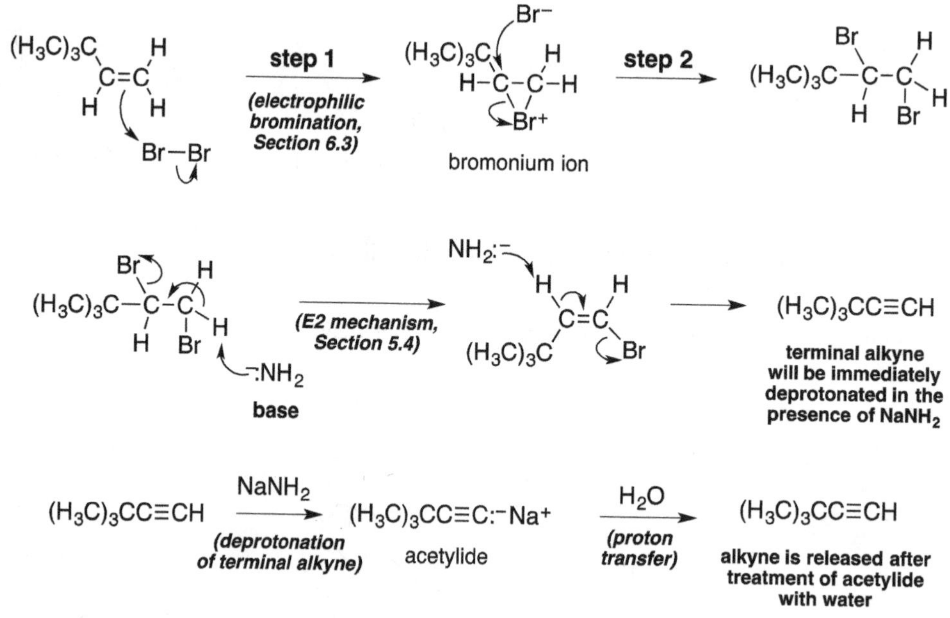

Figure 7.4, reaction 2:

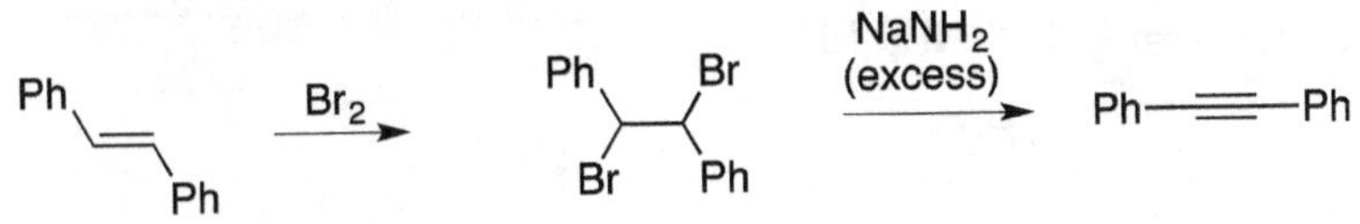

Ph—CH=CH—Ph $\xrightarrow{\text{Br}_2}$ Ph—CHBr—CHBr—Ph $\xrightarrow[\text{(excess)}]{\text{NaNH}_2}$ Ph—C≡C—Ph

Mechanism:

$\xrightarrow[\substack{\text{(electrophilic} \\ \text{bromination,} \\ \text{Section 6.3)}}]{\text{Br}_2}$

base :NH$_2$ $\xrightarrow{\text{1st elimination}}$

NH$_2$:⁻ $\xrightarrow{\text{2nd elimination}}$ Ph—C≡C—Ph

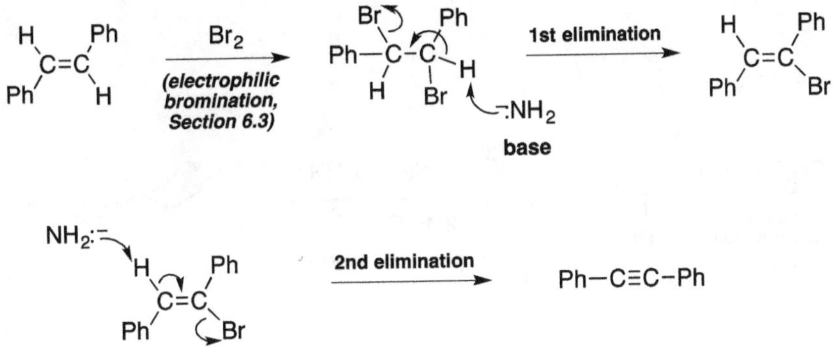

Problem 7.4. Explain the following observation:

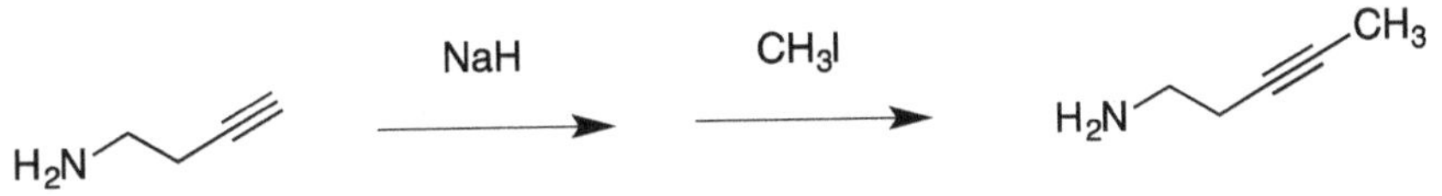

$\xrightarrow{\text{NaH}}$ $\xrightarrow{\text{CH}_3\text{I}}$

however:

$\xrightarrow{\text{NaH}}$ $\xrightarrow{\text{CH}_3\text{I}}$

Solution:

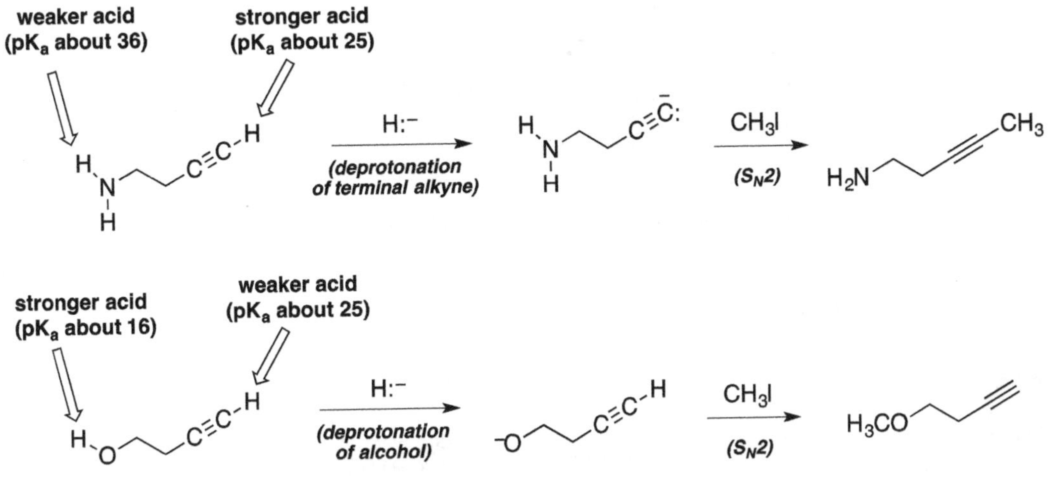

weaker acid
(pK$_a$ about 36)   stronger acid
(pK$_a$ about 25)

$\xrightarrow[\substack{\textit{(deprotonation} \\ \textit{of terminal alkyne)}}]{\text{H:}^-}$ $\xrightarrow[(S_N2)]{\text{CH}_3\text{I}}$

stronger acid
(pK$_a$ about 16)   weaker acid
(pK$_a$ about 25)

$\xrightarrow[\substack{\textit{(deprotonation} \\ \textit{of alcohol)}}]{\text{H:}^-}$ $\xrightarrow[(S_N2)]{\text{CH}_3\text{I}}$

Problem 7.5. Provide the products of the following transformations:

a)

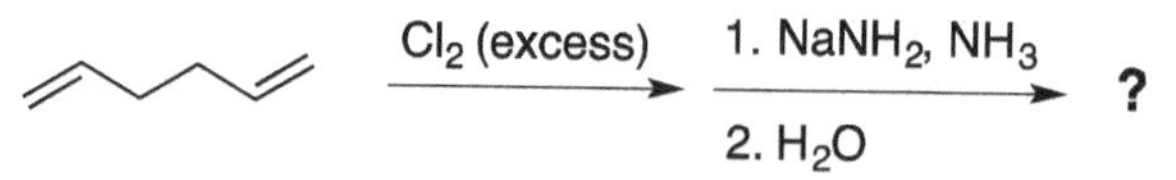

$\xrightarrow{\text{Cl}_2 \text{ (excess)}}$ $\xrightarrow[\text{2. H}_2\text{O}]{\text{1. NaNH}_2, \text{ NH}_3}$ **?**

b) $CH_3C\equiv CH$ $\xrightarrow{H_3CCH_2CH_2CH_2{}^-Li^+}$ $\xrightarrow{D_2O}$ **?**

Solution:

a)

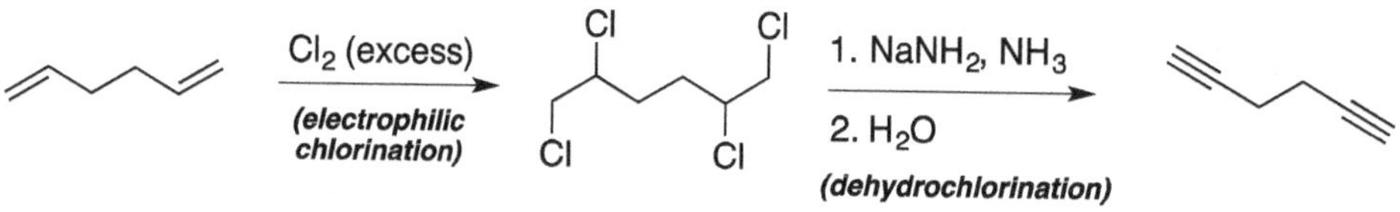

$\xrightarrow[\substack{\textit{(electrophilic)} \\ \textit{chlorination}}]{\text{Cl}_2 \text{ (excess)}}$ $\xrightarrow[\substack{\text{2. H}_2\text{O} \\ \textit{(dehydrochlorination)}}]{\text{1. NaNH}_2, \text{ NH}_3}$

b)

$CH_3C\equiv CH$ $\xrightarrow[\substack{\textit{(deprotonation)} \\ \textit{of terminal alkyne}}]{H_3CCH_2CH_2CH_2{}^-Li^+}$ $CH_3C\equiv C{:}^-$ $\xrightarrow[\textit{(D$^+$ transfer)}]{D_2O}$ $CH_3C\equiv CD$

$D = {}^2H$ (deuterium, isotope of hydrogen)

Problem 7.6. Why does the attempt to synthesize 2,2-dimethyl-3-hexyne via the sequence of reactions shown below fail? Explain why and provide an alternative approach to synthesize this compound.

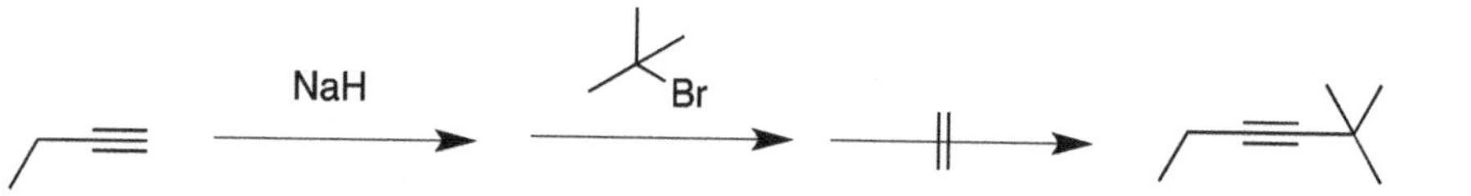

$\xrightarrow{\text{NaH}}$

2,2-dimethyl-3-hexyne
(not formed)

Solution:

$CH_3CH_2C\equiv CH$ $\xrightarrow[\textit{(deprotonation)}]{\text{NaH}}$ $CH_3CH_2C\equiv C{:}^-$

1-butyne   alkynyl anion   3° bromoalkane

S_N2 *reaction of alkynyl anion with 3° substrate is not possible because of steric hindrance*

Alternative approach:

$(CH_3)_3CC\equiv CH$ $\xrightarrow[\textit{(deprotonation)}]{\text{NaH}}$ $(CH_3)_3CC\equiv C{:}^-$ $\xrightarrow[\substack{\textit{(S$_N$2 reaction} \\ \textit{Section 5.2)}}]{\substack{CH_3CH_2Br \\ \textbf{1° bromoalkane}}}$ $(CH_3)_3CC\equiv CCH_2CH_3$

3,3-dimethyl-1-butyne   alkynyl anion   2,2-dimethyl-3-hexyne

Problem 7.7. Propose detailed mechanisms for the reactions shown in Figures 7.7, 7.10, and 7.11.

Solution:

Figure 7.7, Reaction 1:

$$HC{\equiv}CH + HCl\ (1\ mol) \longrightarrow H_2C{=}CHCl$$

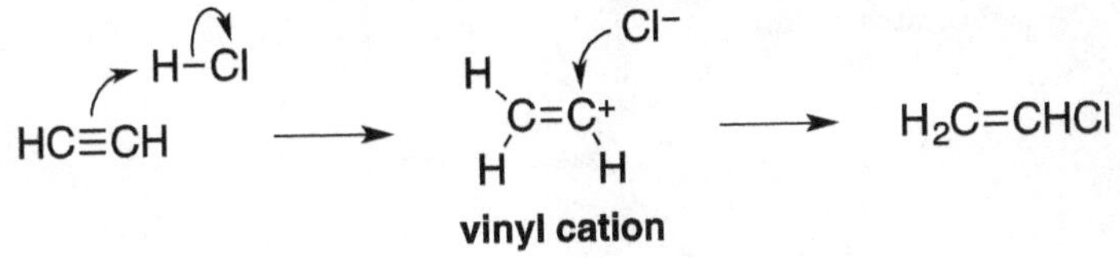
H–Cl
HC≡CH
Cl⁻
H
C=C+
H H
vinyl cation
H2C=CHCl

Figure 7.7, Reaction 2:

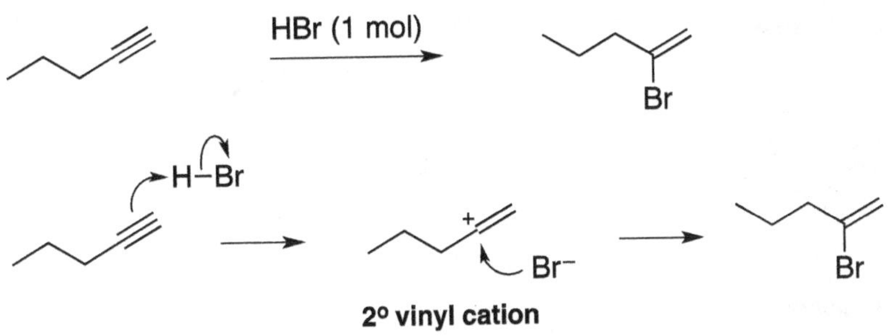
HBr (1 mol)
Br
H–Br
Br⁻
2° vinyl cation
Br

Figure 7.7, Reaction 3:

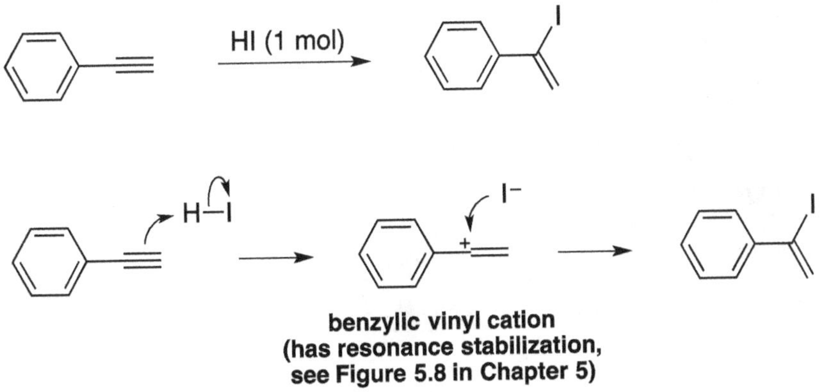
HI (1 mol)
I
H–I
I⁻
benzylic vinyl cation
(has resonance stabilization,
see Figure 5.8 in Chapter 5)
I

Figure 7.10, Reaction 1:

$$HC \equiv CH \xrightarrow[\text{HgSO}_4 \text{ (catalyst)}]{\text{H}_2\text{SO}_4, \text{H}_2\text{O}} \underset{\text{H}_3\text{C}}{\overset{\text{O}}{\|}}\text{C}-\text{H}$$

vinyl cation   oxonium cation   *(proton transfer)*   enol

keto-enol tautomerization

acetaldehyde

Figure 7.10, Reaction 2:

$$\xrightarrow[\text{HgSO}_4 \text{ (catalyst)}]{\text{H}_2\text{SO}_4, \text{H}_2\text{O}}$$

keto-enol tautomerization

Figure 7.10, Reaction 3:

$$\xrightarrow{\text{H}_2\text{SO}_4, \text{H}_2\text{O}}$$

keto-enol tautomerization

Figure 7.11, Reaction 1:

1-propyne

1. BH₃, THF
2. H₂O₂, NaOH, H₂O

enol

HO⁻, H₂O

keto-enol tautomerism

propanal

Simplified mechanism:

BH₃

(hydroboration step, see Section 6.4)

vinylborane

H₂O₂

(oxidation step, see Section 6.4)

enol

keto-enol tautomerization

Figure 7.11, Reaction 2:

ethynylbenzene

1. BH₃, THF
2. H₂O₂, NaOH, H₂O

2-phenylacetaldehyde

Simplified mechanism:

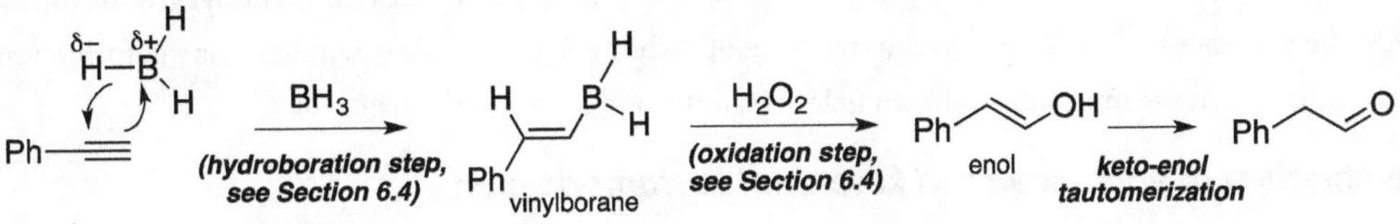

Ph—≡

$\delta-$ $\delta+$
H—B
H
H

BH₃

(hydroboration step, see Section 6.4)

Ph
vinylborane

H
B
H
H

H₂O₂

(oxidation step, see Section 6.4)

Ph⁀OH

enol

keto-enol tautomerization

Ph⁀O

Problem 7.8. Draw the enol form of the following compounds:

a) 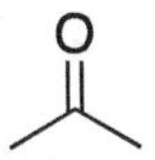   b) 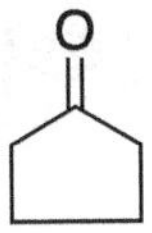   c) 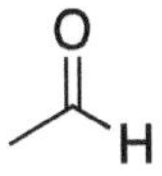   d)

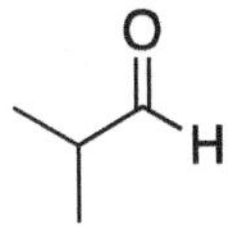

Solution:

a)

OH

enol

b)

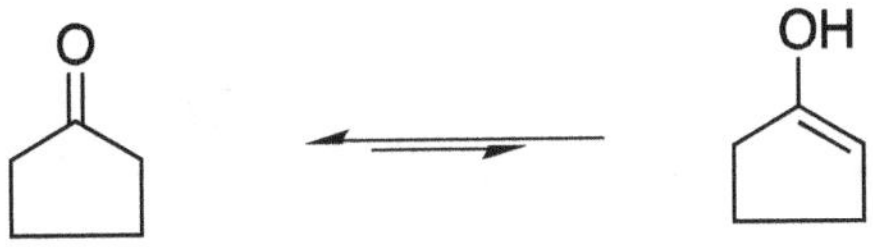

OH

enol

c)

OH
H

enol

d)

OH
H

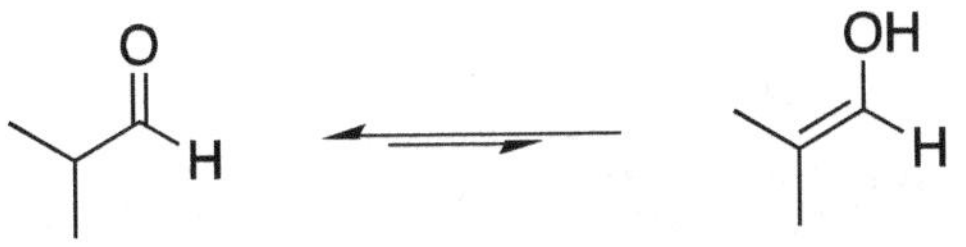

enol

Problem 7.9. Explain why the following carbonyl compounds do not have an enol form.

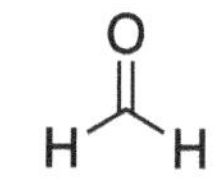

formaldehyde 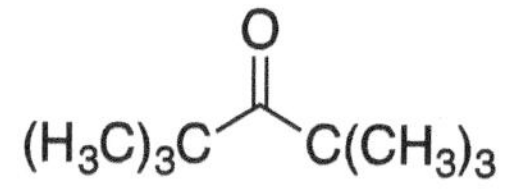   di-*tert*-butyl ketone 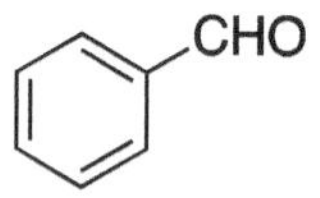   benzaldehyde

Solution:

All these carbonyl compounds lack the hydrogen atom at the carbon atom adjacent to the carbonyl group (the so-called α-position). The presence of α-hydrogen in the structure of carbonyl compounds is required for the formation of the enol form as explained in the mechanism shown below (see also Figure 7.9 in the textbook):

Mechanism of acid-catalyzed keto-enol tautomerization:

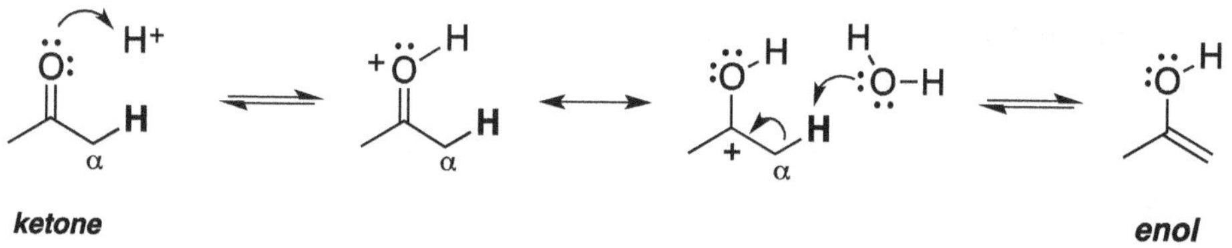

ketone   enol

Problem 7.10. Determine which reagents are required to obtain the indicated products in high yield.

a)

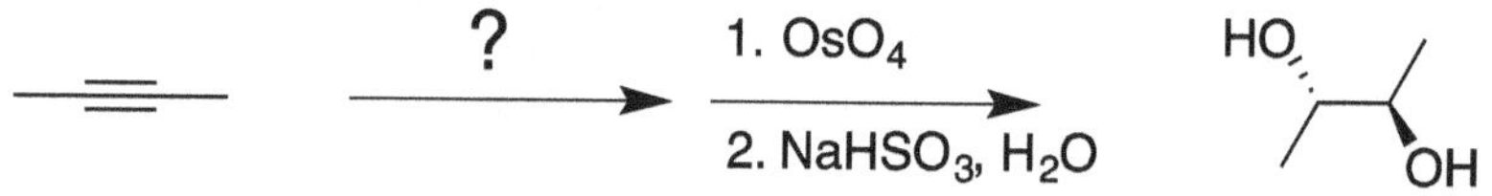

b)

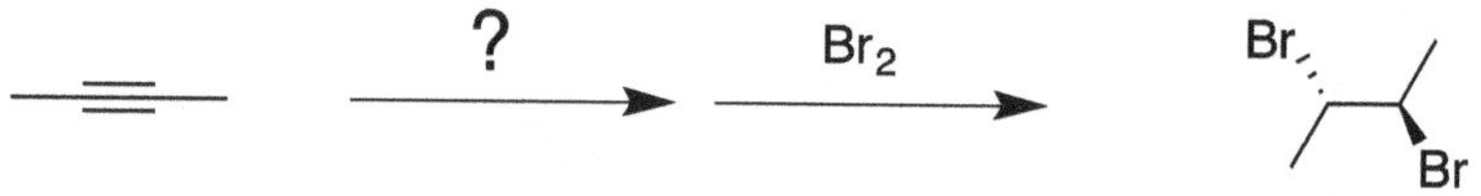

c)

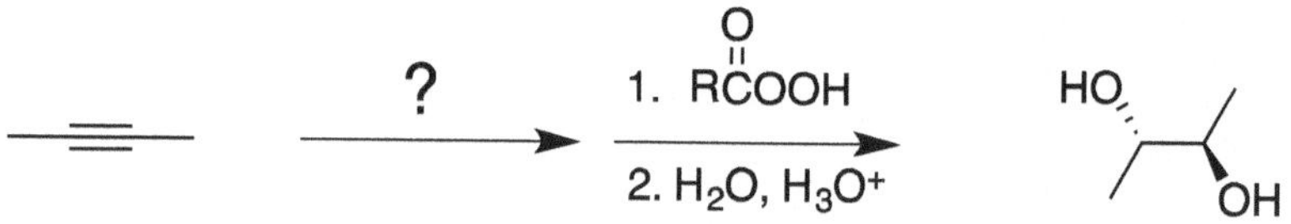

Solution:

a)

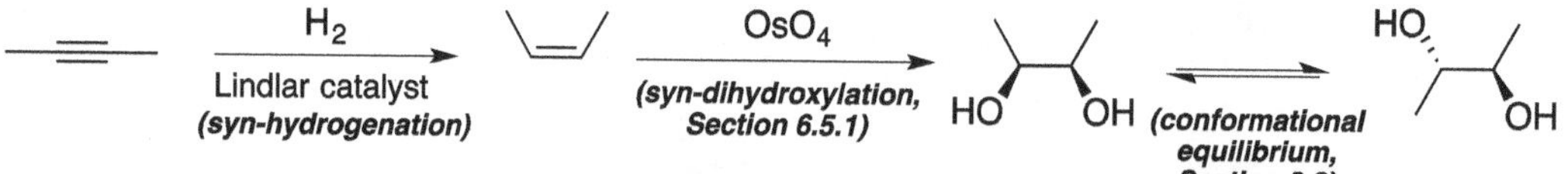

H_2
Lindlar catalyst
(syn-hydrogenation)

OsO_4
(syn-dihydroxylation, Section 6.5.1)

(conformational equilibrium, Section 3.3)

b)

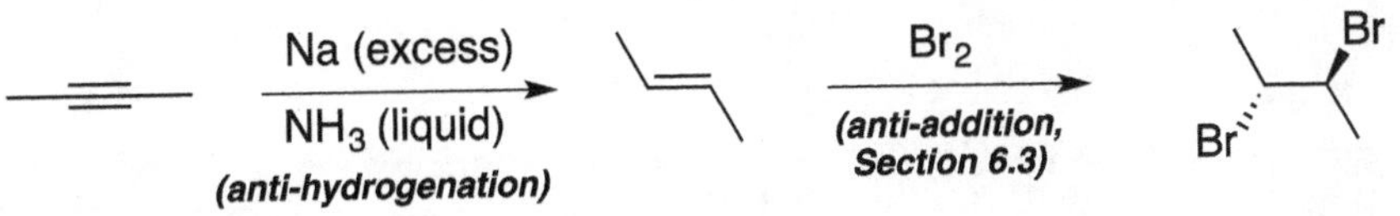

c)

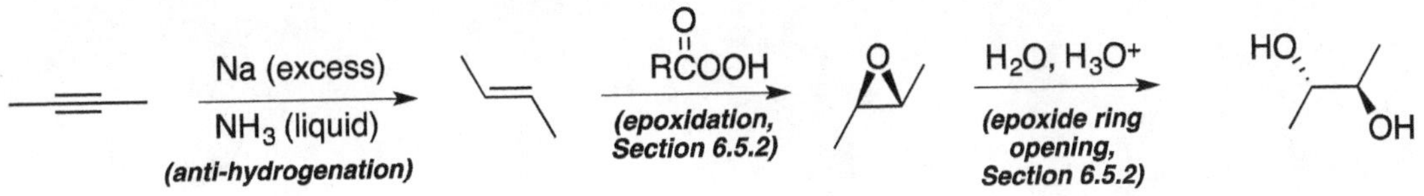

Problem 7.11. Provide the product of the following transformation:

$$\text{NBS} \xrightarrow{\text{light}} \quad HC{\equiv}C{-}Na^+ \quad \xrightarrow{\begin{array}{c}1.\ BH_3 \\ 2.\ NaOH,\ H_2O_2\end{array}} \quad ?$$

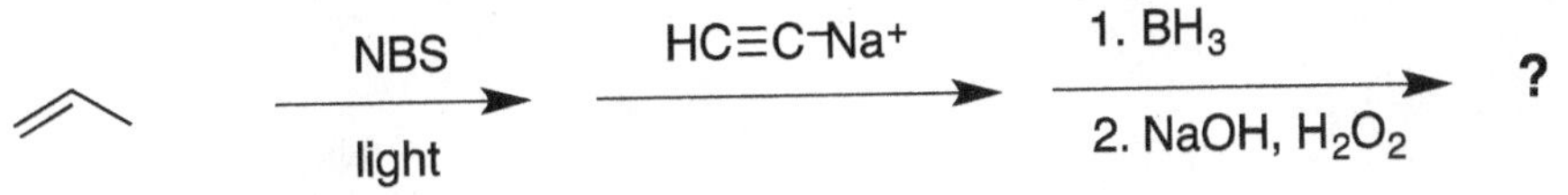

Solution:

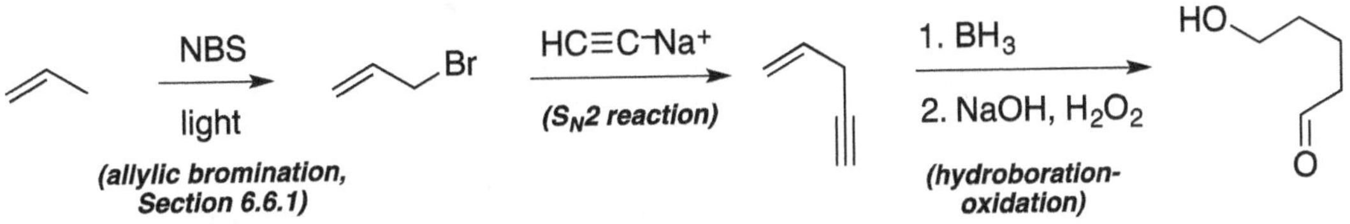

Problem 7.12. Provide the products of the following transformations:

a) $H_3C{-}C{\equiv}CH$ $\xrightarrow{\text{NaH}}$ $\xrightarrow[\text{2. }H_2O]{1.\ \triangle\!O}$ $\xrightarrow[\text{Lindlar cat.}]{H_2}$?

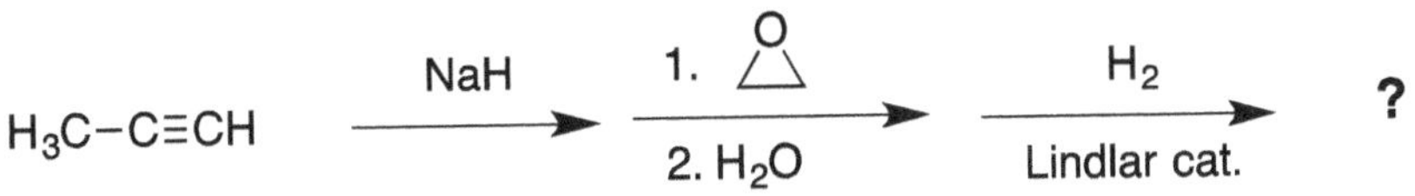

b) $\xrightarrow{\text{NaH}}$ $\xrightarrow{CH_3I}$ $\xrightarrow[\text{NH}_3]{\text{Na}}$?

c) $\xrightarrow{\text{NaH}}$ $\xrightarrow{D_2O}$ $\xrightarrow[\text{Pd}]{H_2}$?

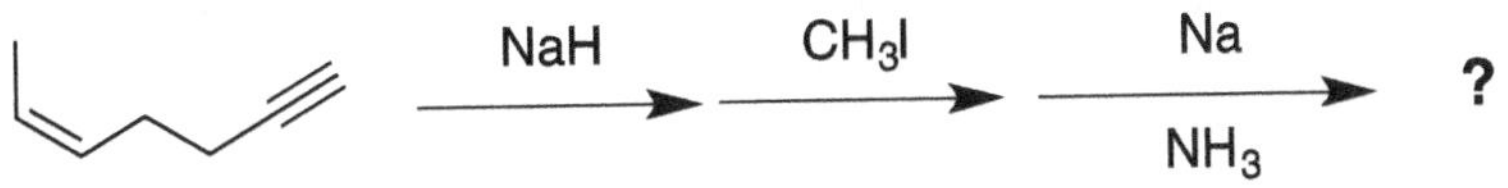

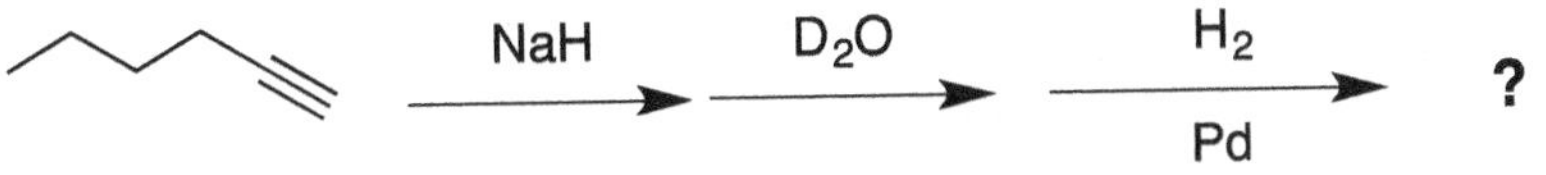

Solution:

a)

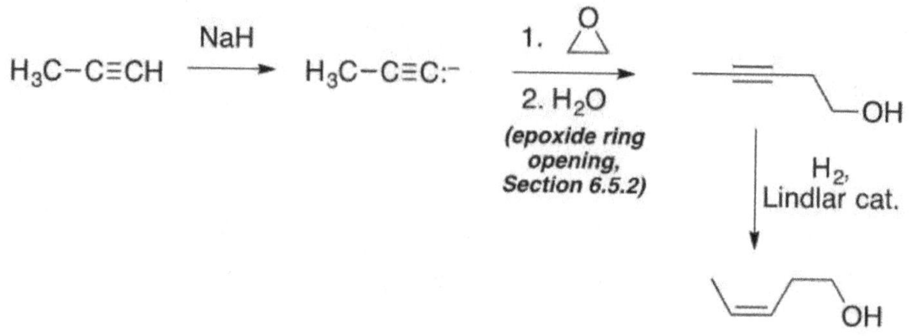

$H_3C-C\equiv CH$ → [NaH] → $H_3C-C\equiv C:^-$ →

1. [epoxide O]
2. H_2O
(epoxide ring opening, Section 6.5.2)

→ (alkyne-OH)

→ [H_2, Lindlar cat.] → (cis-alkene-OH)

b)

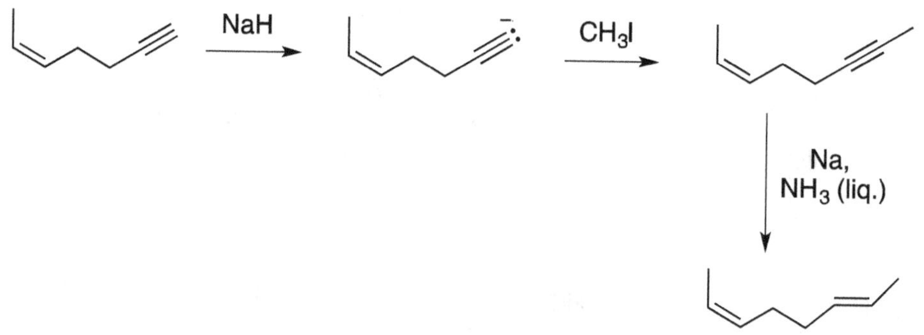

(cis-alkene-alkyne) → [NaH] → (anion) → [CH_3I] → (methylated alkyne)

→ [Na, NH_3 (liq.)] → (diene)

c)

(hexyne) → [NaH] → (anion) → [D_2O, *(D⁺ transfer)*] → (alkyne-D)

→ [H_2, Pd] → (alkane-D)

D = ^2H (deuterium, isotope of hydrogen)

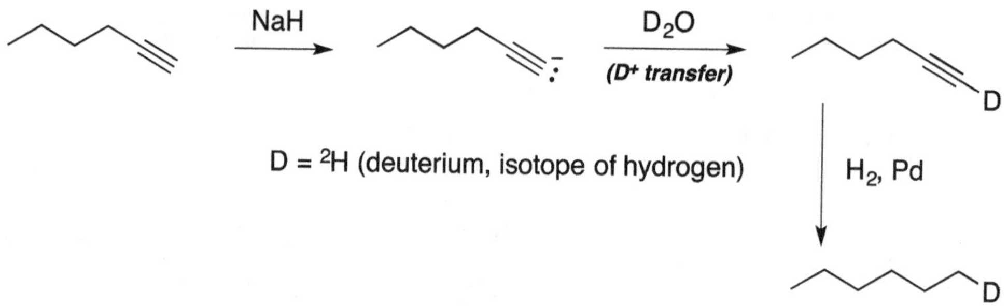

Problem 7.13. Provide the reagents and reaction conditions to accomplish the following syntheses in high yield:

a)

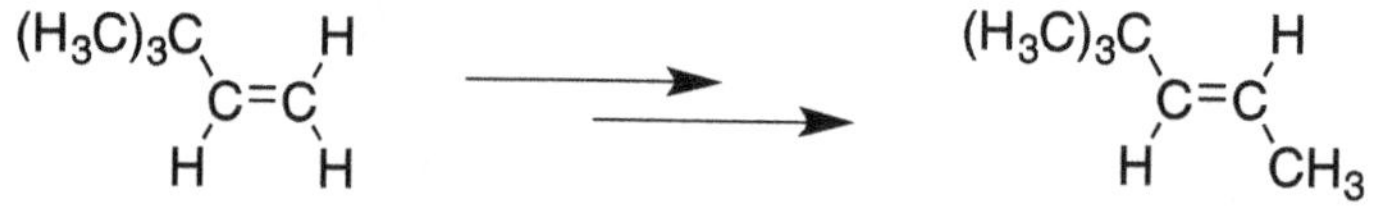

$(H_3C)_3C$, H / $C=C$ / H, H → $(H_3C)_3C$, H / $C=C$ / H, CH_3

b)

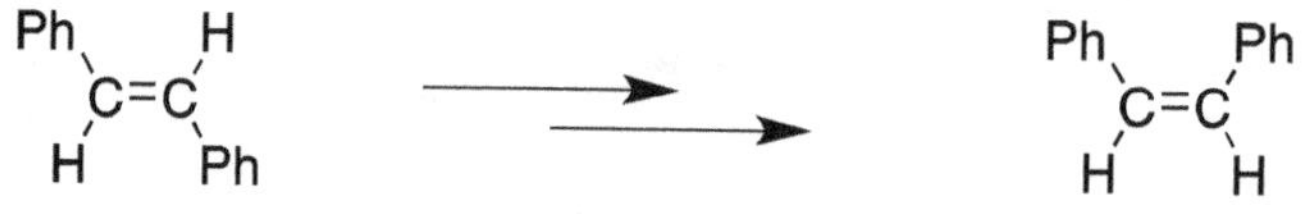

Ph, H / $C=C$ / H, Ph → Ph, Ph / $C=C$ / H, H

c)

$2\ PhCH_2Br$ and $HC\equiv CH$ → $2\ PhCH_2CHO$

Solution:

a)

b)

c)

7.2. Additional Problems for Chapter 7 (for answers see Ch 17)

Problem 7.14. Select the most suitable sequence of reactions that can be used to convert 1-pentene to 1-pentyne.

    a) treatment with HBr; followed by treatment with NaOH

    b) treatment with Br_2; followed by treatment with $NaNH_2$

    c) treatment with Br_2; followed by treatment with H_2SO_4

    d) treatment with Br_2 and H_2O; followed by treatment with NaOH

    e) treatment with Br_2; followed by treatment with NaOH

    f) treatment with HBr; followed by treatment with $NaNH_2$

Problem 7.15. What is the correct assignment of the *acid, base, conjugate acid* and *conjugate base* in the following equilibrium?

$$H_3C-C\equiv C-H \quad + \quad {}^-\ddot{N}H_2 \quad \rightleftharpoons \quad H_3C-C\equiv C:^- \quad + \quad :NH_3$$

          1   **2**   **3**   **4**

Problem 7.16. What is the best choice of reagent(s) to perform the following transformation?

a) H_2/ Pt   b) H_2/ Lindlar catalyst   c) Na/ NH_3(liq)

d) BH_3; followed by H_2O_2/ NaOH   e) Br_2; followed by 2 mol $NaNH_2$

Problem 7.17. Fill one reagent in each box to complete the transformation in the following scheme.

Alcohols

8.1. Chapter 8 Problems and Solutions

Problem 8.1. Which of the following is a 2° alcohol?

Ethylene glycol, ethyl alcohol, cyclopentanol, 2-methyl-2-propanol

Solution:

Structures of these compounds are shown below:

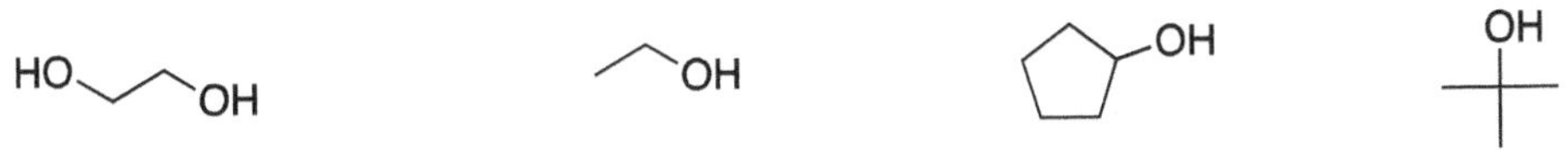

ethylene glycol (IUPAC name: ethane-1,2-diol)	ethyl alcohol (IUPAC name: ethanol)	cyclopentanol	2-methyl-2-propanol
1° alcohol	*1° alcohol*	*2° alcohol*	*3° alcohol*

A **secondary alcohol** has two carbon atoms and one hydrogen atom substituted onto the OH-bearing carbon. Therefore, only cyclopentanol is a secondary alcohol.

Problem 8.2. Sort the following according to increasing boiling point. List the molecule with the lowest boiling point first.

1,2,3-propantriol, hexane, 1-pentanol, 1,2-butandiol

Solution:

All compounds in this problem have similar molecular masses. Thus the boiling points are solely dependent on the intramolecular forces. The more hydroxyl groups are present in the molecule the higher the boiling point is due to increased hydrogen bonding:

hexane (bp 68 °C) < 1-pentanol (bp: 138 °C) < 1,2-butandiol (bp 195 °C) < 1,2,3-propantriol (bp 290 °C).

Problem 8.3. For each reaction provide the IUPAC name of the major product. If applicable, indicate stereochemistry.

a)

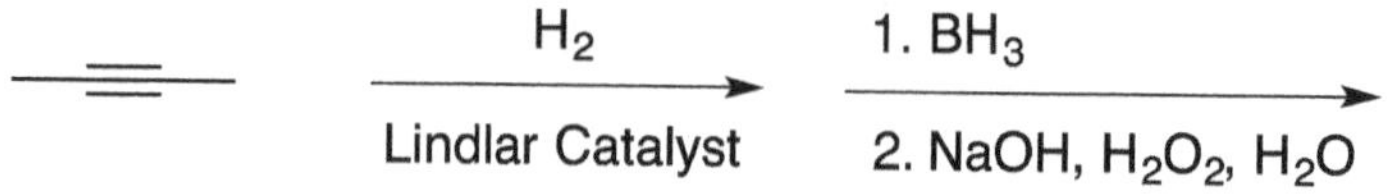

b)

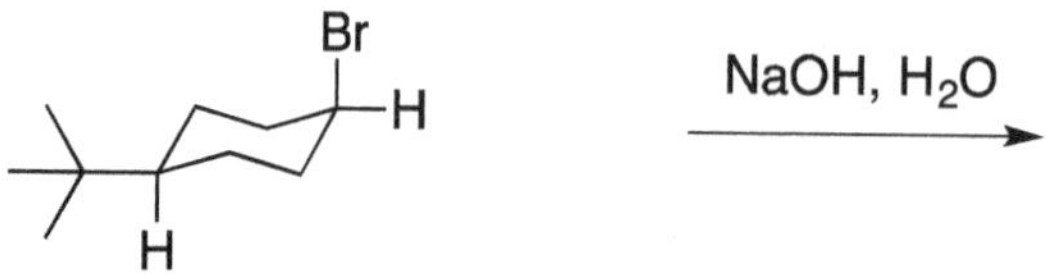

c)

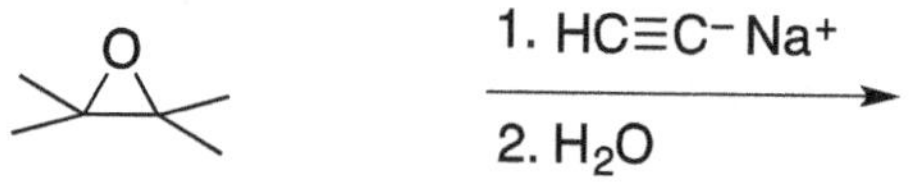

d)

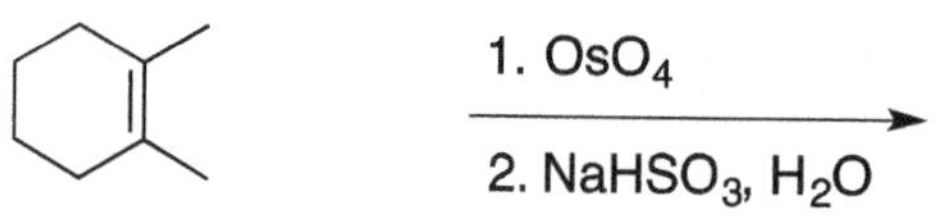

Solution:

a)

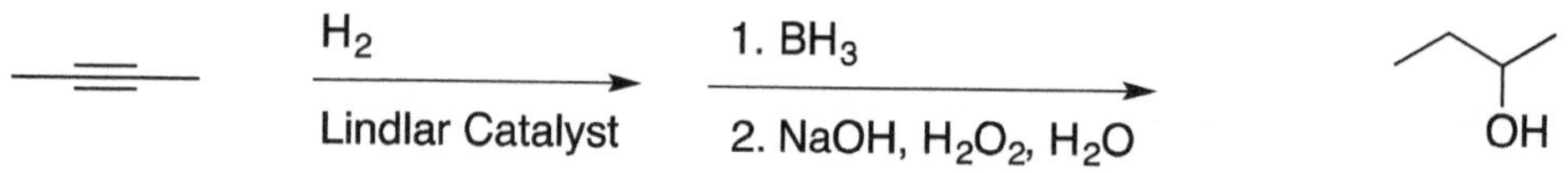

2-butanol

b)

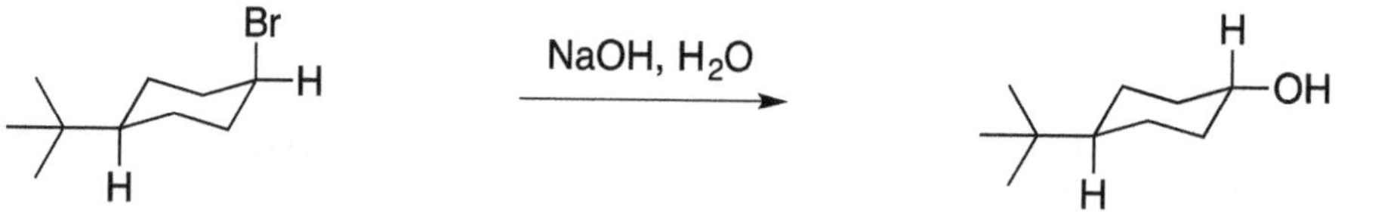

trans-4-(tert-butyl)cyclohexanol

c)

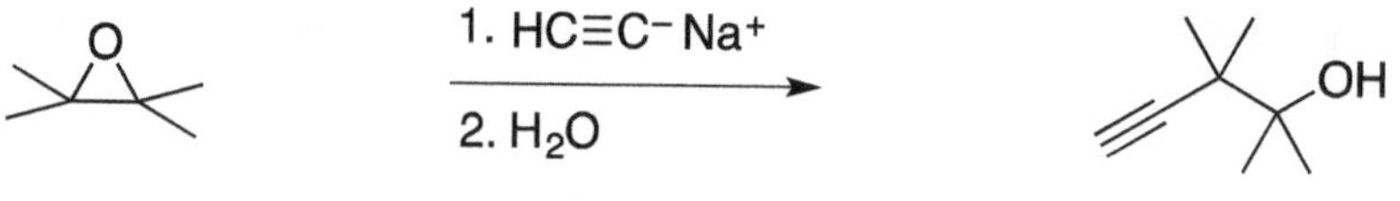

2,3,3-trimethyl-4-pentyn-2-ol

d)

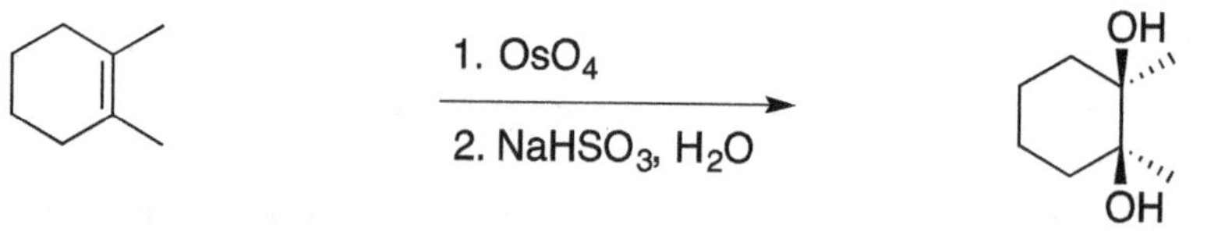

cis-1,2-dimethylcyclohexane-1,2-diol

Problem 8.4.

a) Arrange the alcohols below according to increasing acidity. List the least acidic compounds first.

methanol   trifluoromethanol   *tert*-butanol

b) Sort the conjugated bases of these alcohols according to increasing basicity. List the least basic species first.

Solution:
a) *tert*-butanol $(pK_a\ 17)$ < methanol $(pK_a\ 15.5)$ < trifluoromethanol $(pK_a\ 12.4)$
b) CF_3O^- (weakest base) < CH_3O^- < $(CH_3)_3CO^-$ (strongest base)

Alcohols with electron-withdrawing substituents have higher acidity (see Figure 2.6 in Section 2.3). The anions of stronger acids have weaker acidity.

Problem 8.5. Sort the following ions according increasing basicity. List the least basic ion first.

CH_3NH^- CH_3^- CH_3O^- $HCOO^-$

Solution:
$HCOO^- < CH_3O^- < CH_3NH^- < CH_3^-$

Problem 8.6. a) Give the product and write the mechanism for the following transformation:

b) What would be the outcome of the above transformation if *trans*-2-methyl-cyclohexanol was used instead of the haloalkane?

Solution:
a) The major product of this reaction sequence is (R)-3-methylcyclohexene.

(*R*)-3-methylcyclohexene

Mechanism:

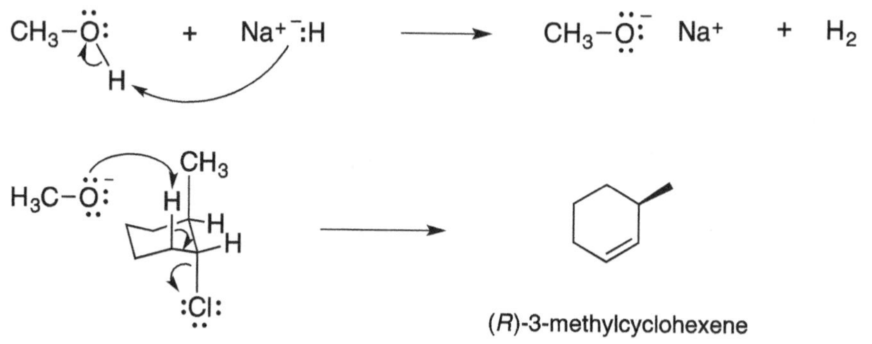

(R)-3-methylcyclohexene

b) Methanol and *trans*-2-methylcyclohexanol have similar pK$_a$ values. Treatment of *trans*-2-methylcyclohexa-nol with sodium methoxide (NaOCH$_3$) will result in a partial deprotonation of the cyclohexanol compound. Elimination will not occur because of the absence of the required leaving group (e.g., Cl).

Problem 8.7. Provide the major product in each of the following reactions:

a)

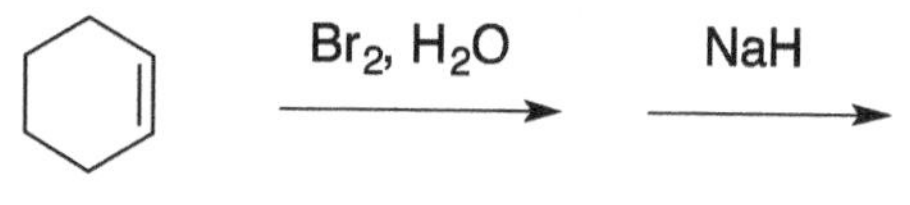

Br$_2$, H$_2$O   NaH

b)

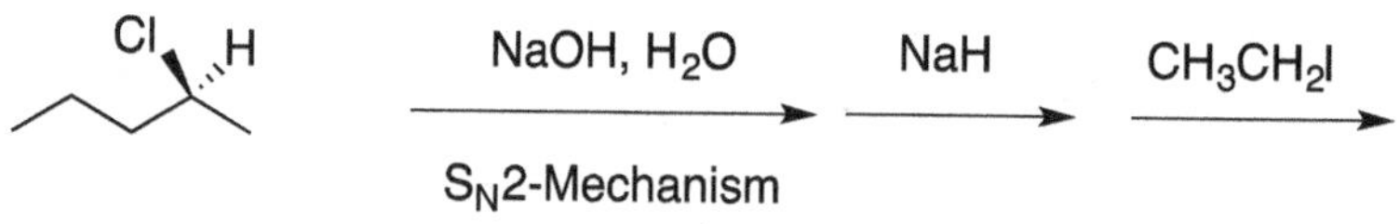

NaOH, H$_2$O   NaH   CH$_3$CH$_2$I

S$_N$2-Mechanism

c)

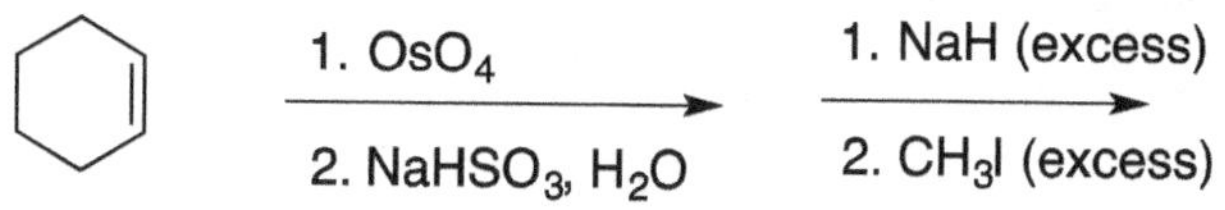

1. OsO$_4$ 1. NaH (excess)

2. NaHSO$_3$, H$_2$O   2. CH$_3$I (excess)

Solution:

a)

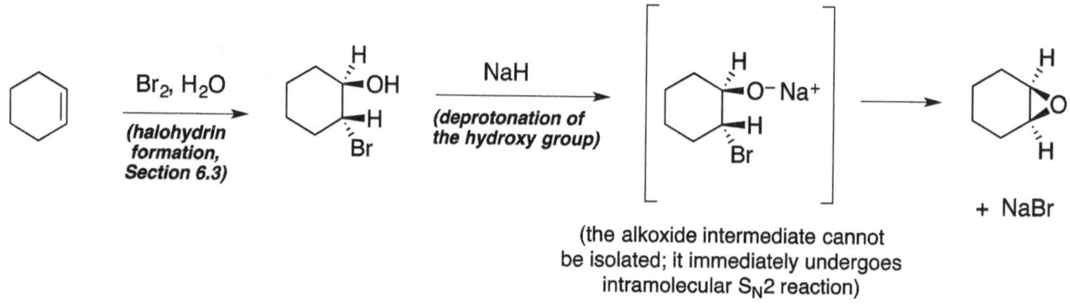

Br$_2$, H$_2$O
(halohydrin formation, Section 6.3)

NaH
(deprotonation of the hydroxy group)

(the alkoxide intermediate cannot be isolated; it immediately undergoes intramolecular S$_N$2 reaction)

+ NaBr

b)

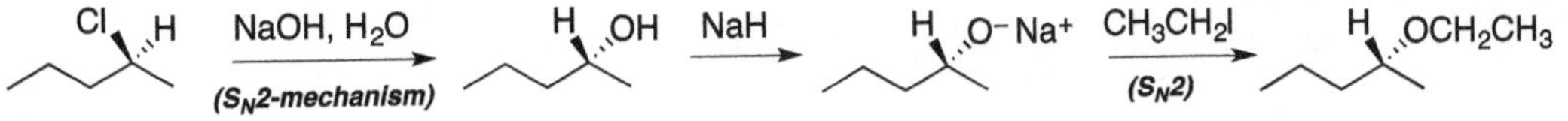

(S$_N$2-mechanism)

c)

1. OsO$_4$

2. NaHSO$_3$, H$_2$O

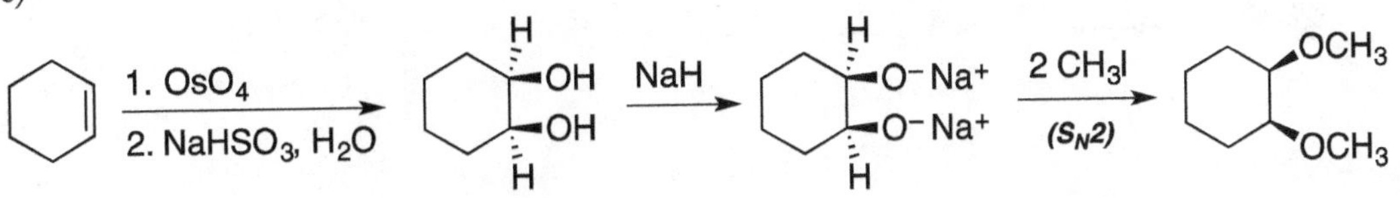

(dihydroxylation of alkenes; see Section 6.5.3)

Problem 8.8. Propose a mechanism for the formation of diethyl ether from ethanol in the presence of sulfuric acid as catalyst.

Solution:

The condensation of two molecules of ethanol results in formation of one molecule of diethyl ether and one molecule of water. Experimentally, since this reaction is an equilibrium reaction the water needs to be removed from the reaction mixture.

Mechanism:

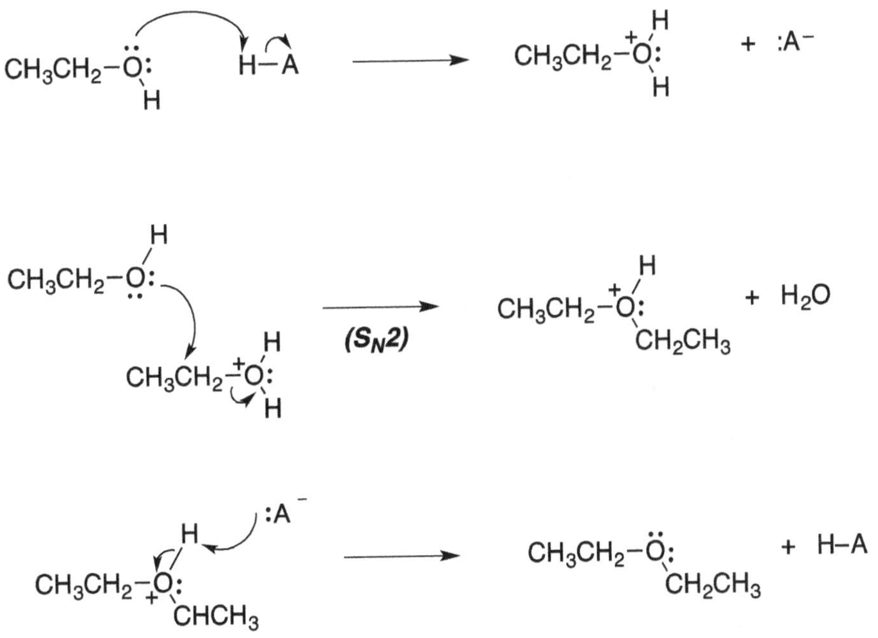

$$CH_3CH_2-\overset{..}{\underset{H}{O}}: \quad H-A \longrightarrow CH_3CH_2-\overset{H}{\overset{+}{O}}: \quad + \quad :A^-$$

$$CH_3CH_2-\overset{H}{\underset{..}{O}}: \quad CH_3CH_2-\overset{H}{\underset{H}{\overset{+}{O}}}: \quad \xrightarrow{(S_N2)} \quad CH_3CH_2-\overset{H}{\overset{+}{O}}:{CH_2CH_3} \quad + \quad H_2O$$

$$CH_3CH_2-\overset{H}{\underset{CHCH_3}{\overset{+}{O}}}: \quad :A^- \longrightarrow CH_3CH_2-\overset{..}{O}:{CH_2CH_3} \quad + \quad H-A$$

H–A = H$_2$SO$_4$ (sulfuric acid)

Problem 8.9. Suggest a mechanism that accounts for the formation of 2-bromo-2-methylbutane from 3-methyl-2-butanol and HBr.

Solution:

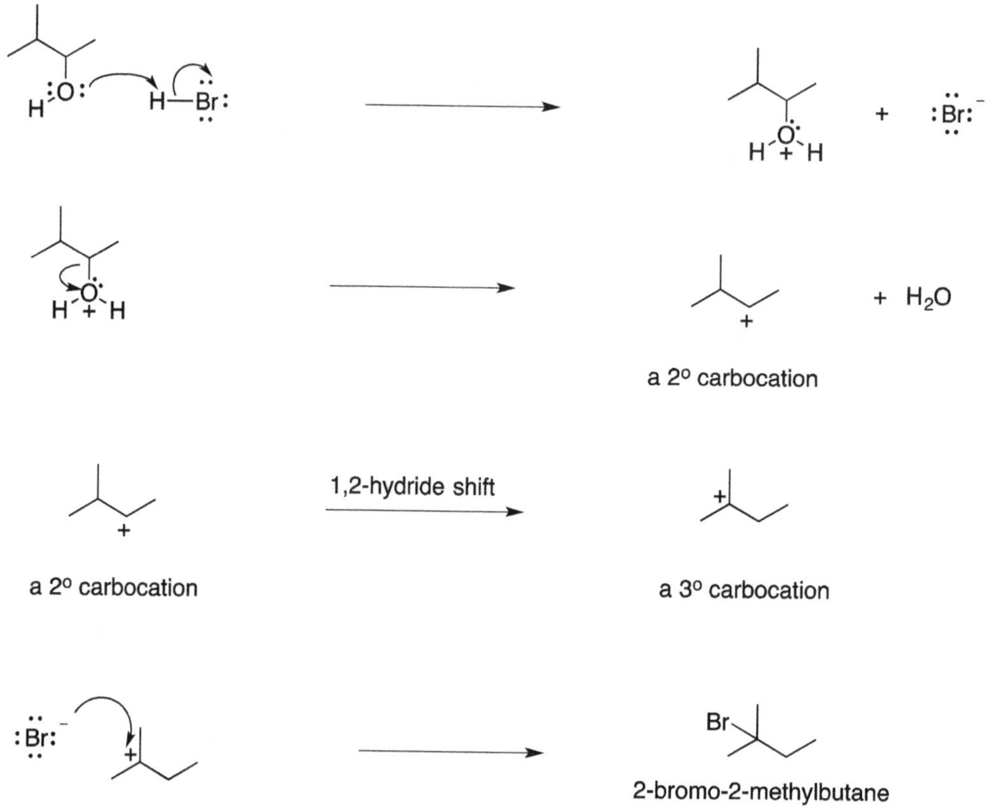

a 2° carbocation

a 2° carbocation

1,2-hydride shift

a 3° carbocation

2-bromo-2-methylbutane

Problem 8.10. Provide the major product in each of the following reactions:

a) 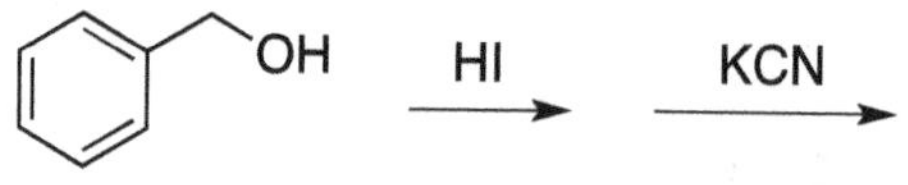 OH   HI   KCN

b) 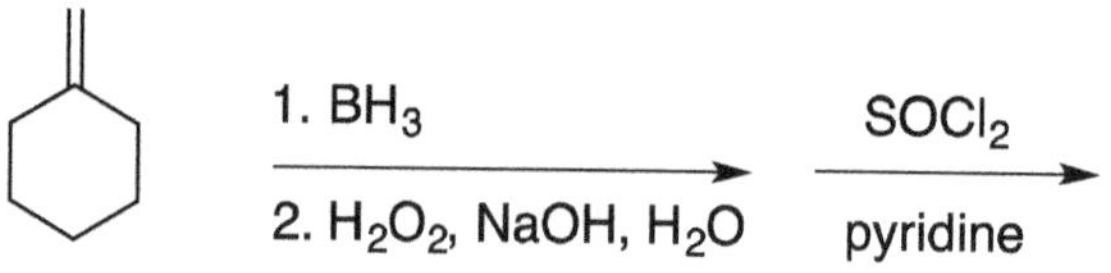   1. BH₃ / 2. H₂O₂, NaOH, H₂O   SOCl₂ / pyridine

c) 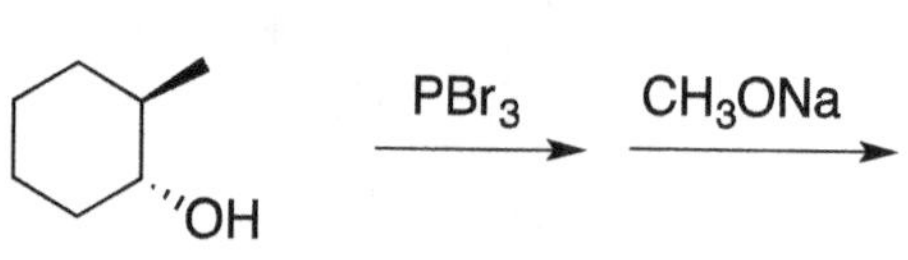 ''OH   PBr₃   CH₃ONa

d) 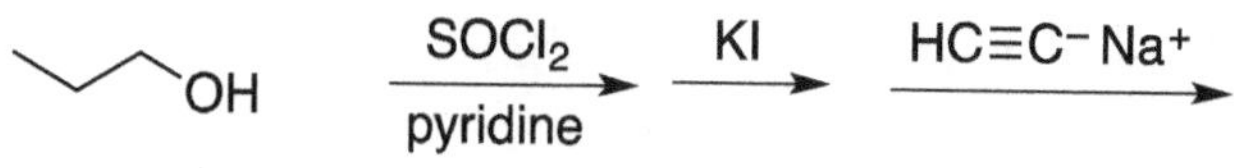 OH   SOCl₂ / pyridine   KI   HC≡C⁻Na⁺

Solution:

a)

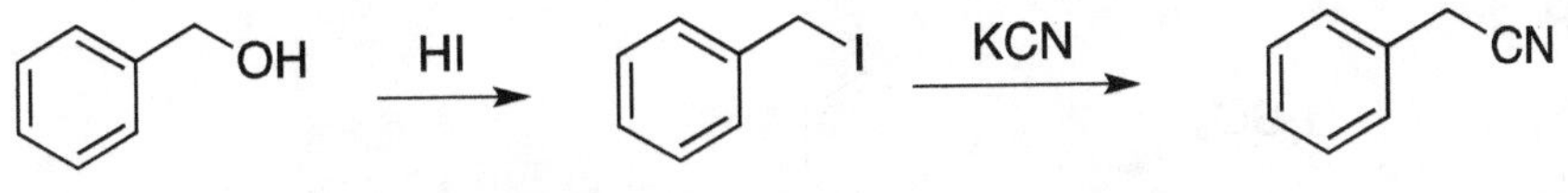

OH
HI
I
KCN
CN

b)

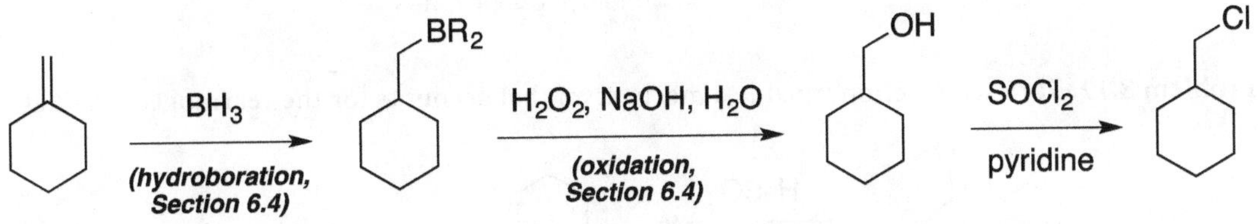

BH3
(hydroboration, Section 6.4)
BR2
H2O2, NaOH, H2O
(oxidation, Section 6.4)
OH
SOCl2
pyridine
Cl

c)

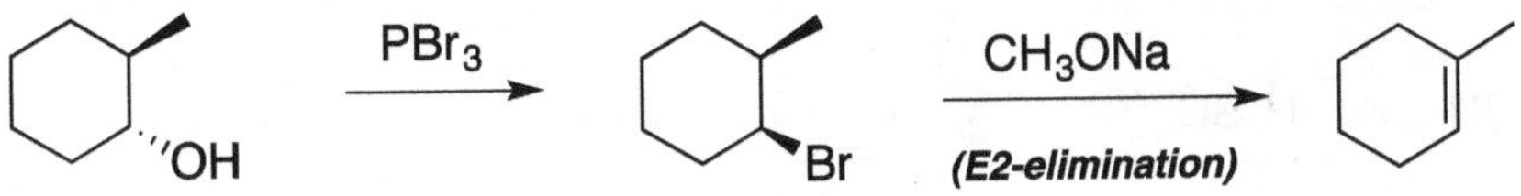

OH
PBr3
Br
CH3ONa
(E2-elimination)

d)

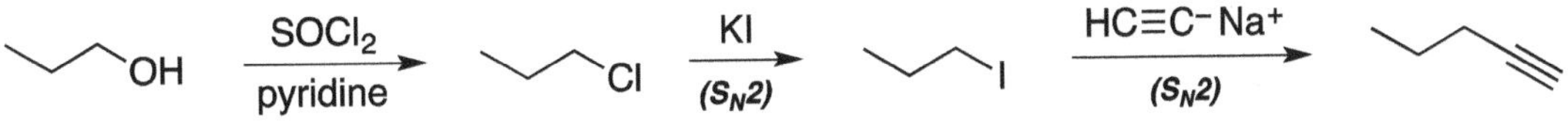

OH
SOCl2
pyridine
Cl
KI
(SN2)
I
HC≡C- Na+
(SN2)

Problem 8.11. Provide major products in the following reactions.

a)

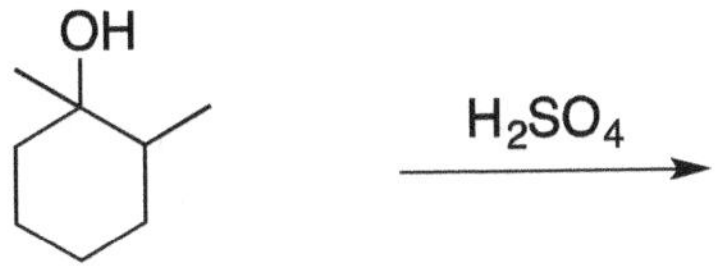

OH
H2SO4

b)

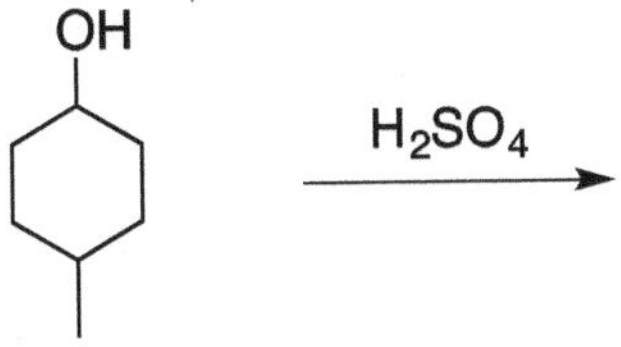

OH
H2SO4

Solution:

a)

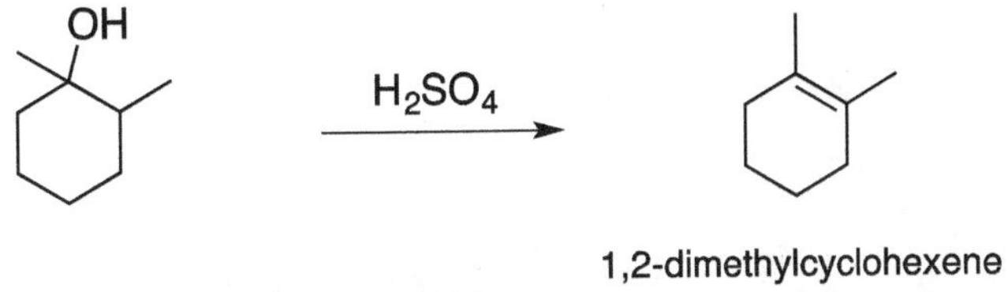

OH
H2SO4
1,2-dimethylcyclohexene

According to Zaitsev's rule (see Section 5.4 of the textbook), the most highly substituted alkene (1,2-dimethylcyclo-hexene) is expected to be the major product in this E1 elimination reaction.

b)

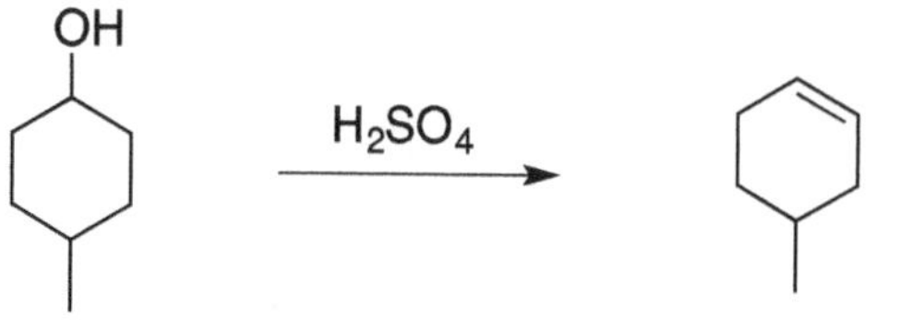

OH

H_2SO_4

4-methylcyclohexene

Problem 8.12. For each reaction provide a mechanism that accounts for the rearranged product.

a)

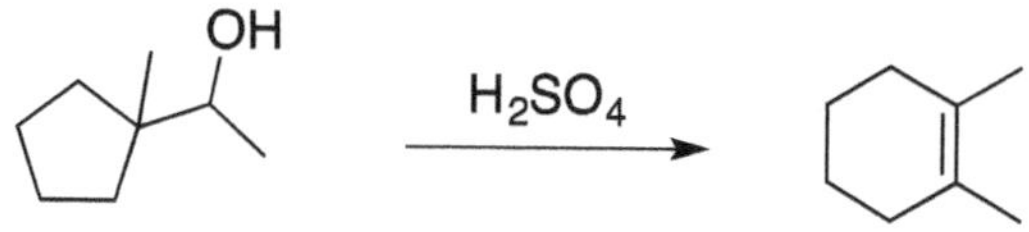

OH

H_2SO_4

b)

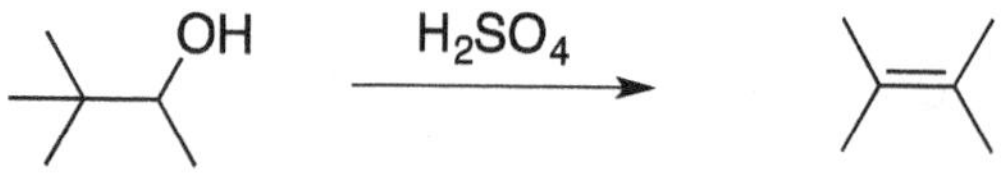

OH

H_2SO_4

Solution:
a)

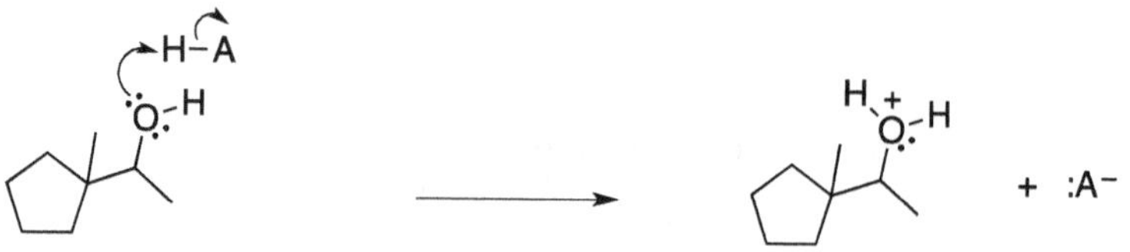

H–A

O–H

H, +, O–H

+ :A⁻

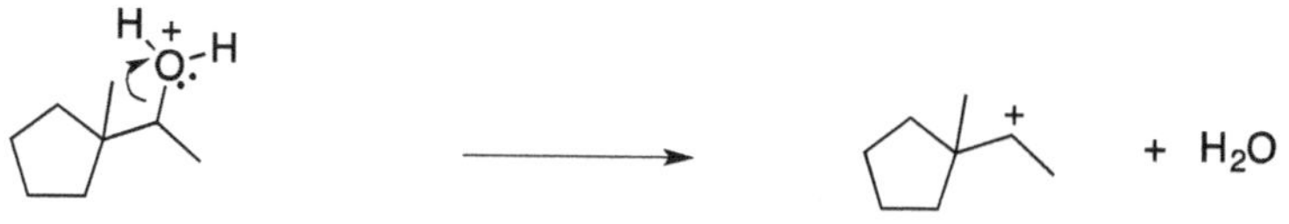

H, +, O–H

+ H₂O

2° carbocation

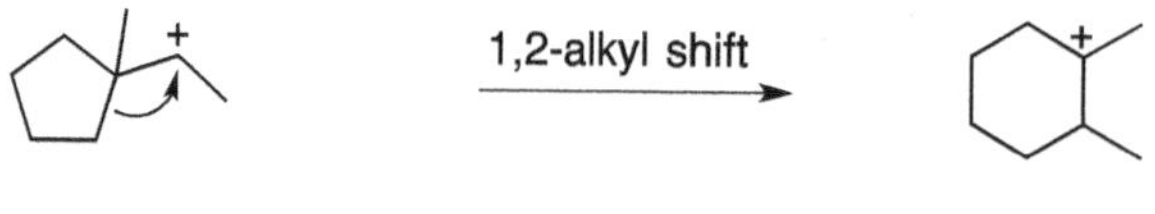

2° carbocation

1,2-alkyl shift

3° carbocation

H

A:⁻

+ HA

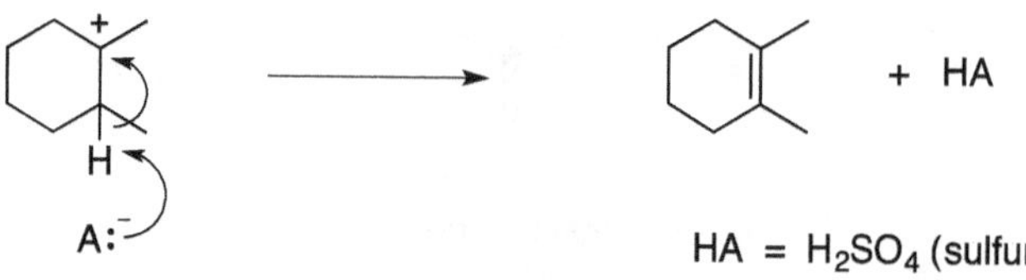

HA = H_2SO_4 (sulfuric acid)

b)

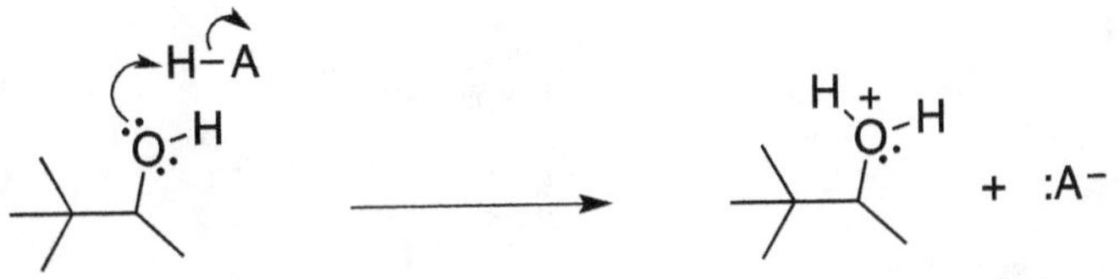
H–A
O–H
H
O–H
+ :A⁻

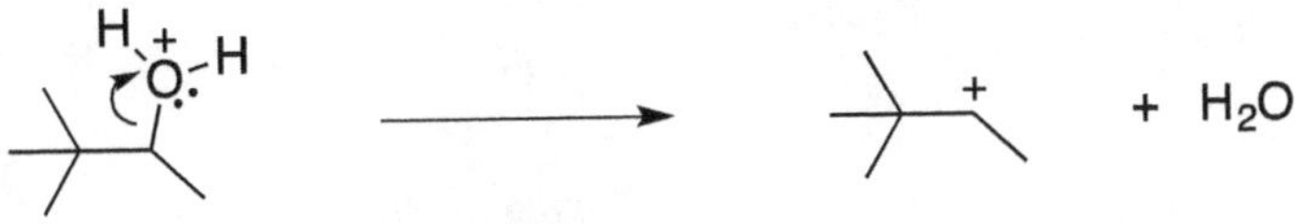
H
O–H
+
+ H_2O

2° carbocation

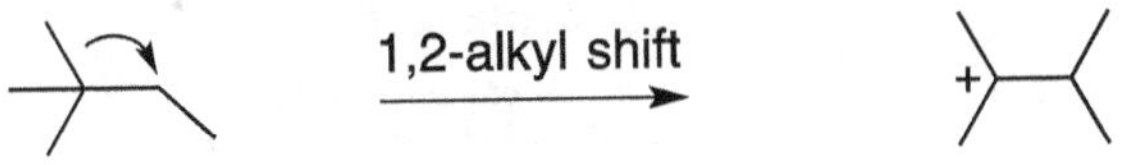
1,2-alkyl shift
+

2° carbocation

3° carbocation

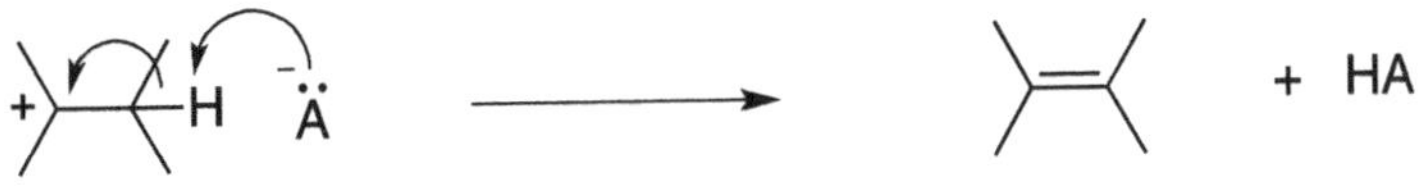
+
H
A
+ HA

HA = H_2SO_4 (sulfuric acid)

Problem 8.13. Provide major products in the following reactions:

a)

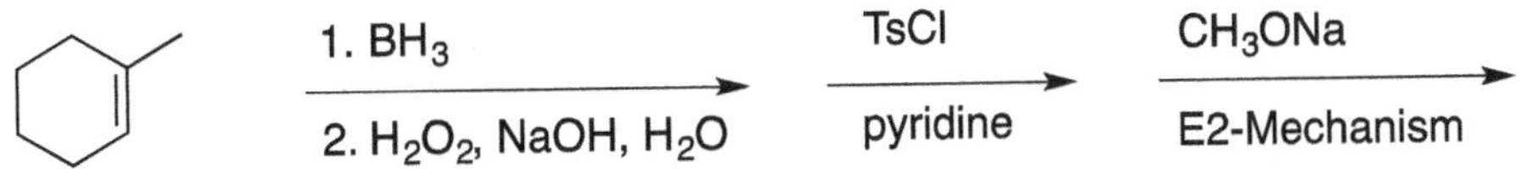
1. BH_3
2. H_2O_2, NaOH, H_2O
TsCl
pyridine
CH_3ONa
E2-Mechanism

b)

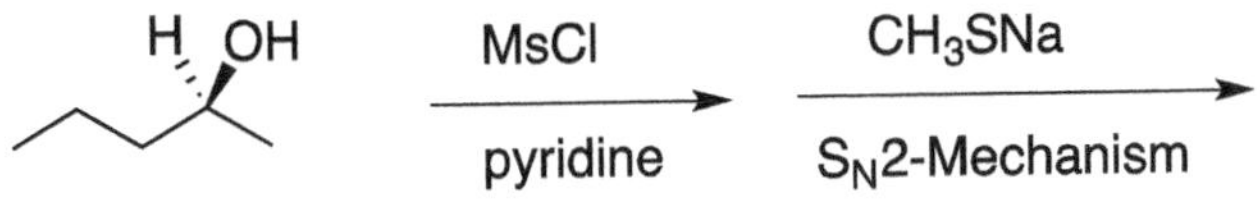
H
OH
MsCl
pyridine
CH_3SNa
S_N2-Mechanism

Solution:

a)

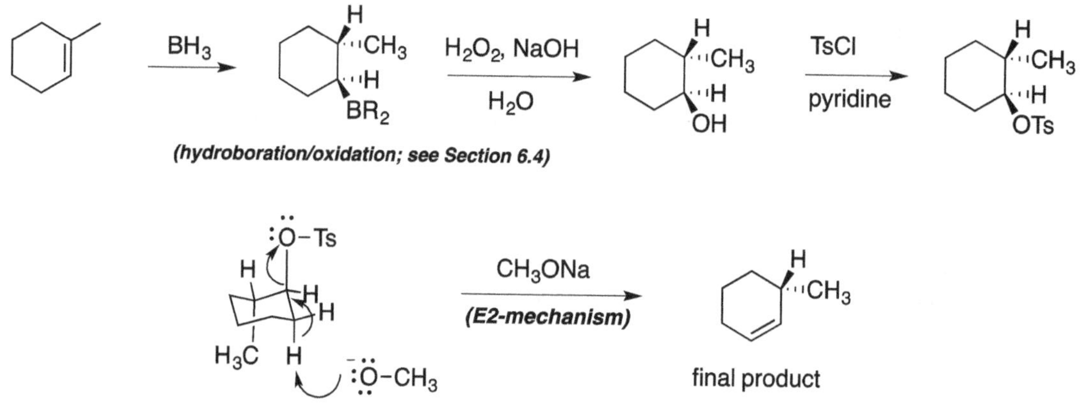

(hydroboration/oxidation; see Section 6.4)

b)

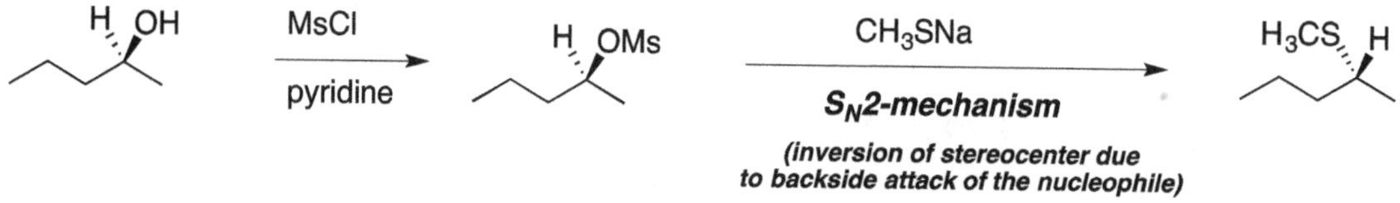

Problem 8.14. Propose a mechanism for the oxidation of a 1° alcohol to aldehyde using IBX.

Solution:

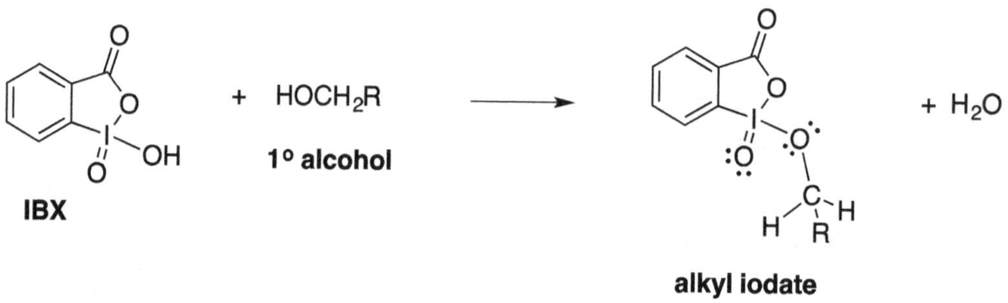

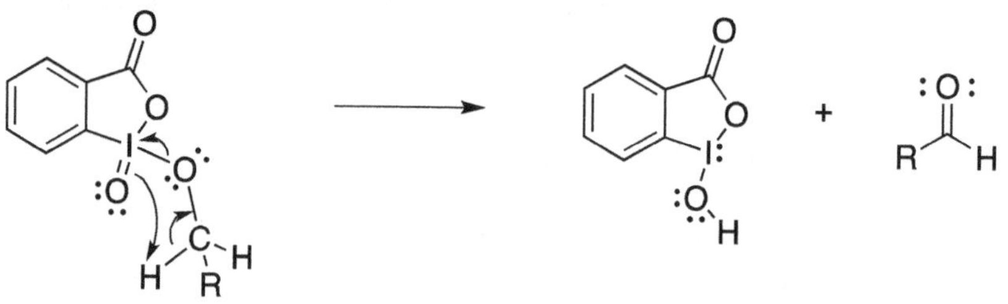

Problem 8.15. Provide major products in the following reactions:

a)

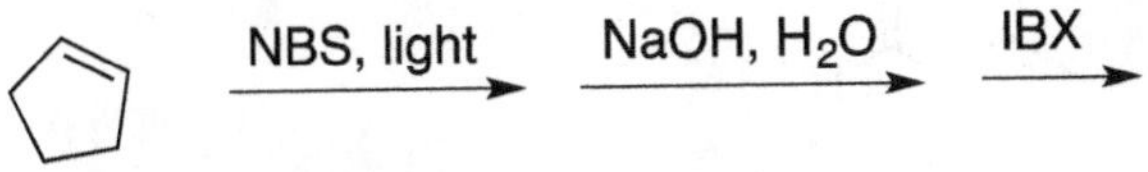

NBS, light → NaOH, H$_2$O → IBX →

b)

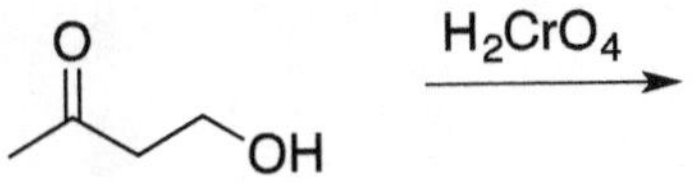

H$_2$CrO$_4$ →

c)

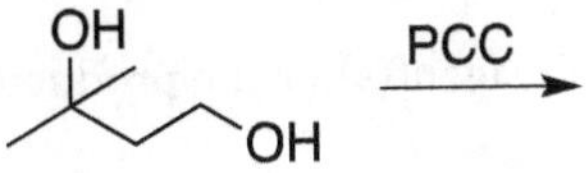

PCC →

Solution:

a)

NBS, light → NaOH, H$_2$O → IBX →

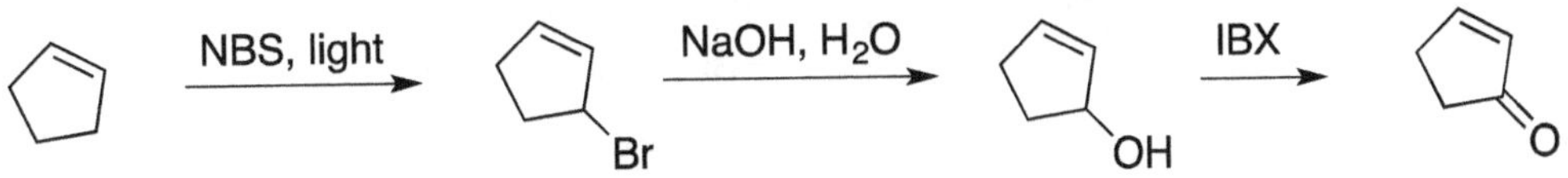

The first step in this reaction sequence is an allylic bromination (see Section 6.6.1 of the textbook). The second step of sequence is nucleophilic substitution reaction with the hydroxide ion (HO⁻) as nucleophile resulting in a 2° allylic alcohol, which is oxidized in the third step to give a ketone.

b)

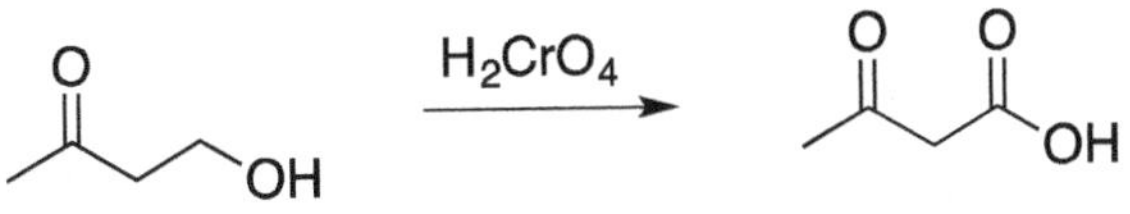

H$_2$CrO$_4$ →

acetoacetic acid

The starting material contains a ketone functional group and a 1° alcohol functional group. Only the 1° alcohol group is oxidized. Based on our knowledge to this point, the oxidation product is acetoacetic acid. We will learn in a later chapter this compound is unstable and will spontaneously loose CO$_2$ to form acetone:

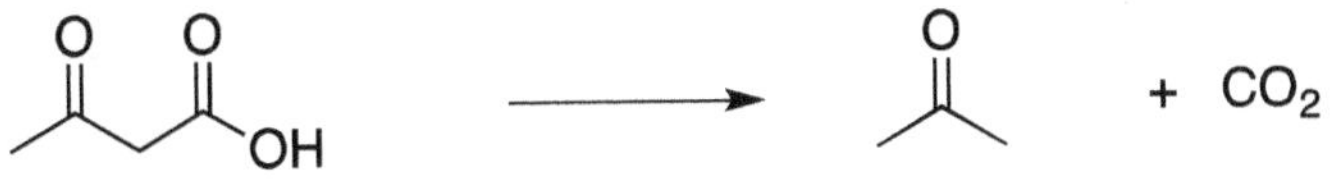

acetoacetic acid → acetone + CO$_2$

c)

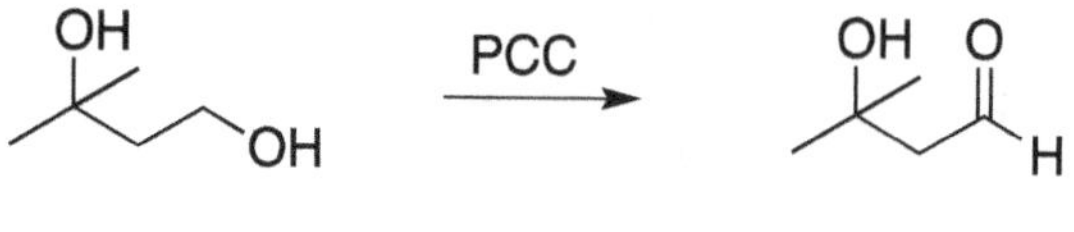

The starting material contains a 3° tertiary alcohol functional group and a 1° alcohol functional group. Only the 1° alcohol functional group is oxidized by PCC to a give an aldehyde.

8.2. Additional Problems for Chapter 8 (for answers see Ch 17)

Problem 8.16. Complete the following reactions by filling in the reagent(s) or the product(s) for each reaction.

a)

b)

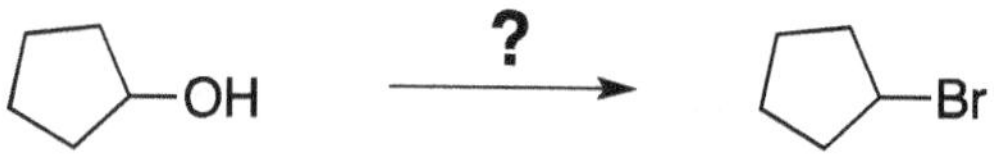

c)

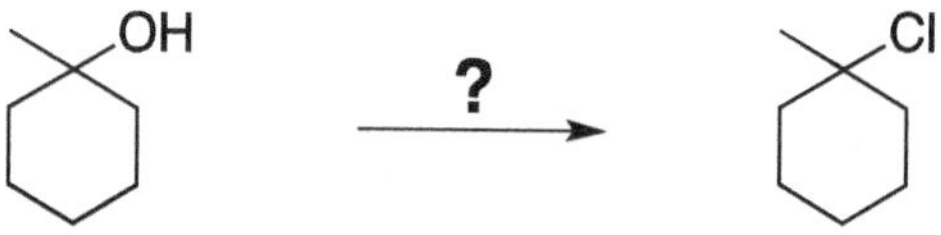

d)

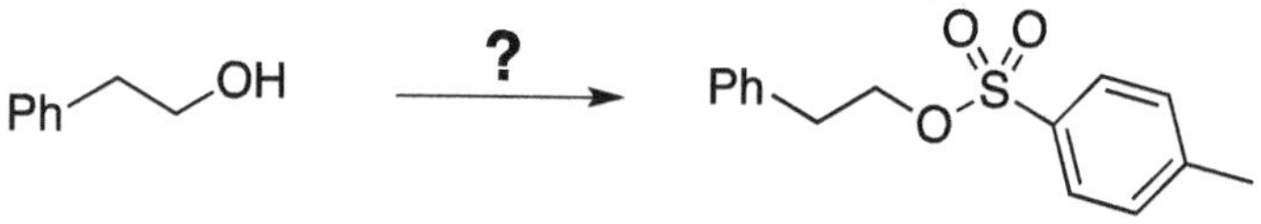

e)

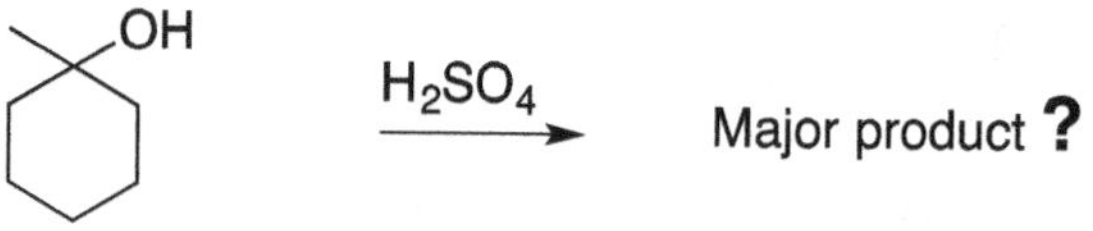

Major product ?

f)

Major product ? Minor product ?

g)

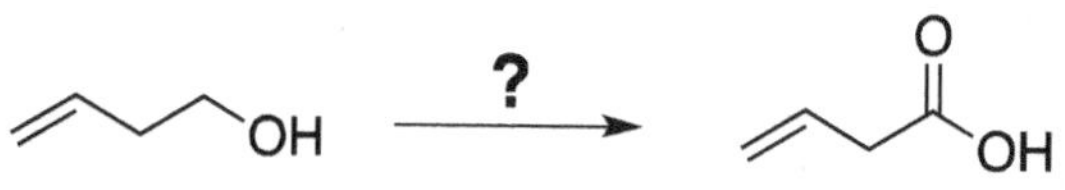

h)

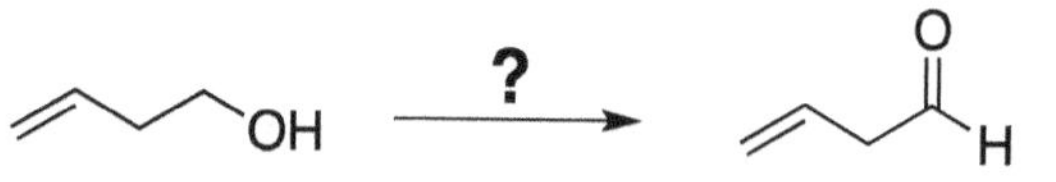

i)

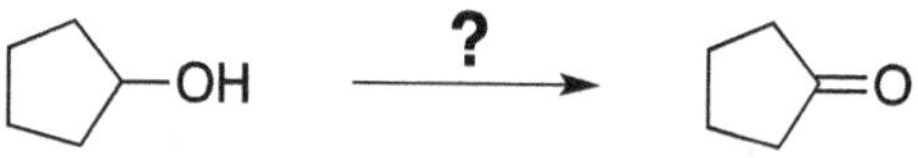

Problem 8.17. Provide reagents that can be used in each nucleophilic substitution reaction in the following scheme to achieve the desired stereochemical outcome.

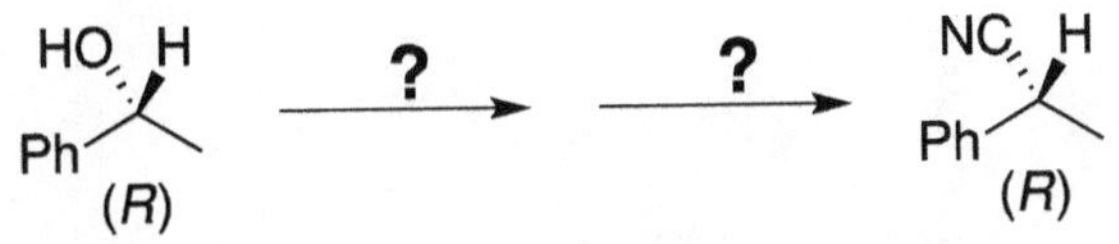

HO H
 \ /
  C ···· H
 /
Ph
(R)   —?→   —?→   NC H
                     \ /
                      C ···· H
                     /
                    Ph
                    (R)

(NOTE: Net retention in configuration at the chiral center in the substitution product)

HO H
 \ /
  C
 /
Ph (R)   —?→   —?→   H CN
                        \ /
                         C
                        /
                      Ph (S)

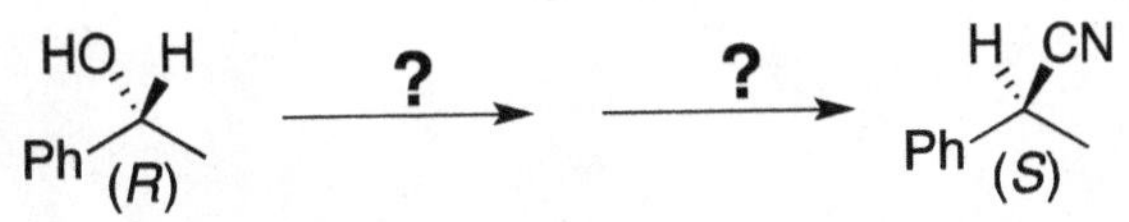

(NOTE: Net inversion in configuration at the chiral center in the substitution product)

Spectroscopy of Organic Compounds

9.1. Chapter 9 Problems and Solutions

Problem 9.1. How many signals do you expect in the ^{13}C NMR spectrum for each of the following compounds:

a) 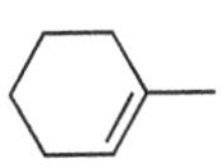   b) 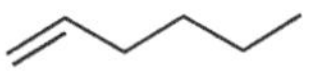   c) 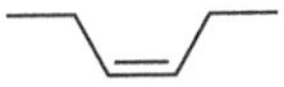   d)

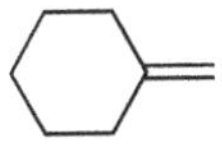

Solution:

a) 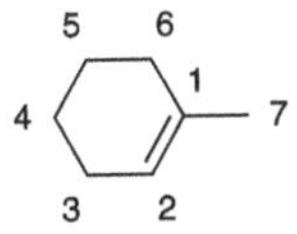   b) 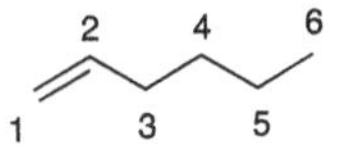   c) 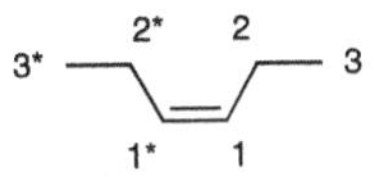   d)

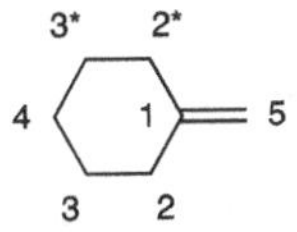

1 and 1* are equivalent;
2 and 2* are equivalent;
3 and 3* are equivalent

2 and 2* are equivalent
3 and 3* are equivalent

7 signals   **6 signals**   **3 signals**   **5 signals**

Problem 9.2. For each compound below, determine the number of the signals and the integration.

a) $CH_3CH_2COOCH_3$ b) $(CH_3)_2CHCOOH$
c) $CH_3CH_2OCOCH_3$ d) $CH_3OCH_2COCH_3$

Solution:

^{13}C NMR spectra are usually not integrated.

a) $CH_3CH_2COOCH_3$; ^{13}C NMR: 4 signals; ^{1}H NMR: 3 signals; integration: 3:2:3
b) $(CH_3)_2CHCOOH$; ^{13}C NMR: 3 signals; ^{1}H NMR: 3 signals; integration: 6:1:1
c) $CH_3CH_2OCOCH_3$; ^{13}C NMR: 4 signals; ^{1}H NMR: 3 signals; integration: 3:2:3
d) $CH_3OCH_2COCH_3$; ^{13}C NMR: 4 signals; ^{1}H NMR: 3 signals; integration: 3:2:3

Problem 9.3. Identify the ^{1}H NMR spectrum for each of the following compounds:

I) CH_3CH_2Cl II) $(CH_3)_2CHCl$ III) $CH_3CH_2CH_2Cl$ IV) $CH_3CH_2CH_2CH_2Cl$

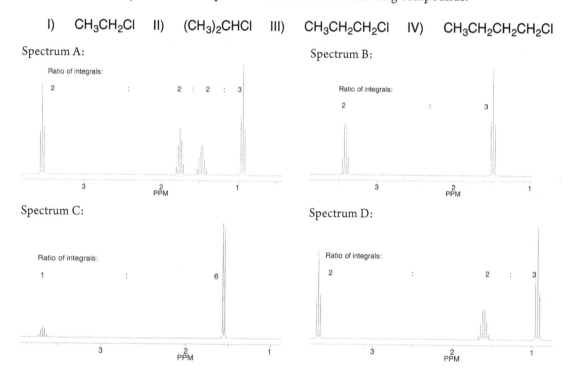

Solution:

Expected number of signals, signal splitting, and integration:

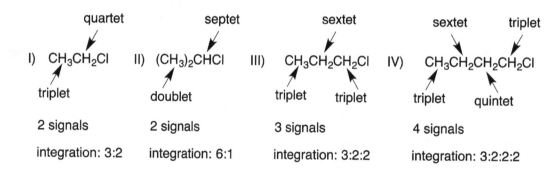

Spectrum A:

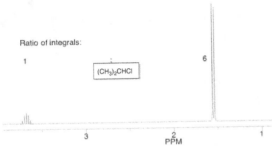

Spectrum B:

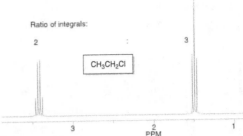

Spectrum C:

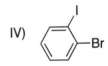

Spectrum D:

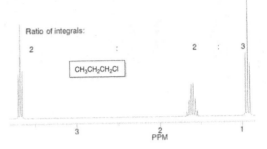

Problem 9.4. Identify the ^{1}H NMR spectrum for each of the following compounds:

I)

Br
I

II)

I

III) Br—〈 〉—Cl

IV)

I
Br

Spectrum A: Ratio of integrals: 2:2

Spectrum B: Ratio of integrals: 1:1:1:1

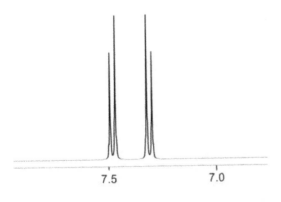

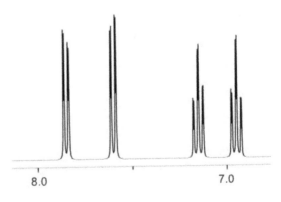

Spectrum C: Ratio of integrals: 1:1:1:1   Spectrum D: Ratio of integrals: 2:1:2

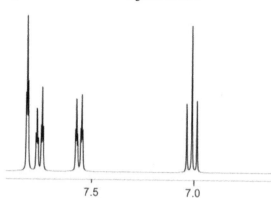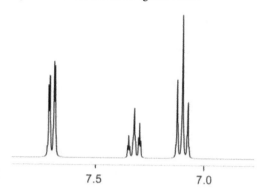

Solution:

Approach:

1. Number of signals.

Expected number of signals:

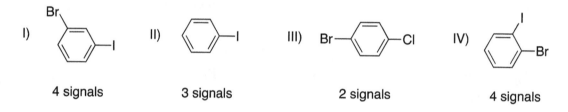

I) 4 signals

II) 3 signals

III) 2 signals

IV) 4 signals

Number of signals in the spectra:

      Spectrum A: 2 signals   Spectrum B: 4 signals
      Spectrum C: 4 signals   Spectrum D: 3 signals

2. Integration.

Expected ratio of integrals:

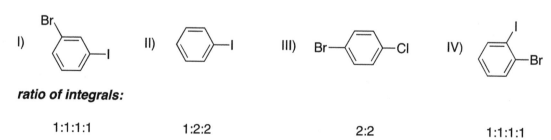

I) **ratio of integrals:**
    1:1:1:1

II) 1:2:2

III) 2:2

IV) 1:1:1:1

Observed ratio of integrals:

Spectrum A: 2:2   Spectrum B: 1:1:1:1
Spectrum C: 1:1:1:1   Spectrum D: 2:1:2

3. Equivalent hydrogens.

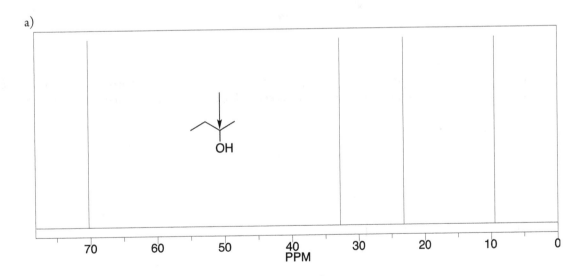

I)

all hydrogens
are different

4 signals

II) 1 and 1* are equivalent
3 and 3* are equivalent

3 signals

III) 1 and 1* are equivalent
2 and 2* are equivalent

2 signals

IV) all hydrogens
are different

4 signals

4. Final solution:

Spectrum A matches compound III
Spectrum B matches compound IV
Spectrum C matches compound I
Spectrum D matches compound II

Problem 9.5. For each compound, identify the signal of the indicated carbon atom in the ^{13}C NMR spectrum.

a)

b)

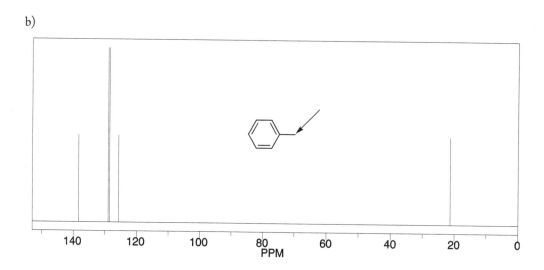

c)

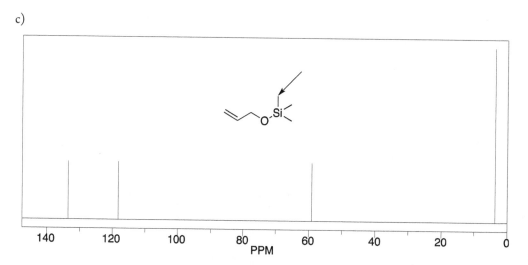

Solution:

a) The indicated atom is connected to the oxygen of the hydroxyl. Compared to the other carbon atoms present in the molecule, this atom will have the largest chemical shift due to the high electronegativity of oxygen.

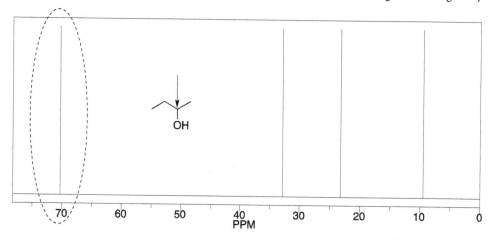

b) The indicated atom is part of an alkyl group. Alkyl groups have most commonly a chemical shift between 0 and 70 ppm.

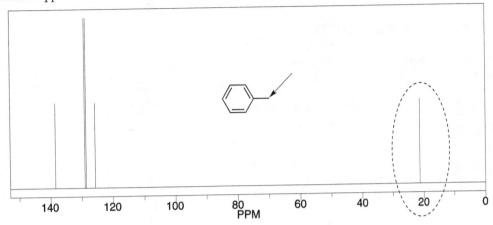

c) The indicated atom is attached to a silicon atom, an element with lower electronegativity than carbon. Compared to the other carbon atoms present in the molecule this atom will have the smallest chemical shift.

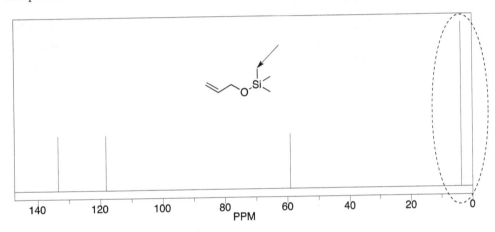

Problem 9.6. Provide the structures, based on the molecular formula and the ^{1}H NMR spectrum.

a)

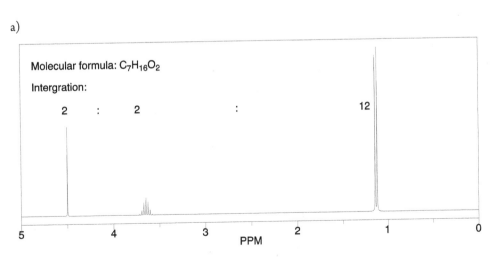

b)

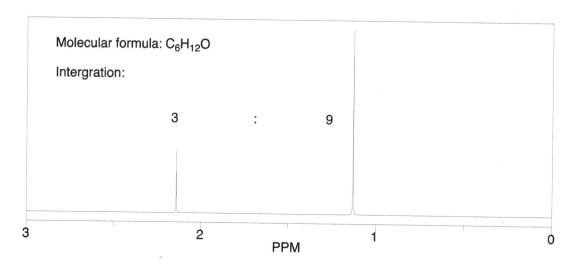

Molecular formula: $C_6H_{12}O$

Intergration:

3 : 9

3   2   PPM   1   0

Solution:

a) The ¹H NMR shows a septet and a doublet with a ratio of integrals of 1:6, which is very characteristic for an isopropyl group. According to the molecular formula we have 16 protons in the molecule. We need to double all values of the integrals to achieve the number of protons present in the molecule. Therefore, our ratio of integrals changes from 1:1:6 to 2:2:12. There will be two isopropyl groups present in the molecule; and the singlet at 4.5 ppm is due to a methylene group.

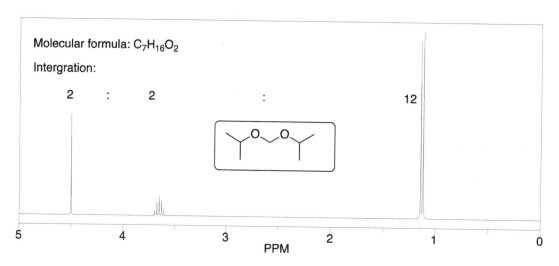

Molecular formula: $C_7H_{16}O_2$

Intergration:

2 : 2 : 12

5   4   3   PPM   2   1   0

b) The ¹H NMR contains a singlet with an integration of 3 (a methyl group) and a singlet with an integration of 9 (*tert*-butyl group).

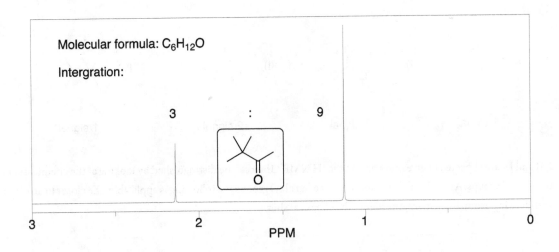

Molecular formula: $C_6H_{12}O$

Intergration:

3 : 9

Problem 9.7. For each compound, identify the corresponding ¹H NMR spectrum.

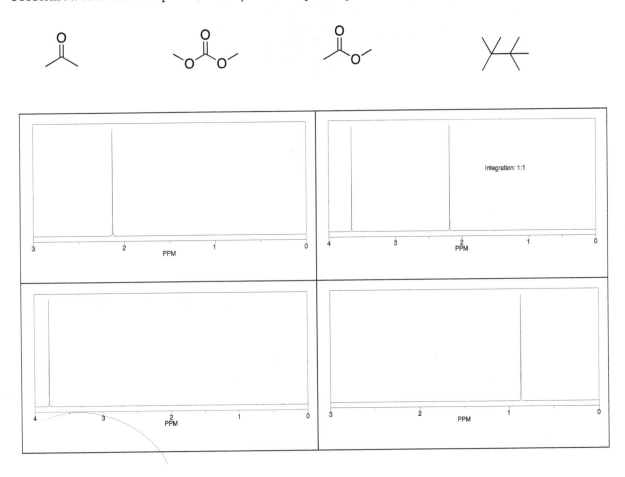

Integration: 1:1

Solution:

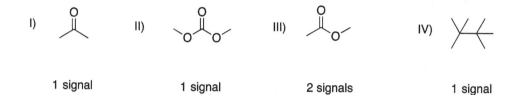

I)	II)	III)	IV)
1 signal	1 signal	2 signals	1 signal

I, II and IV are expected to give one signal in the ¹H NMR. They can be distinguished by looking at the chemical shift of the methyl groups. As a rule of thumb for protons of an alkyl groups the following is applicable: the closer to an electron withdrawing group or element, the higher the chemical shift.

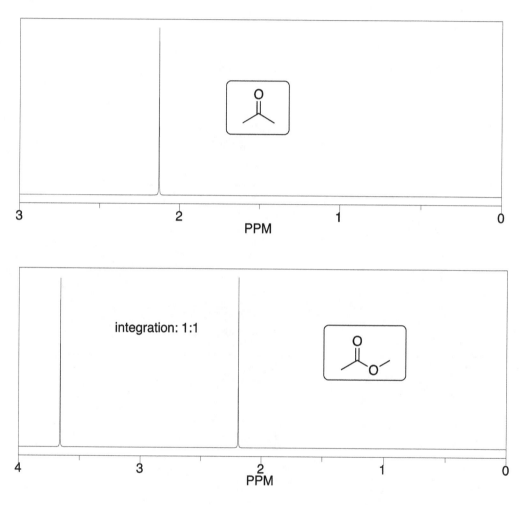

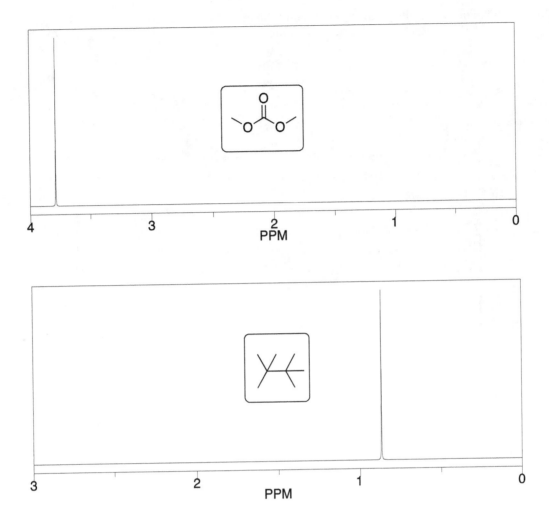

Problem 9.8. What is the structure of this compound?

    IR: strong absorption at 3350 cm^{-1}
    Mass spectrum: molecular ion m/z = 32.

Solution:
The IR spectrum shows a band at 3350 cm^{-1} which could be due to NH or OH stretch. However, according to the mass spectrum the molecular ion (m/z = 32) is even. Therefore, the compound cannot contain nitrogen. The absorption in the IR is due to an OH stretch. We can determine the molecular formula to be CH$_4$O: 32 (molecular ion) – 17 (OH) = 15, which is the mass of a methyl group (CH$_3$). Thus, the answer is methanol (CH$_3$OH).

Problem 9.9. For each of the following compounds identify the corresponding mass spectrum:

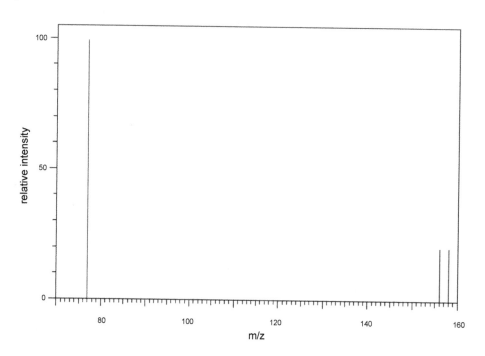

Mass spectrum A:

Mass spectrum B:

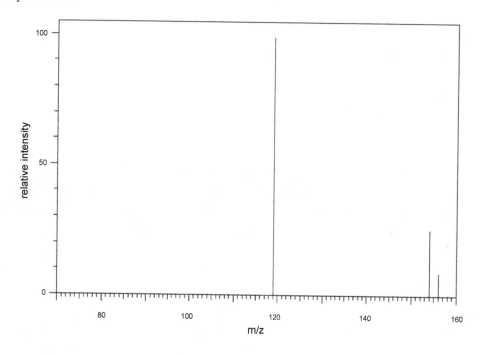

Mass spectrum C:

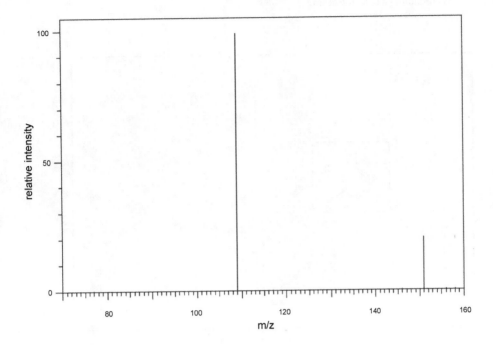

Solution:

Mass spectrum A: The peaks with equal intensity at m/z = 156 and m/z = 158 (two mass units apart) are very characteristic for ions containing a bromine atom. The base peak in the spectrum at m/z = 77, characteristic for a phenyl group $(C_6H_5^+)$.

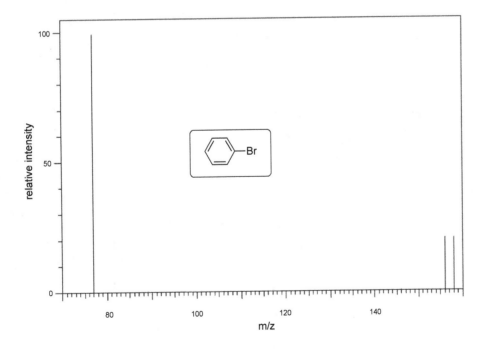

Mass spectrum B: The peaks with intensity of a 3:1 ratio at m/z = 154 and m/z = 156 (two mass units apart) are very characteristic for ions containing a chlorine atom.

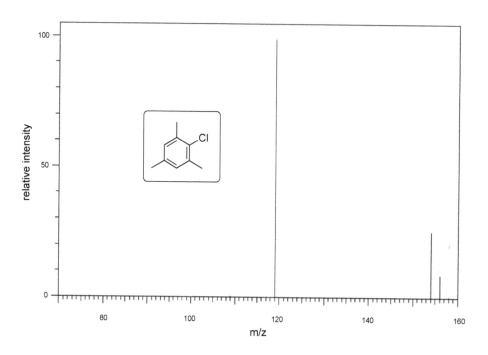

Mass spectrum C: Odd molecular ion is in agreement with presence of an odd number nitrogen atoms.

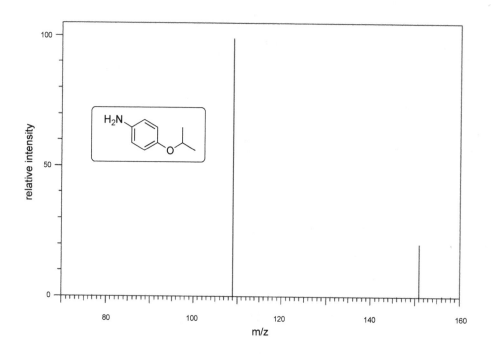

Problem 9.10. What are the structures of these two compounds?

The mass spectrum shows a molecular ion with m/z = 88, indicating that these compounds are isomers.

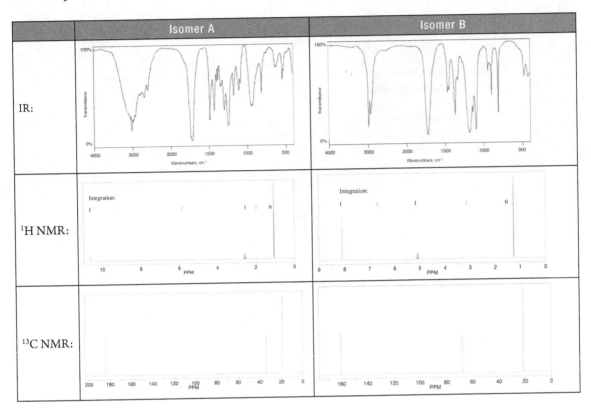

Solution:

The mass spectrum shows a molecular ion with m/z = 88, indicating that these compounds are isomers. The even number for molecular ion indicates that there cannot be an odd number of nitrogen atoms present in the molecule.

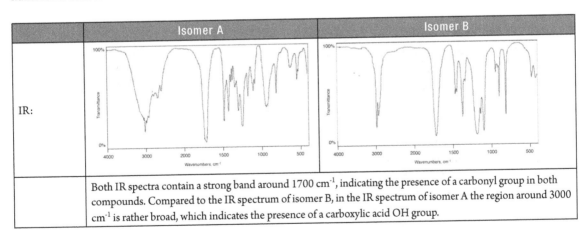

	Isomer A	Isomer B
IR:		
	Both IR spectra contain a strong band around 1700 cm^{-1}, indicating the presence of a carbonyl group in both compounds. Compared to the IR spectrum of isomer B, in the IR spectrum of isomer A the region around 3000 cm^{-1} is rather broad, which indicates the presence of a carboxylic acid OH group.	

¹H NMR:	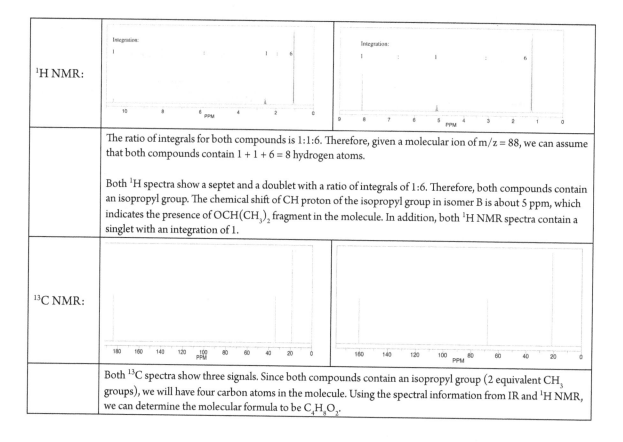

The ratio of integrals for both compounds is 1:1:6. Therefore, given a molecular ion of m/z = 88, we can assume that both compounds contain 1 + 1 + 6 = 8 hydrogen atoms.

Both ¹H spectra show a septet and a doublet with a ratio of integrals of 1:6. Therefore, both compounds contain an isopropyl group. The chemical shift of CH proton of the isopropyl group in isomer B is about 5 ppm, which indicates the presence of $OCH(CH_3)_2$ fragment in the molecule. In addition, both ¹H NMR spectra contain a singlet with an integration of 1.

¹³C NMR:

Both ¹³C spectra show three signals. Since both compounds contain an isopropyl group (2 equivalent CH_3 groups), we will have four carbon atoms in the molecule. Using the spectral information from IR and ¹H NMR, we can determine the molecular formula to be $C_4H_8O_2$.

Isomer A: assignment of the ¹H NMR data (ppm):   **Isomer B:** assignment of the ¹H NMR data (ppm):

Isomer A: assignment of the ¹³C NMR data (ppm):   **Isomer B:** assignment of the ¹³C NMR data (ppm):

Problem 9.11. Identify these compounds:

a) Mass spectrum: molecular ion m/z = 99; IR spectrum: Characteristic bands at 2260 cm⁻¹ and 1754 cm⁻¹; ¹³C NMR – 4 signals; ¹H NMR: All signals are singlets.

A)   B)   C)   D)

b) The mass spectrum shows four major peaks: m/z = 159, m/z = 157, m/z = 78 and m/z = 51.

A)　　CI—CN　　B)　　CH_3Br　　C) 　　D)

c) The ratio of integrals in the ¹H NMR spectrum is 2:2:3.

A) 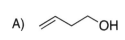　　B) 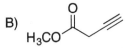　　C)　　D)

d) The structure contains diastereotopic protons.

A)   Ph   B)   Ph   C)   Ph   D)   Ph

e) The ¹H NMR spectrum shows a septet and other signals.

A)　　B)　　C)　　D)

Solution:

a) The molecular ion is odd; therefore the compound needs to contain an odd number of nitrogen atoms.

A)   OH   B) H_3CO C)   OH   D) H_3CO CN

b) The molecular ions are odd; therefore the compound needs to contain an odd number of nitrogen atoms. Choice A has molecular ions of 61 and 63 thus cannot be the answer.

A) CI—CN   B) CH_3Br C)   CI   D)   Br

c) The ratio of integrals in the ¹H NMR spectrum is 2:2:3.

A)   B)   C)   D)   CI

Integration:

3:2:2:3　　　　1:2:2:3　　　　6:1 or 12:2　　　　2:2:3

d) A methylene group needs to be present in the molecule. Using a test group and replacing the protons of the methylene group needs to give diastereomers.

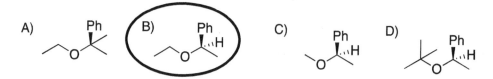

A)   B)   C)   D)

e) A septet is indicative of six nonequivalent hydrogen atoms located three bonds away. Septets are commonly present in the ¹H NMR spectra of compounds with isolated isopropyl groups.

A)   B)   C)   D)

9.2. Additional Problems for Chapter 9 (for answers see Ch 17)

Problem 9.12. Determine/identify (a) number of signals in the ¹H NMR spectrum, (b) number of signals in the ¹³C NMR spectrum, (c) the splitting pattern (also known as multiplicity) of all the ¹H NMR signals, (d) the most deshielded H(s), and (e) the most deshielded C in the following three structures.

Problem 9.13. Determine if the indicated hydrogens in the following structures are related as homotopic, enantiotopic, or diastereotopic.

Problem 9.14. Choose **one** structure from the given set that agrees with the given IR and NMR spectral data:

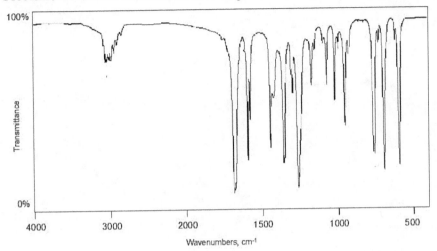

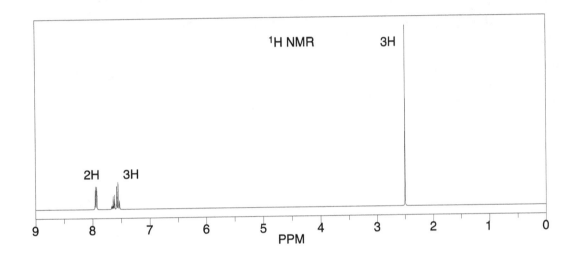

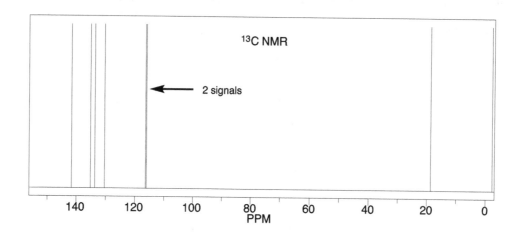

Organometallic Compounds and Transition Metal Catalysis

10.1. Chapter 10 Problems and Solutions

Problem 10.1. Sort the following according increasing basicity:

Solution:
Additional attachment of electron-donating alkyl groups to the carbanionic center leads to a slight increase of the negative charge on carbon. The higher electronic density on carbon corresponds to the higher basicity (see Chapter 2 of the textbook).

Increasing basicity

the electron-donating inductive effect of each CH_3 group adds negative charge on the carbanion

Problem 10.2. Provide the Gilman reagent that gives the indicated products in high yield:

a)

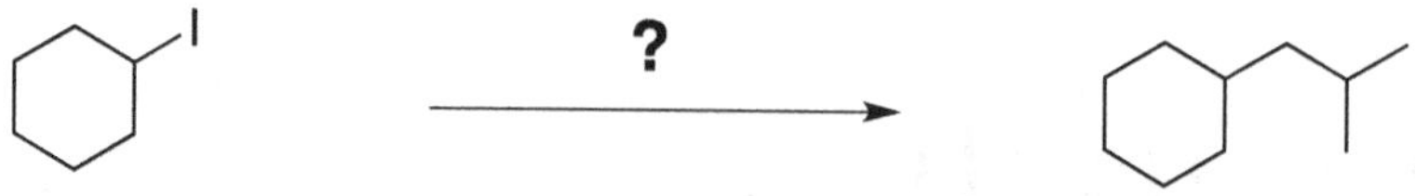
I
?

b)

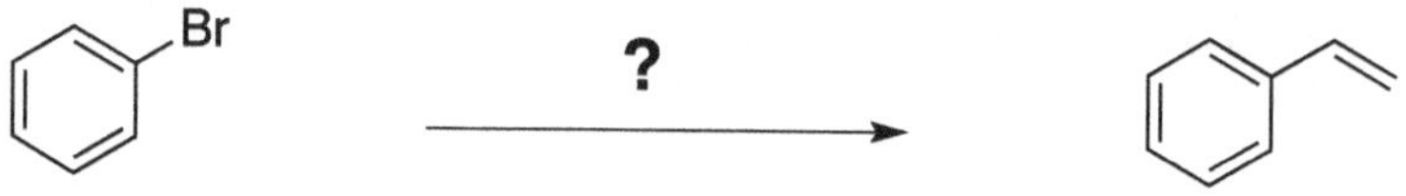
Br
?

Solution:

a)

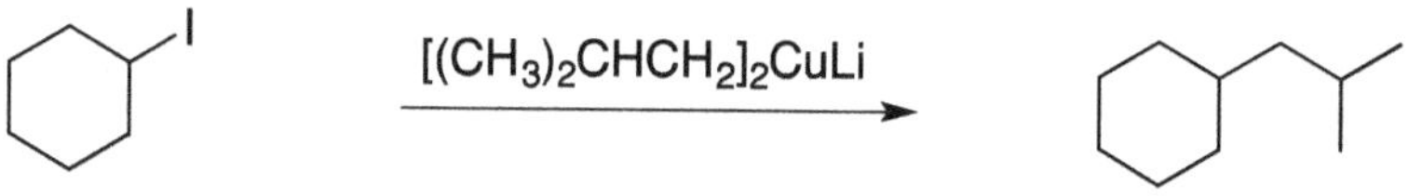
I
[(CH3)2CHCH2]2CuLi

b)

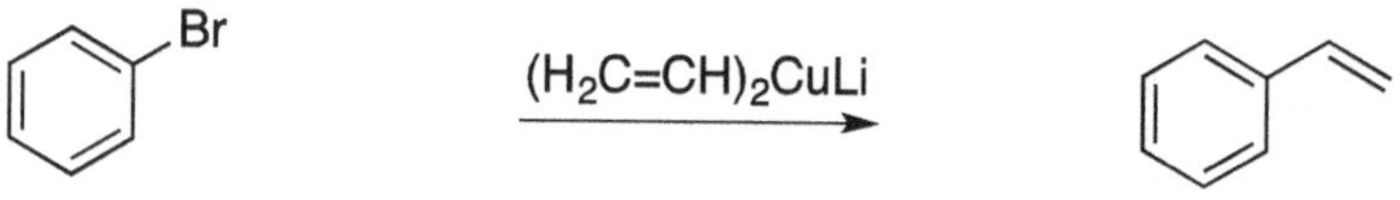
Br
(H2C=CH)2CuLi

Problem 10.3. Provide the products of the following transformations:

a)

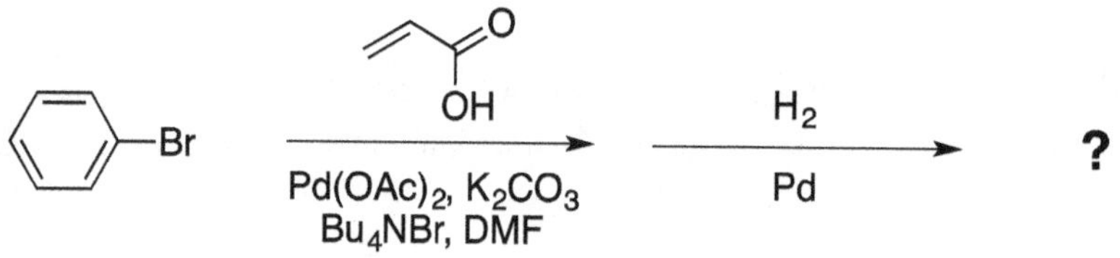
O
OH
Br
Pd(OAc)2, K2CO3
Bu4NBr, DMF
H2
Pd
?

b)

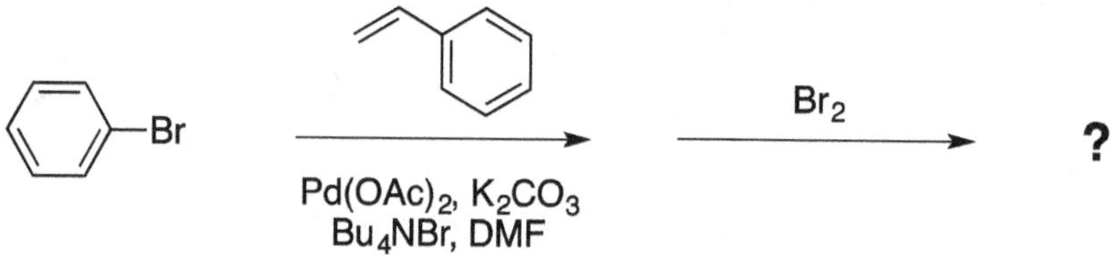
Br
Pd(OAc)2, K2CO3
Bu4NBr, DMF
Br2
?

c)

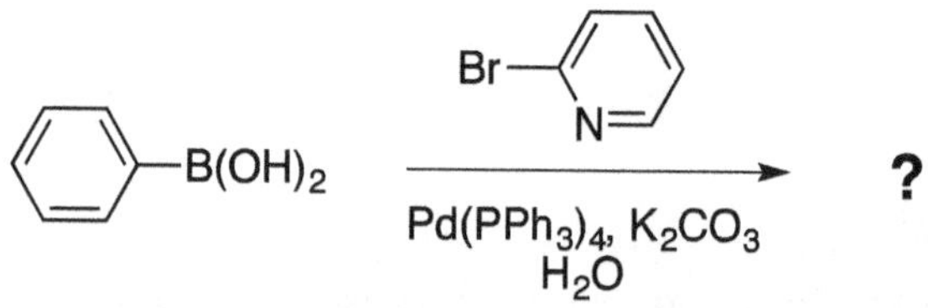
Br
N
B(OH)2
Pd(PPh3)4, K2CO3
H2O
?

Solution:

a)

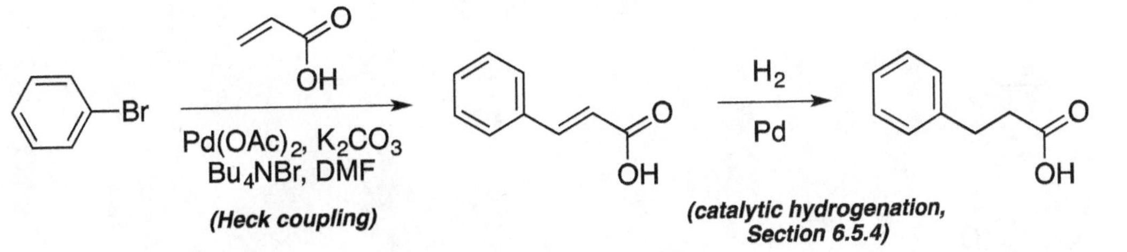

(Heck coupling)

(catalytic hydrogenation, Section 6.5.4)

b)

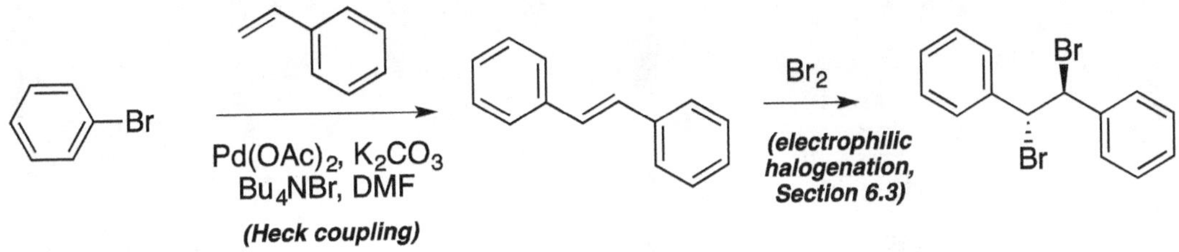

(Heck coupling)

(electrophilic halogenation, Section 6.3)

c)

Pd(PPh₃)₄, K₂CO₃
H₂O

(Suzuki coupling)

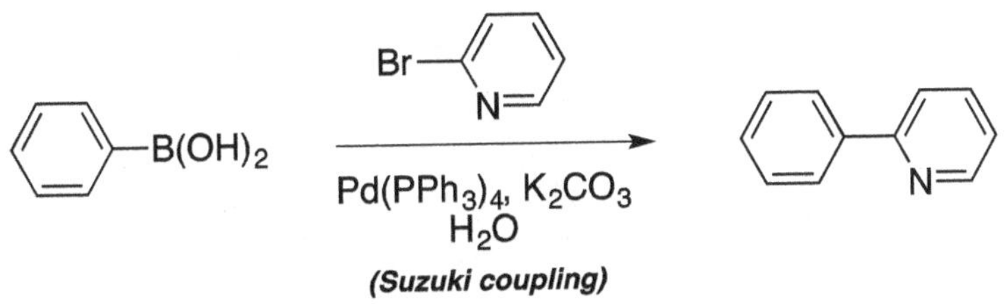

Problem 10.4. Propose mechanism for the formation of dichlorocarbene ($Cl_2C:$) by the reaction of chloroform ($CHCl_3$) with *t*-BuOK.

Solution:

Formation of dichlorocarbene:

dichlorocarbene

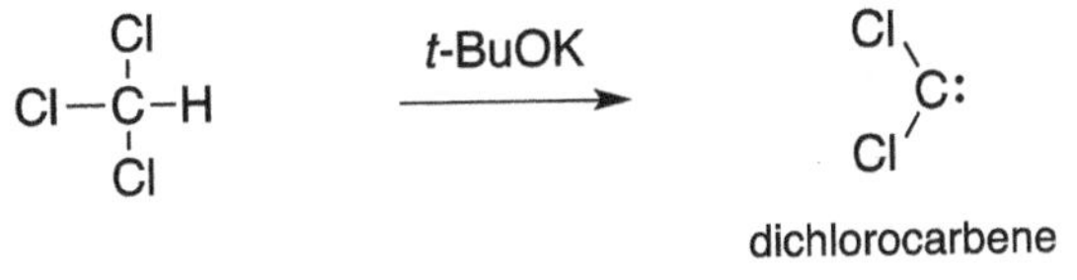

Mechanism:

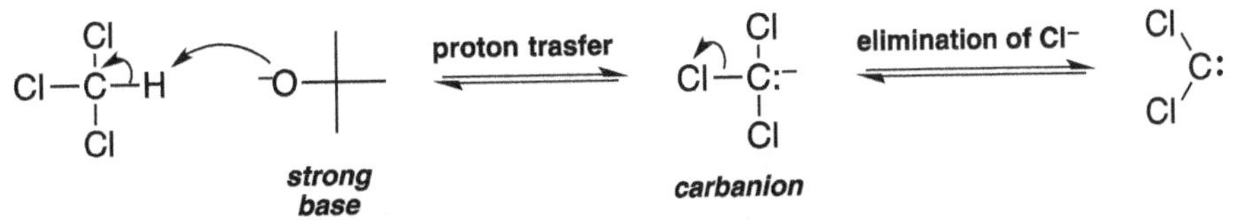

Problem 10.5. How could you synthesize the following molecules by using an alkene and the Simmons–Smith reagent:

a)

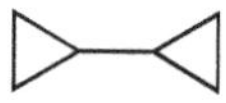

b)

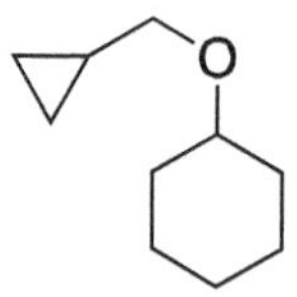

Solution:

a)

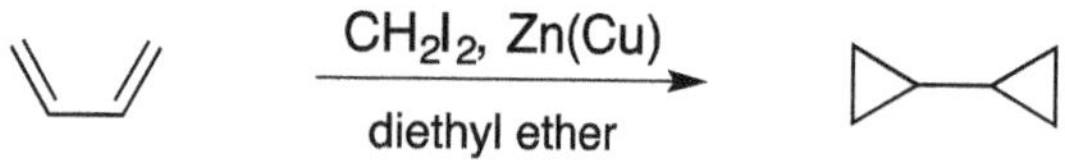

CH_2I_2, Zn(Cu)

diethyl ether

b)

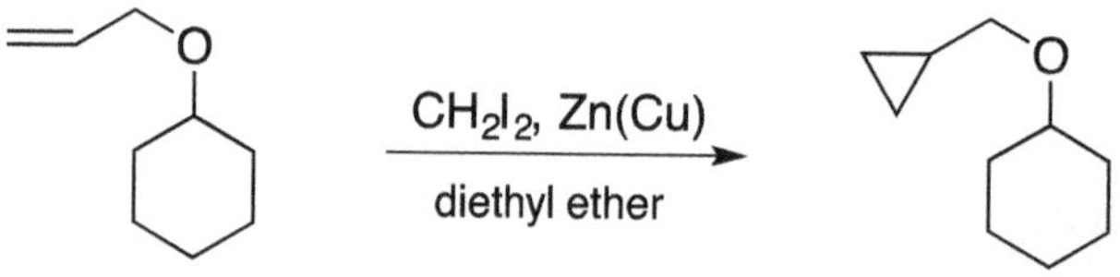

CH_2I_2, Zn(Cu)

diethyl ether

Problem 10.6. What are the products of the following transformations?

a)

H_3CO_2C CO_2CH_3

Grubbs' catalyst

?

b)

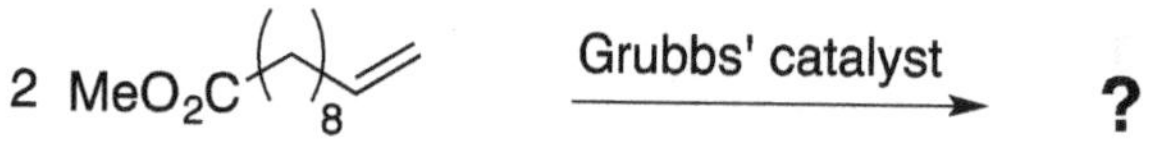

2 MeO_2C $\left(\right)_8$

Grubbs' catalyst

?

c)

+ Bu

Grubbs' catalyst

?

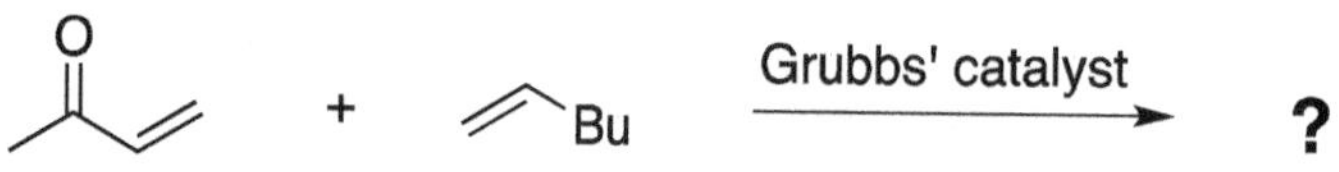

Solution:

a)

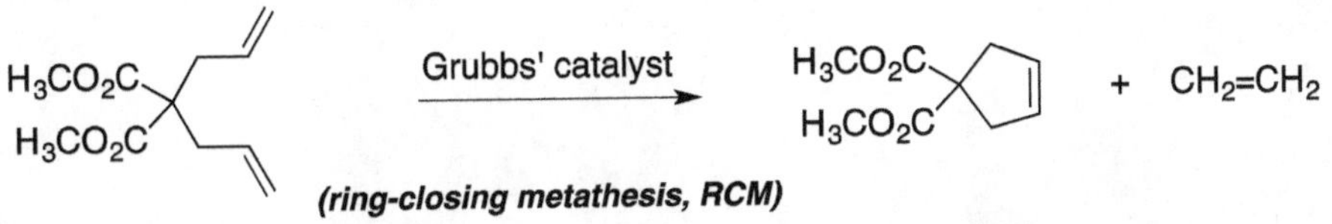

H₃CO₂C and H₃CO₂C groups on a quaternary carbon bearing two allyl groups → **Grubbs' catalyst** → cyclopentene bearing two CO₂CH₃ groups + CH₂=CH₂

(ring-closing metathesis, RCM)

b)

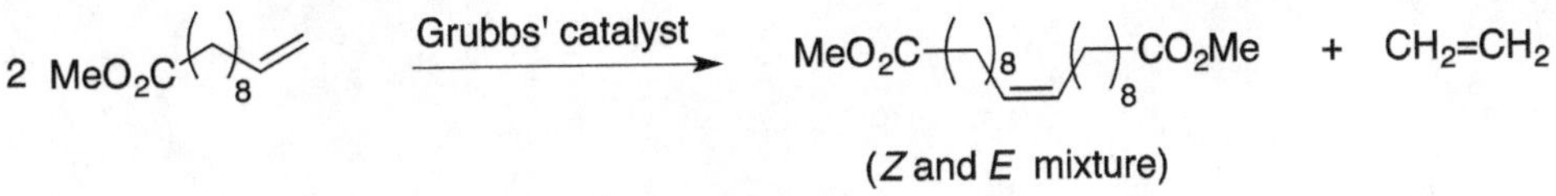

2 MeO₂C-(CH₂)₈-CH=CH₂ → **Grubbs' catalyst** → MeO₂C-(CH₂)₈-CH=CH-(CH₂)₈-CO₂Me + CH₂=CH₂

(Z and E mixture)

c)

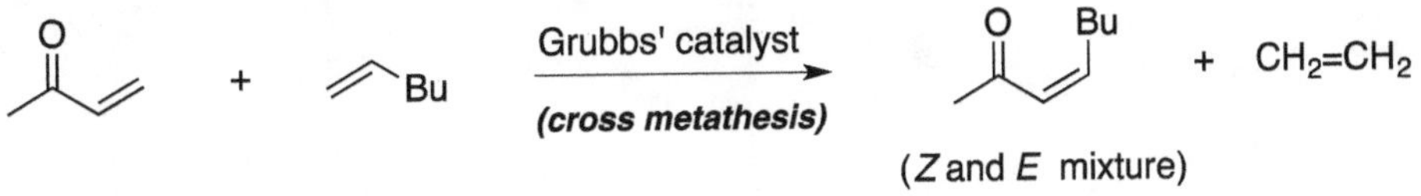

methyl vinyl ketone + CH₂=CH-Bu → **Grubbs' catalyst** → enone with Bu (Z/E) + CH₂=CH₂

(cross metathesis)

(Z and E mixture)

10.2. Additional Problems for Chapter 10 (for answers see Ch 17)

Problem 10.7. What is the major organic product obtained from the following sequence of reactions?

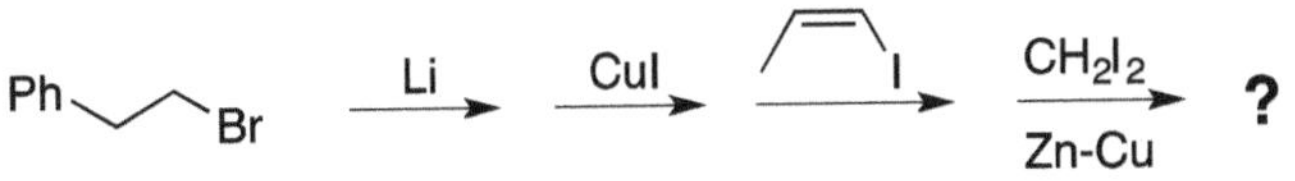

Ph-CH₂CH₂-Br → **Li** → **CuI** → (vinyl iodide) → **CH₂I₂ / Zn-Cu** → **?**

Problem 10.8. Propose a mechanism to account for the formation of product in the following reaction:

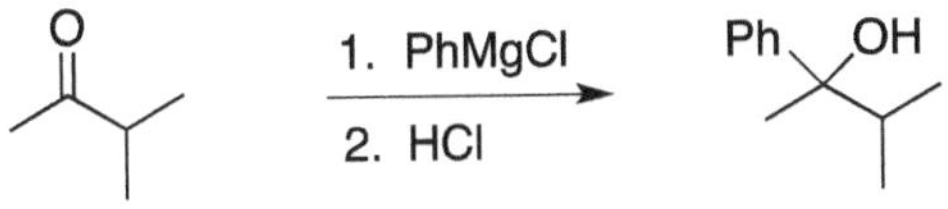

3-methyl-2-butanone → **1. PhMgCl / 2. HCl** → Ph-C(OH) with methyl and isopropyl groups

Problem 10.9. Identify the reagent(s) required to convert the reactant to the indicated product in each reaction.

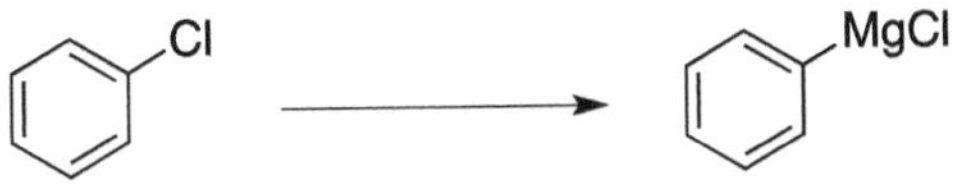

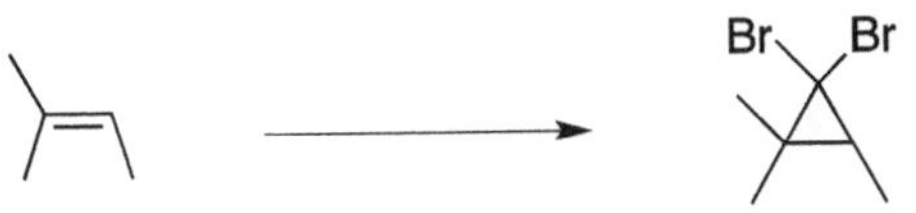

chlorobenzene (Ph–Cl) ⟶ Ph–MgCl

2-methyl-2-butene ⟶ 1,1-dibromo-2,2-dimethylcyclopropane (Br, Br)

butyllithium (Bu–Li) ⟶ (butyl)₂CuLi

Aldehydes and Ketones

11.1. Chapter 11 Problems and Solutions

Problem 11.1. Provide the IUPAC names for the following compounds:

Solution:

3-buten-2-one   3-hydroxybutanal   pentanedial   (*R*)-2,3-dihydroxypropanal

Problem 11.2. Why are ketones, in general, less reactive toward nucleophilic addition to the carbonyl group than aldehydes?

Solution:
Ketones are less reactive toward nucleophilic addition to the carbonyl group than aldehydes for the following two reasons: 1) the carbonyl group in ketones is less electrophilic due to the presence of two electron-donating alkyl groups reducing positive charge on the carbon atom, 2) the two bulky alkyl groups block the carbonyl carbon from nucleophilic attack.

Aldehyde:

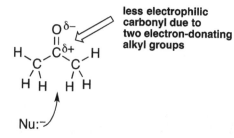

Ketone:

less electrophilic carbonyl due to two electron-donating alkyl groups

steric hindrance due to the presence of two bulky alkyl groups

Problem 11.3. For each of the following provide the IUPAC name of the major product:

a)

1. O_3
2. $(CH_3)_2S$

?

b)

H_2SO_4, H_2O

$HgSO_4$ (catalyst)

?

c)

1. BH_3, THF
2. H_2O_2, NaOH, H_2O

?

d)

HO

OH

IBX

DMSO (solvent)

?

Solution:

a)

1. O_3
2. $(CH_3)_2S$

(ozonolysis, Section 6.5.3)

6-oxoheptanal

b)

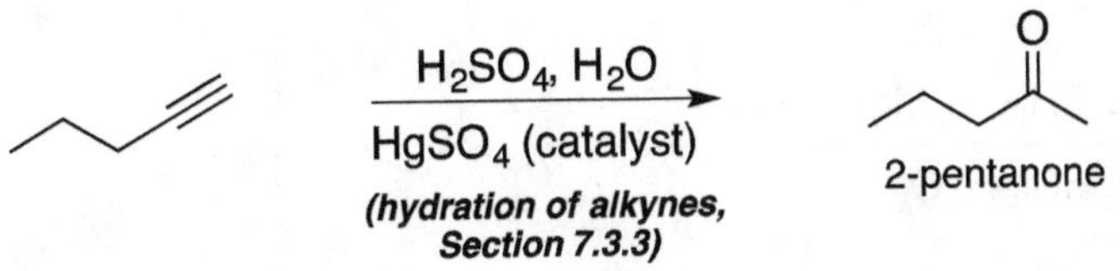

H₂SO₄, H₂O
HgSO₄ (catalyst)
(hydration of alkynes, Section 7.3.3)

2-pentanone

c)

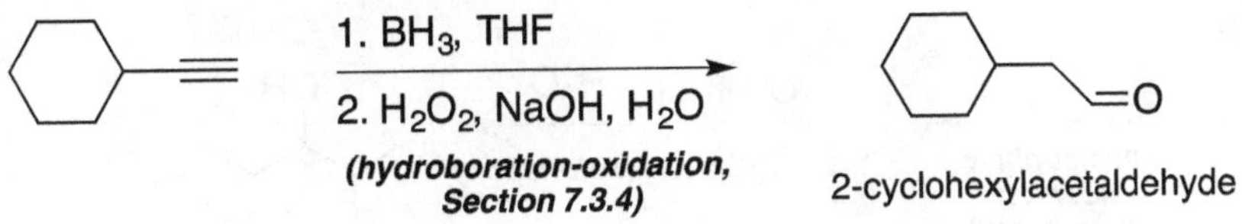

1. BH₃, THF
2. H₂O₂, NaOH, H₂O
(hydroboration-oxidation, Section 7.3.4)

2-cyclohexylacetaldehyde

d)

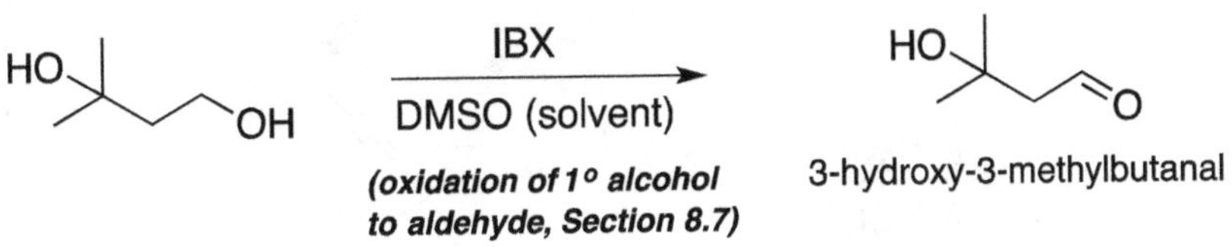

IBX
DMSO (solvent)
(oxidation of 1° alcohol to aldehyde, Section 8.7)

3-hydroxy-3-methylbutanal

Problem 11.4. Propose a mechanism for each reaction shown in Figure 11.3.

Solution:

Abbreviated mechanisms of these reactions are shown below:

Reaction 1:

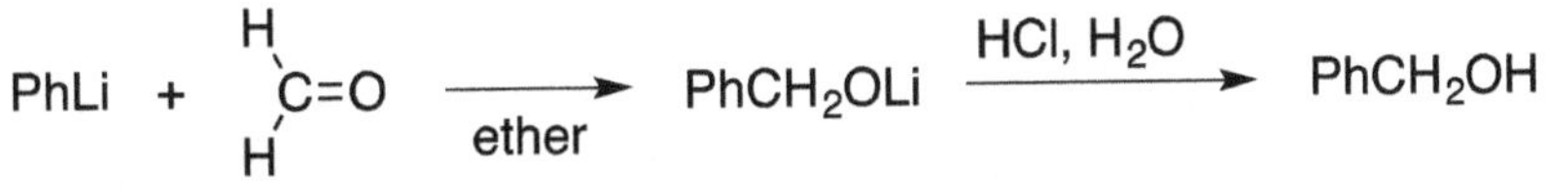

PhLi + (H)C=O(H) →(ether) PhCH₂OLi →(HCl, H₂O) PhCH₂OH

Mechanism:

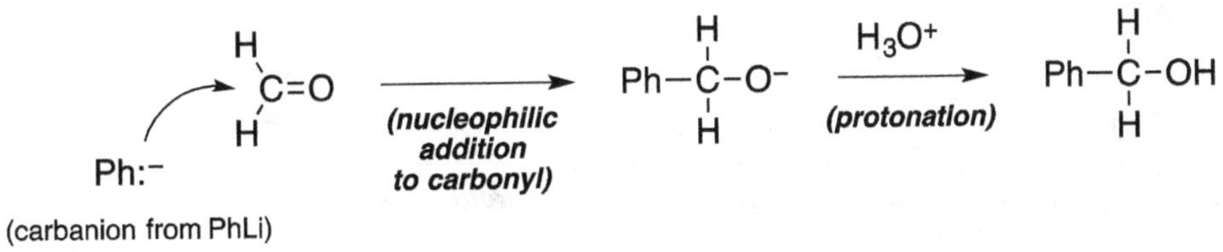

(nucleophilic addition to carbonyl)

Ph–C(H)(H)–O⁻ →(H₃O⁺) *(protonation)* Ph–C(H)(H)–OH

Ph:⁻
(carbanion from PhLi)

Reaction 2:

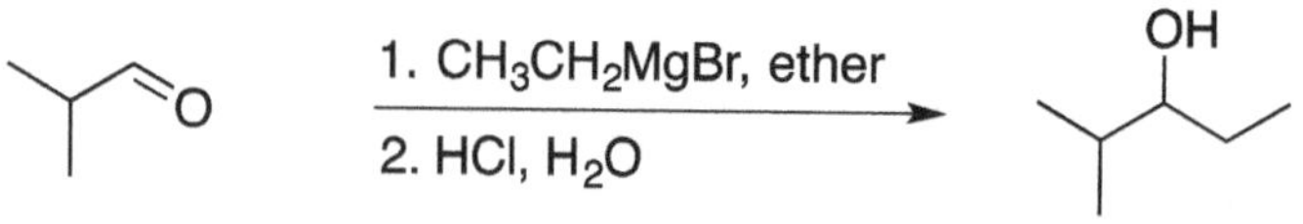

1. CH_3CH_2MgBr, ether
2. HCl, H_2O
O
OH

Mechanism:

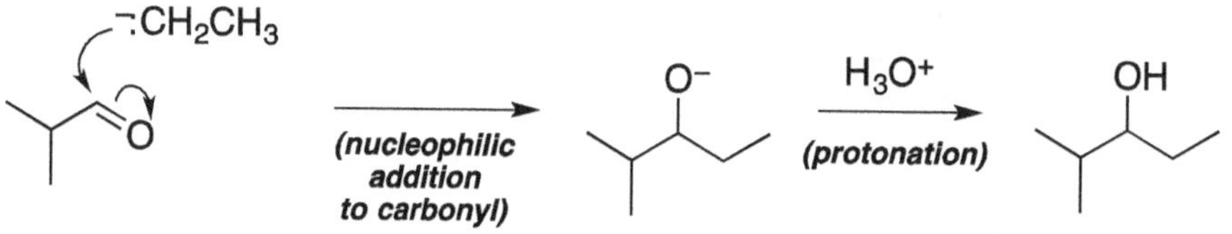

$^{-}$:CH_2CH_3
O
(nucleophilic addition to carbonyl)
O$^-$
H_3O^+
(protonation)
OH

(carbanion from CH_3CH_2MgBr)

Reaction 3:

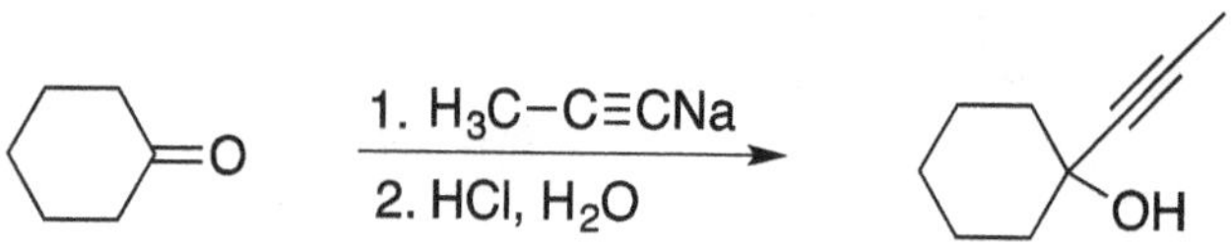

O
1. $H_3C-C\equiv CNa$
2. HCl, H_2O
OH

Mechanism:

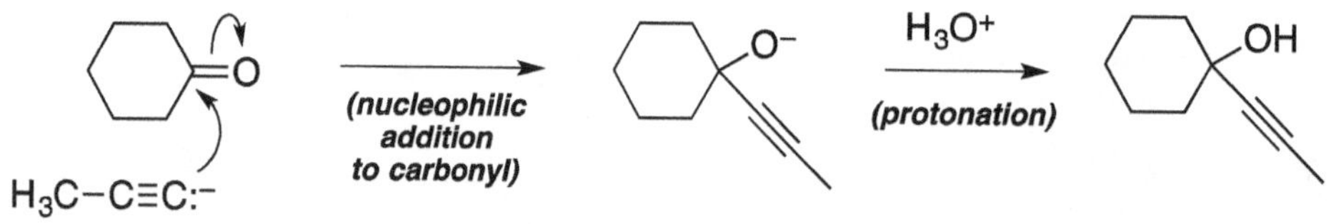

O
$H_3C-C\equiv C:^-$
(nucleophilic addition to carbonyl)
O$^-$
H_3O^+
(protonation)
OH

Reaction 4:

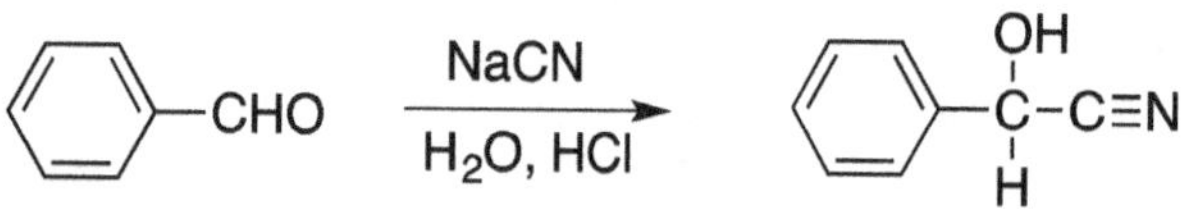

CHO
NaCN
H_2O, HCl
OH
C−C≡N
H

Mechanism:

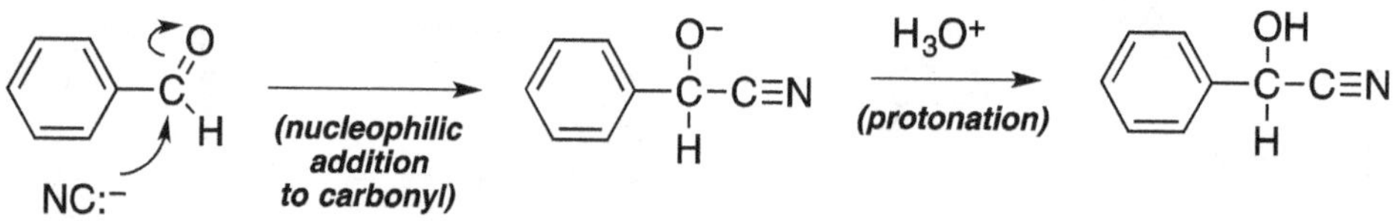

O
C
H
NC:$^-$
(nucleophilic addition to carbonyl)
O$^-$
C−C≡N
H
H_3O^+
(protonation)
OH
C−C≡N
H

Problem 11.5. Use organolithium or Grignard reagents to synthesize each of the compounds:

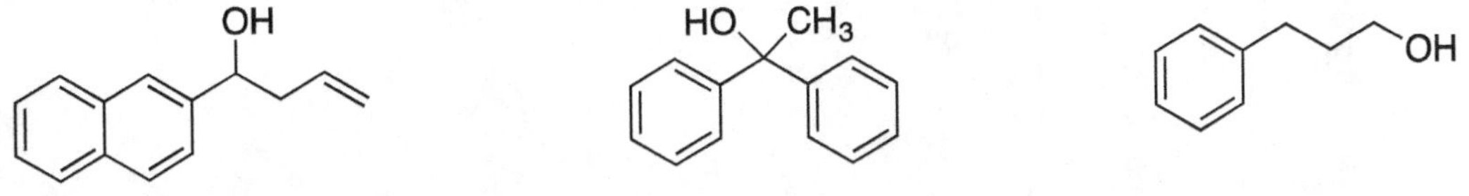

Solution:

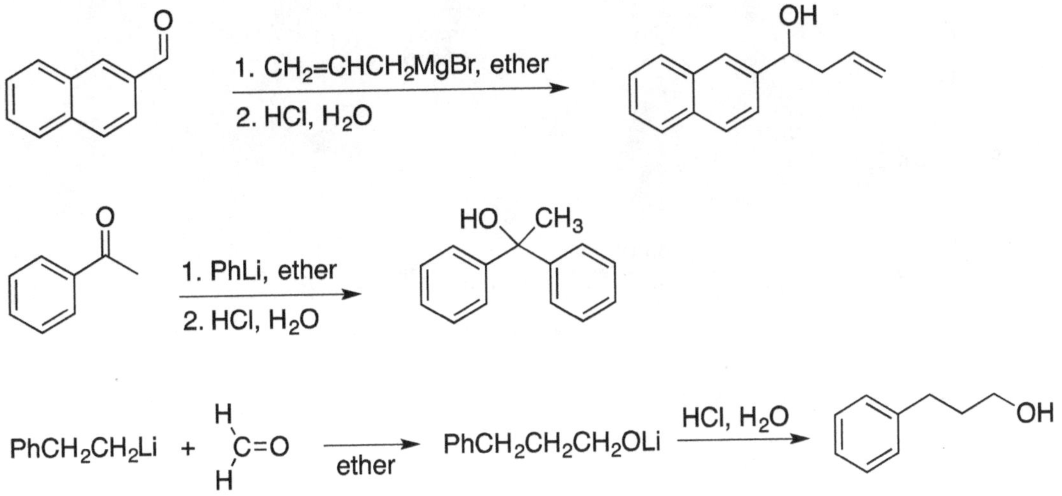

1. CH$_2$=CHCH$_2$MgBr, ether
2. HCl, H$_2$O

1. PhLi, ether
2. HCl, H$_2$O

PhCH$_2$CH$_2$Li + $\overset{H}{\underset{H}{C}}$=O $\xrightarrow{\text{ether}}$ PhCH$_2$CH$_2$CH$_2$OLi $\xrightarrow{\text{HCl, H}_2\text{O}}$

Problem 11.6. Suggest mechanisms for the reactions shown in Figure 11.4.

Solution:
Abbreviated mechanisms of these reactions are shown below:

Reaction 1:

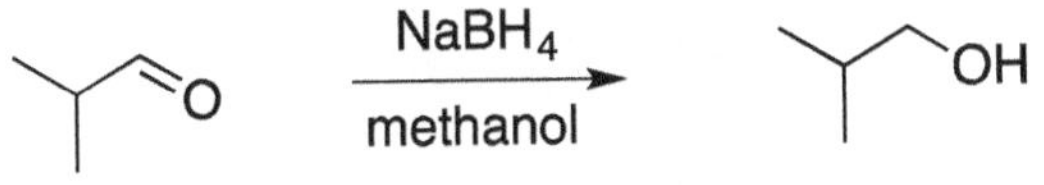

$\xrightarrow[\text{methanol}]{\text{NaBH}_4}$

Mechanism:

H:$^-$

(nucleophilic addition to carbonyl)

H–O–CH$_3$

(proton transfer)

OH + CH$_3$O$^-$

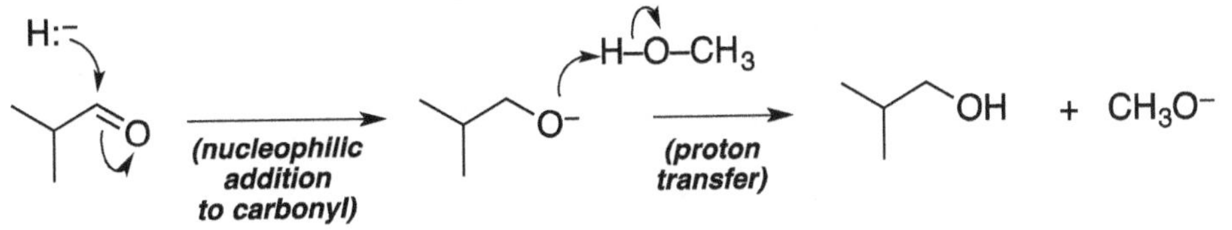

(NaBH$_4$ or LiAlH$_4$ are the sources of H:$^-$)

Reaction 2:

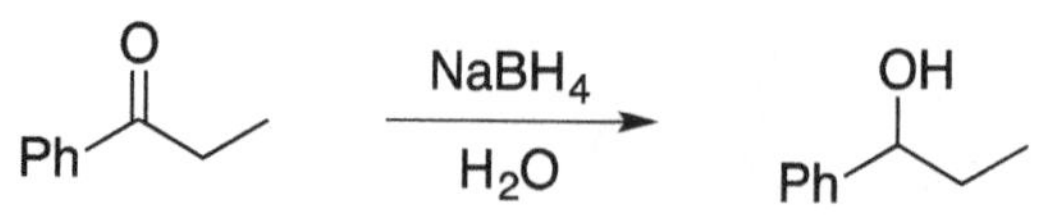

Mechanism:

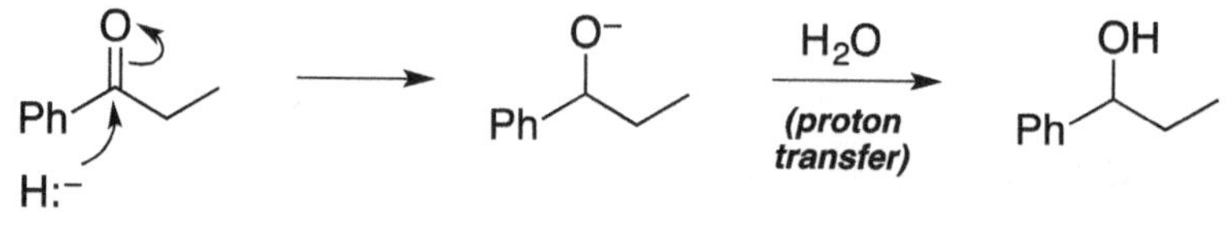

Reaction 3:

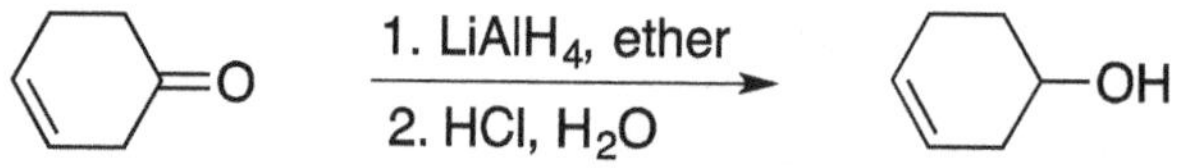

1. LiAlH₄, ether
2. HCl, H₂O

Mechanism:

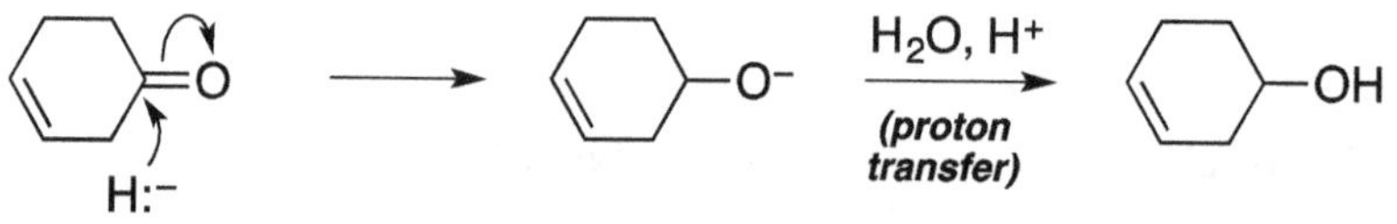

Problem 11.7. The reduction of 2-methylcyclohexanone leads to several stereoisomers. Name each stereoisomer and indicate which are diastereomers and which are enantiomers.

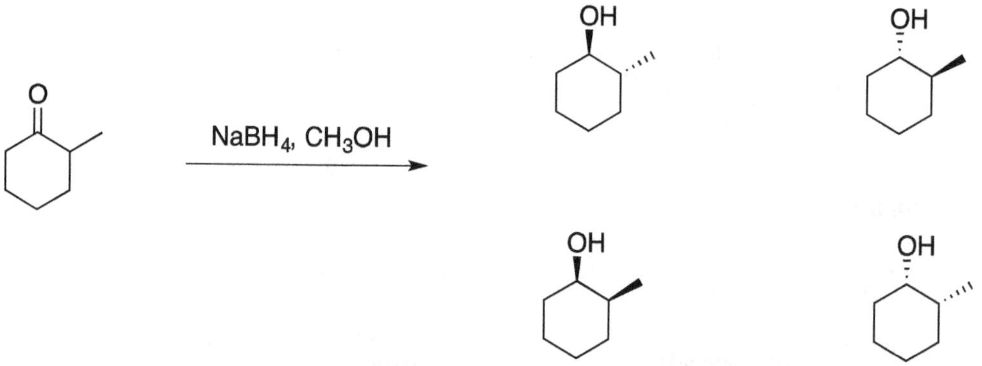

NaBH₄, CH₃OH

Solution:

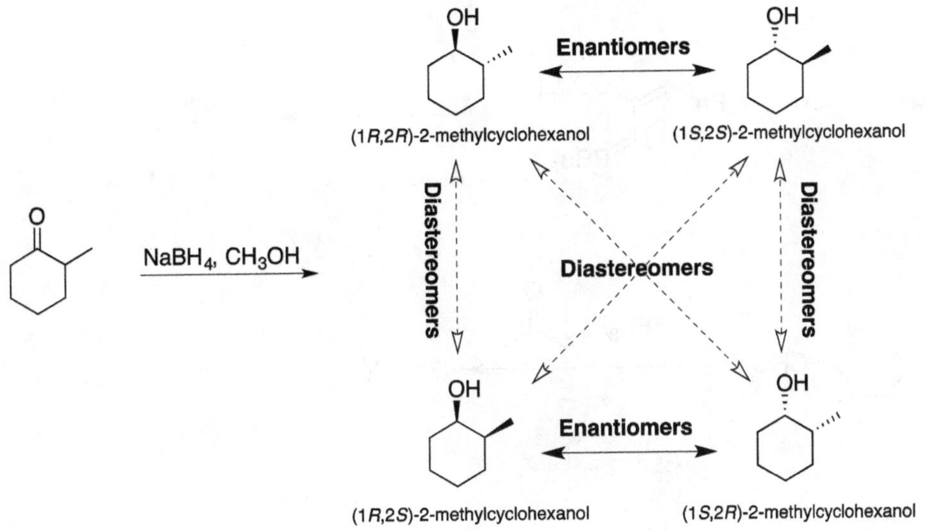

(1R,2R)-2-methylcyclohexanol   (1S,2S)-2-methylcyclohexanol

(1R,2S)-2-methylcyclohexanol   (1S,2R)-2-methylcyclohexanol

Problem 11.8. Each of the following can be prepared by Wittig reaction of a ketone with a phosphonium ylide. Provide the structure of the ketone and the ylide.

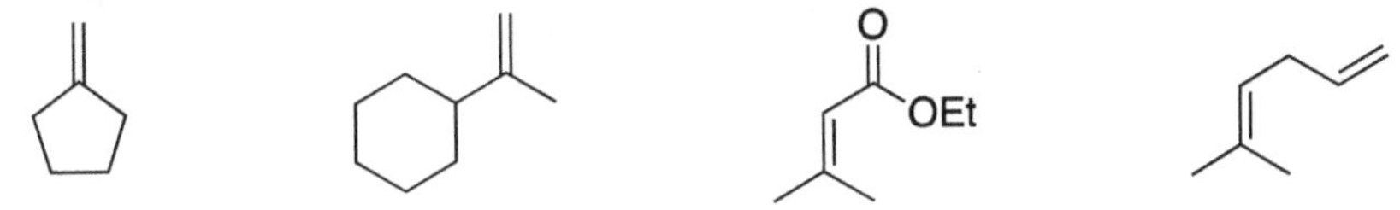

Solution:

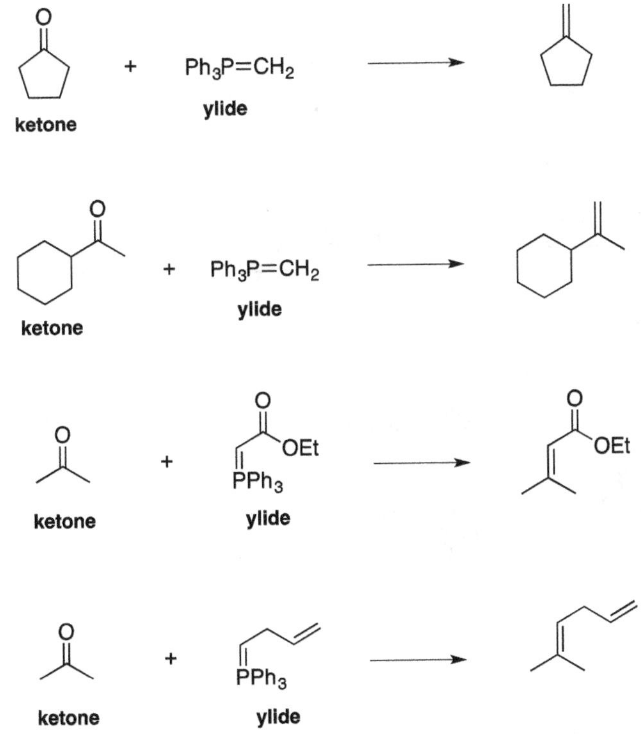

Problem 11.9. Draw the major products in the following reactions:

a)

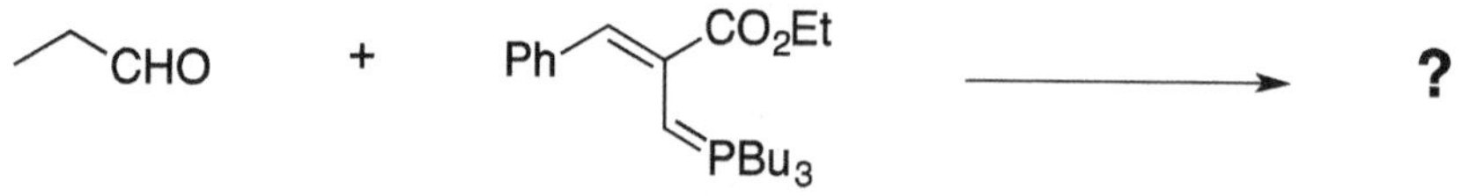

CHO + Ph CO_2Et PBu_3 ⟶ **?**

b)

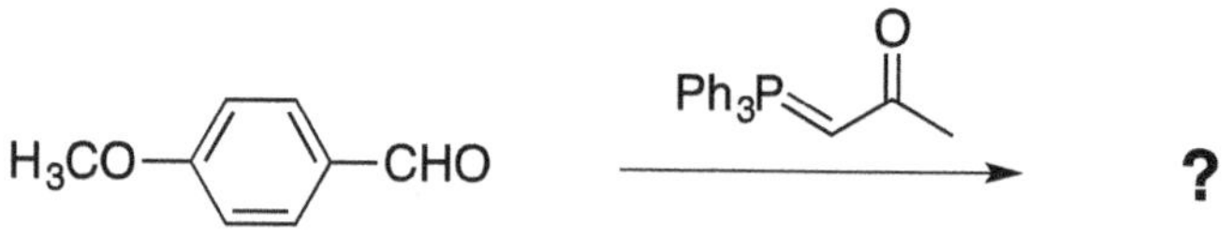

H_3CO—⬡—CHO $\xrightarrow{\text{Ph}_3\text{P} \text{(ketone)}}$ **?**

c)

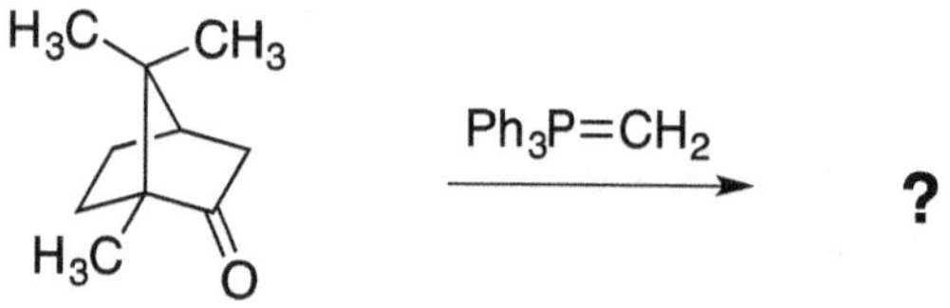

H_3C CH_3 ... H_3C O $\xrightarrow{\text{Ph}_3\text{P}=\text{CH}_2}$ **?**

Solution:

a)

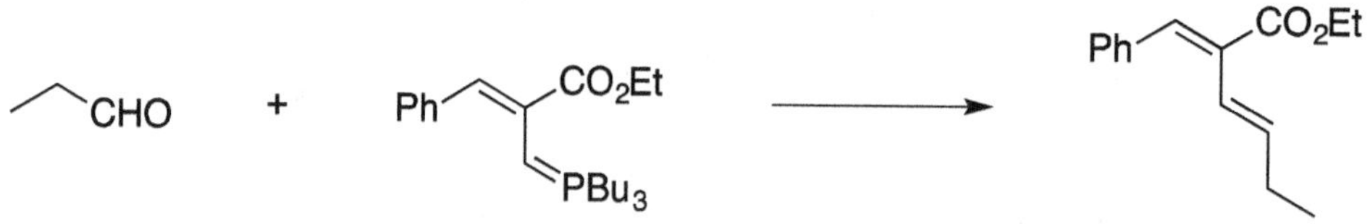

CHO + Ph CO_2Et PBu_3 ⟶ Ph CO_2Et

b)

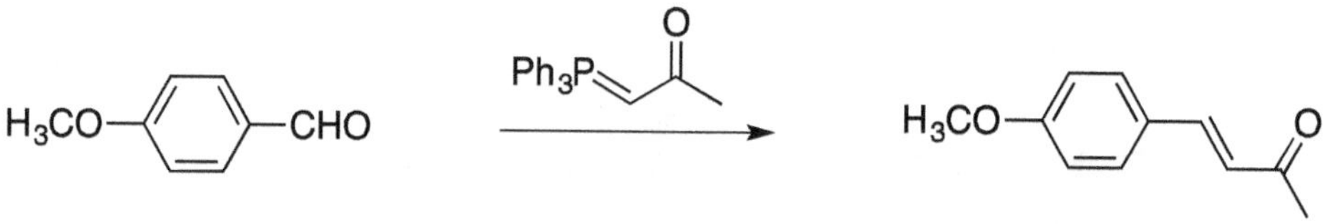

H_3CO—⬡—CHO $\xrightarrow{\text{Ph}_3\text{P} \text{(ketone)}}$ H_3CO—⬡— (enone) O

c)

H_3C CH_3 ... H_3C O $\xrightarrow{\text{Ph}_3\text{P}=\text{CH}_2}$ H_3C CH_3 ... H_3C CH_2

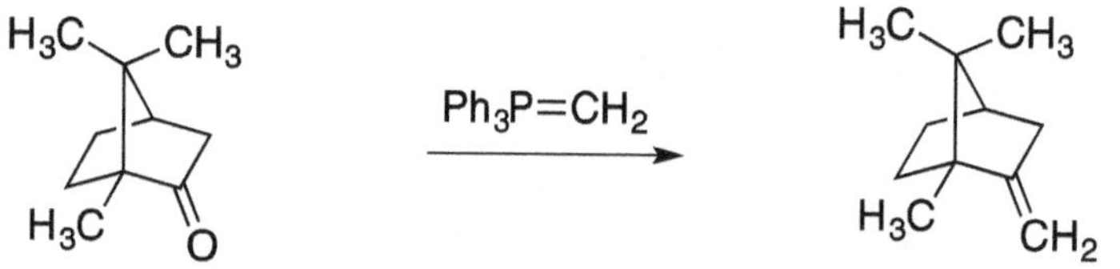

Problem 11.10. You have been assigned to synthesize methylenecyclohexane in high yield. You consider two approaches for making this compound, using cyclohexanone as a starting material:

Option I:

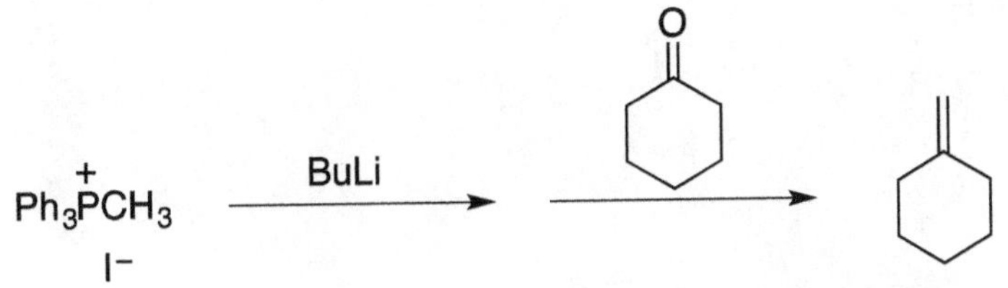

Option II:

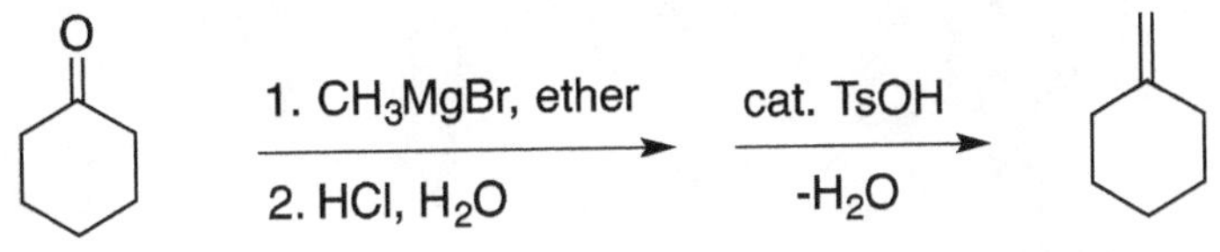

Why would you choose to pursue Option I in order to synthesize methylenecyclohexane from cyclohexanone in high yield?

Solution:

Option I, the Wittig reaction, will produce methylenecyclohexane as the main product in high yield. Option II involves dehydration of alcohol (1-methylcyclohexanol) in the second step. Elimination of water from a 3° alcohol proceeds according to E1 β-elimination mechanism yielding a more stable, more highly substituted alkene as the major product in agreement with Zaitsev's rule (see Section 8.5 of the textbook). Therefore, 1-methylcyclohexene will be the main product in this reaction, while methylenecyclohexane will be formed only in trace amounts.

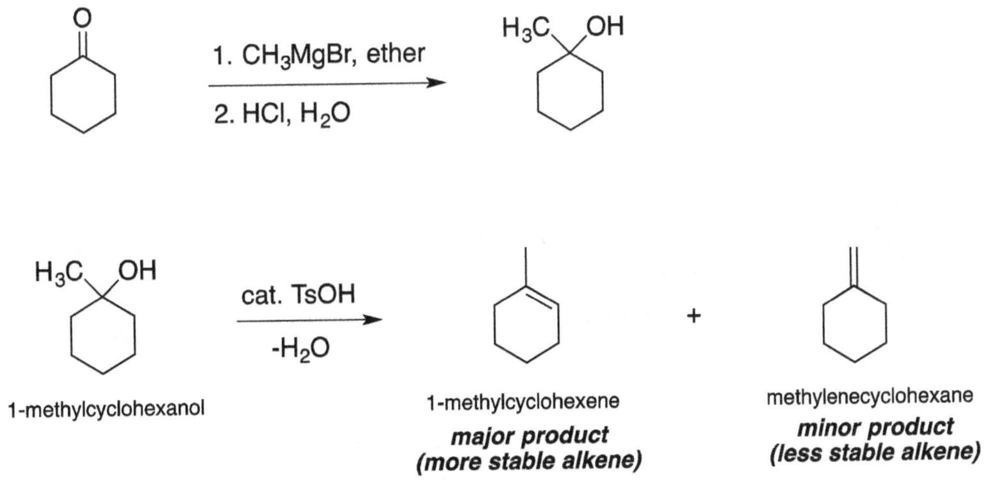

1-methylcyclohexanol

1-methylcyclohexene
major product
(more stable alkene)

methylenecyclohexane
minor product
(less stable alkene)

Problem 11.11. Provide the products of the following transformations:

a)

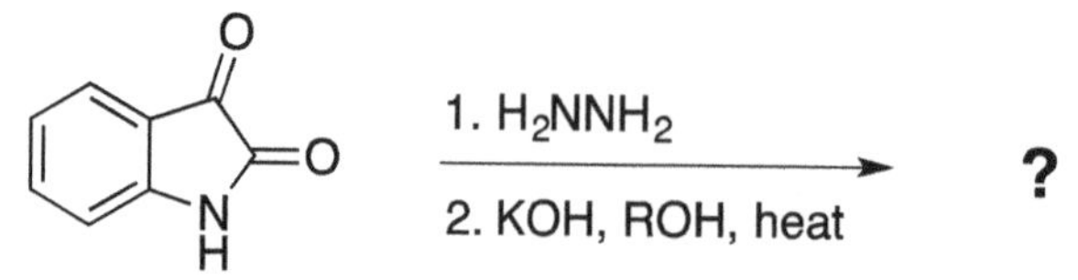

1. H$_2$NNH$_2$

2. KOH, ROH, heat

?

b)

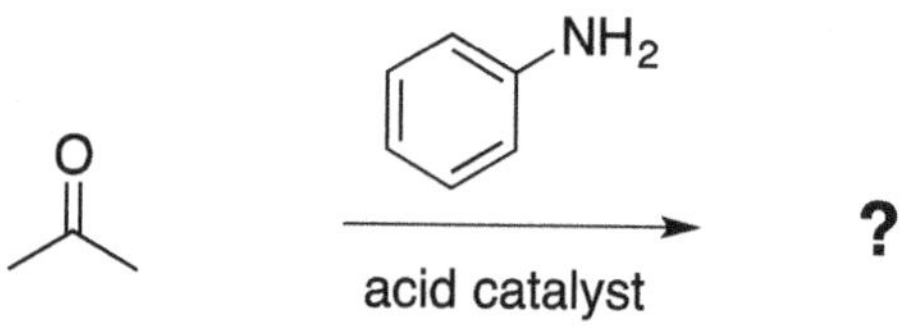

NH$_2$

acid catalyst

?

c)

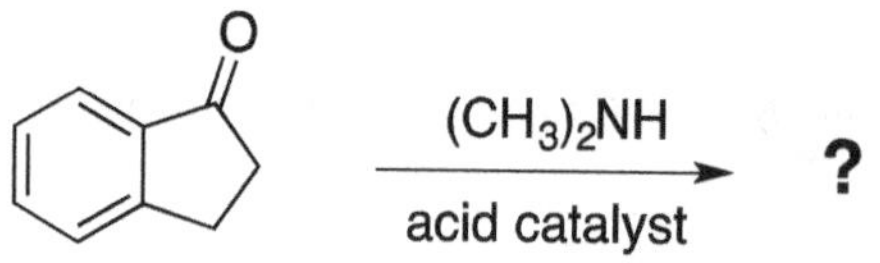

(CH$_3$)$_2$NH

acid catalyst

?

d)

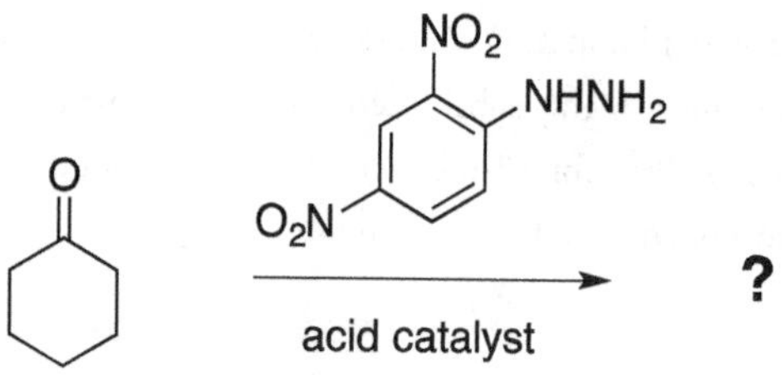

NO$_2$

NHNH$_2$

O$_2$N

acid catalyst

?

Solution:

a)

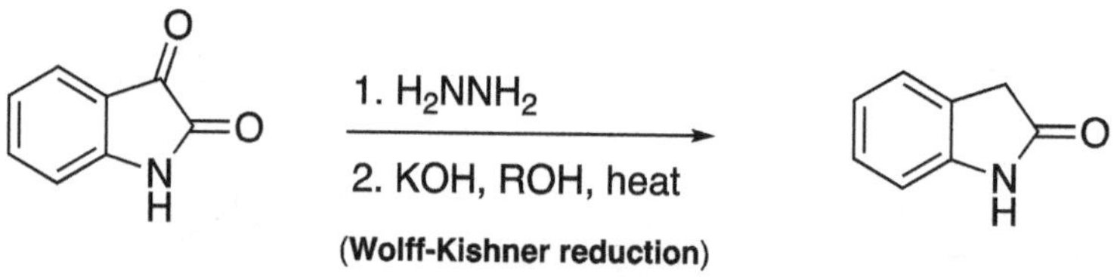

1. H$_2$NNH$_2$

2. KOH, ROH, heat

(Wolff-Kishner reduction)

b)

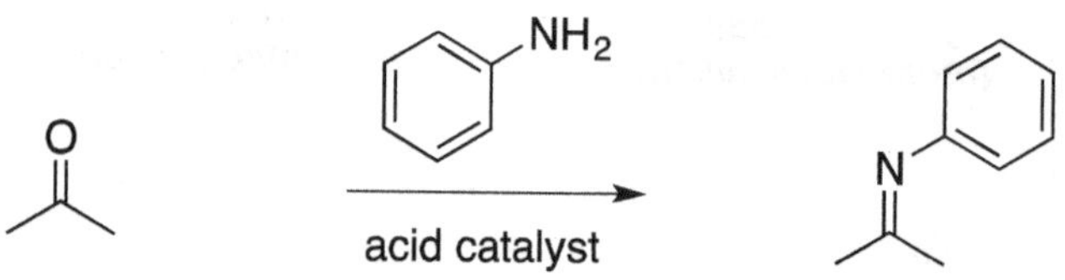

NH$_2$

acid catalyst

c)

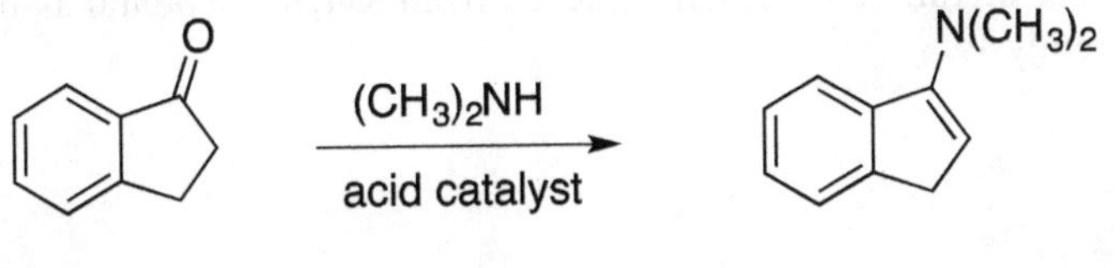

d)

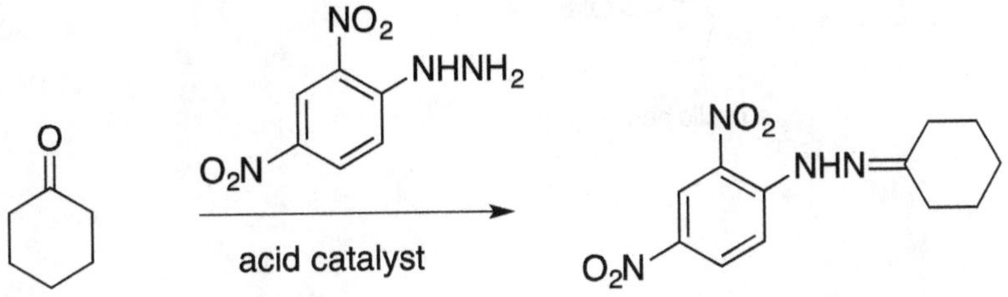

Problem 11.12. Suggest a mechanism for the formation of formaldehyde hydrate $H_2C(OH)_2$ in the reaction of formaldehyde with water.

Solution:

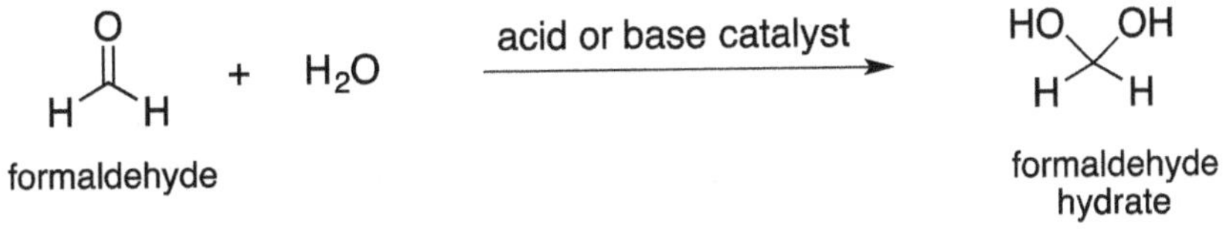

formaldehyde   acid or base catalyst   formaldehyde hydrate

Mechanism:

a) acid catalysis

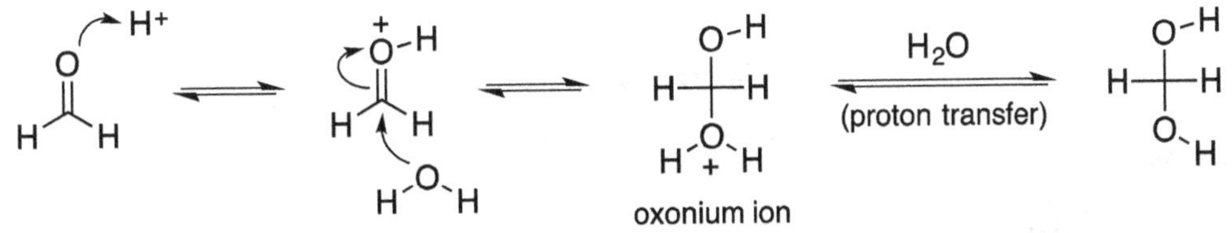

oxonium ion

b) base catalysis

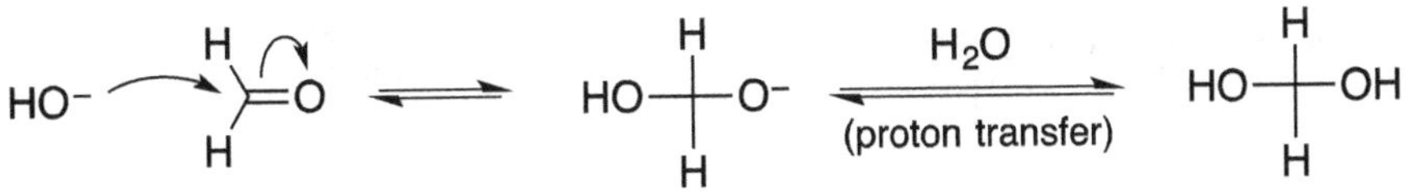

Problem 11.13. Suggest mechanisms for the formation of five-membered cyclic hemiacetal from 4-hydroxybutanal (Figure 11.10), and six-membered cyclic hemiacetal from 5-hydroxypentanal, under conditions of acid catalysis and base catalysis.

Solution:

Reaction 1:

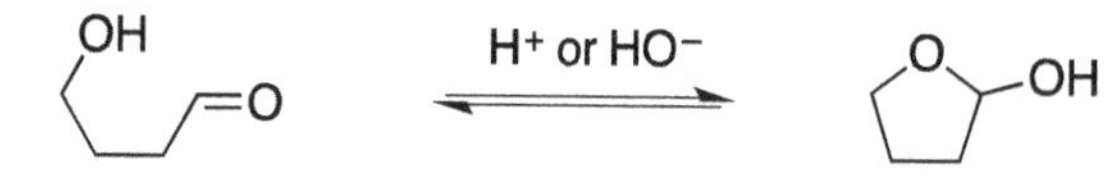

4-hydroxybutanal   a cyclic hemiacetal

Mechanism:

a) acid catalysis

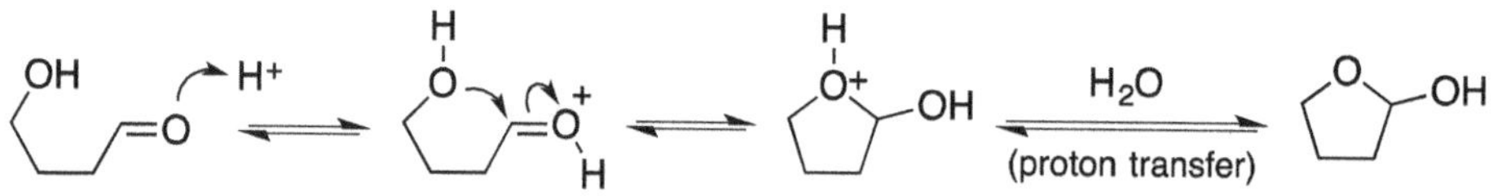

b) base catalysis

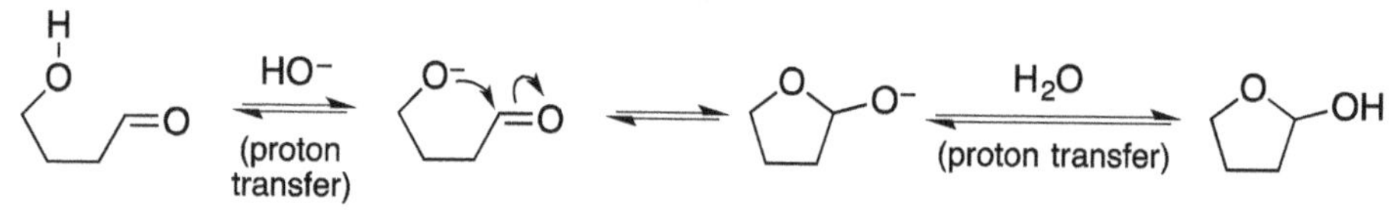

Reaction 2:

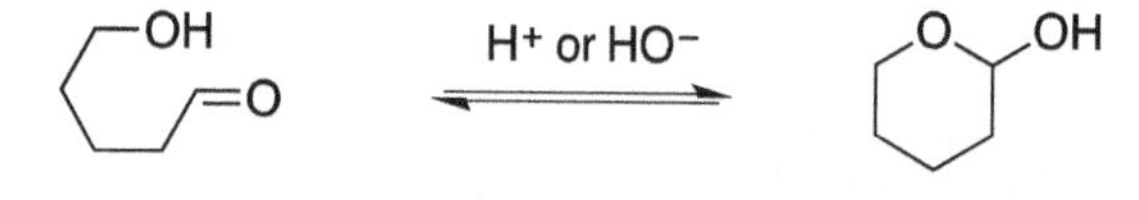

5-hydroxypentanal   a cyclic hemiacetal

Mechanism:

a) acid catalysis

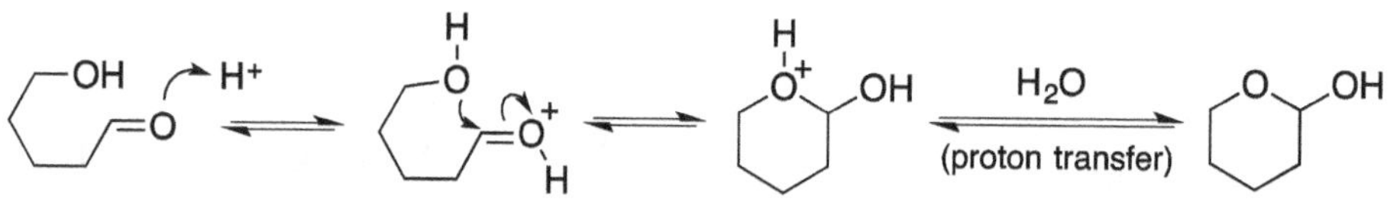

b) base catalysis

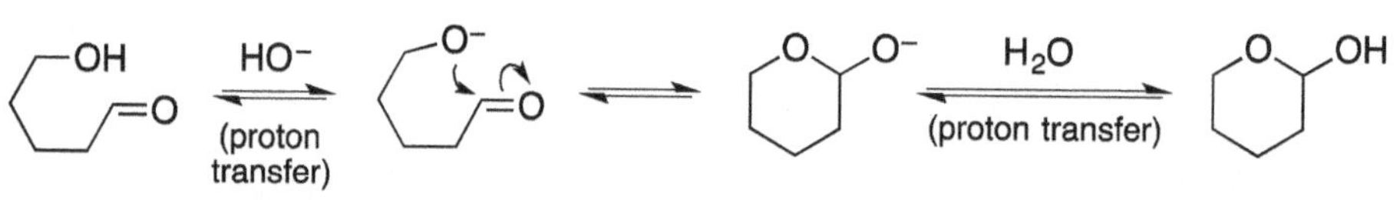

Problem 11.14. Suggest mechanisms for the reactions shown in Figure 11.11.

Solution:

Reaction 1:

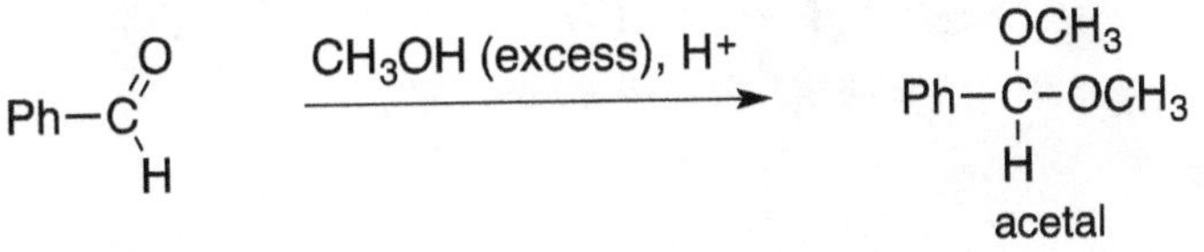

Ph–C(=O)H
CH3OH (excess), H+
Ph–C(OCH3)(OCH3)–H
acetal

Mechanism:

CH3OH
H+
a hemiacetal
oxonium ion
–H2O
carbocation
(stabilized by resonance)
oxonium ion
H2O or CH3OH
(proton transfer)
acetal

Reaction 2:

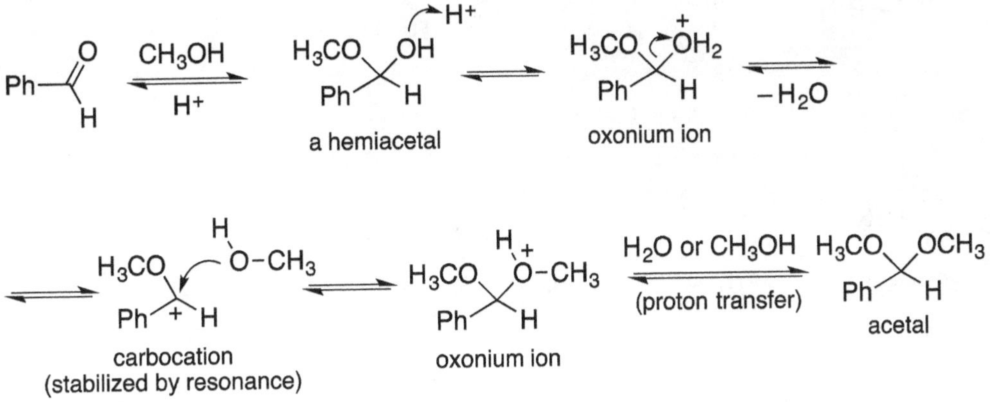

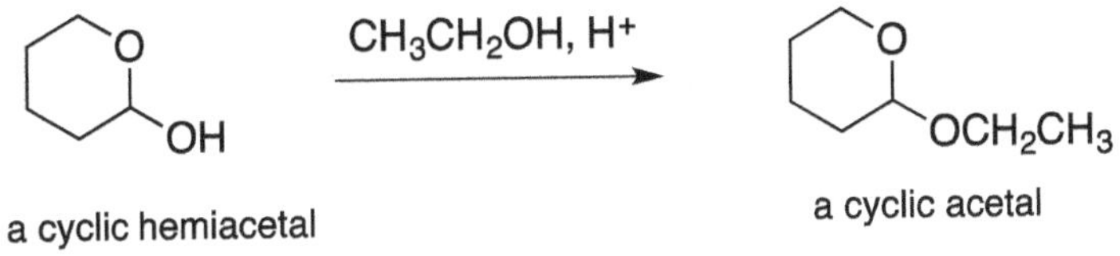

CH3CH2OH, H+
OH
OCH2CH3
a cyclic hemiacetal
a cyclic acetal

Mechanism:

H+
oxonium ion
–H2O
O–Et
carbocation
(stabilized by resonance)
oxonium ion
H2O or EtOH
(proton transfer)
OEt
a cyclic acetal

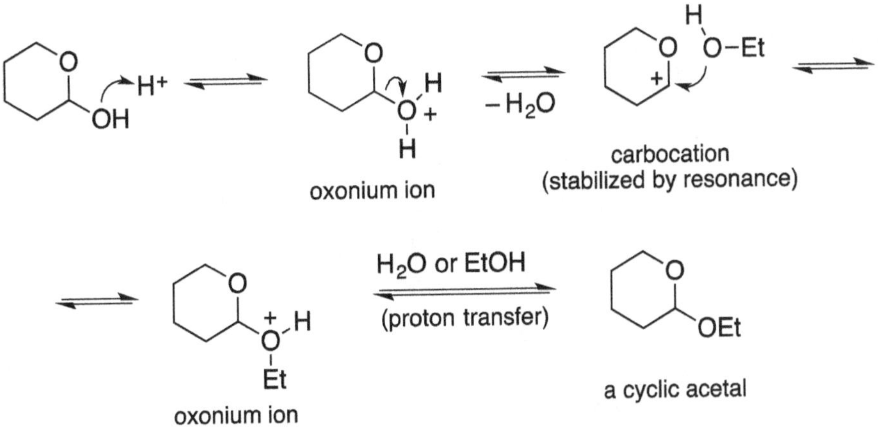

Problem 11.15. Provide the structure of the missing reactants:

a)

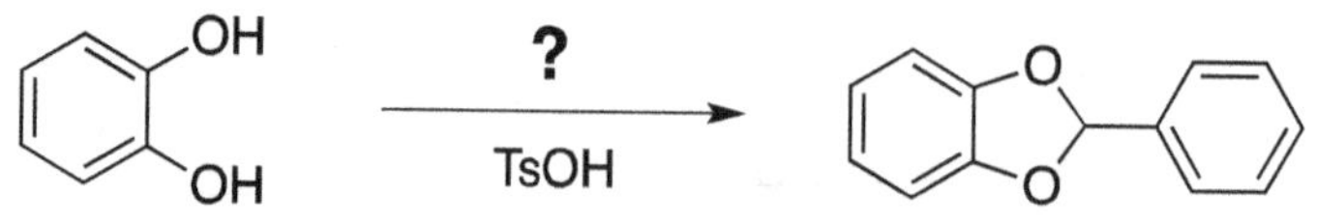

b)

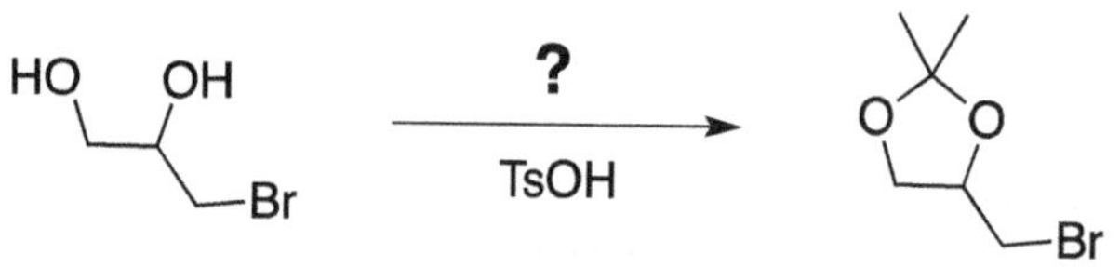

Solution:

a)

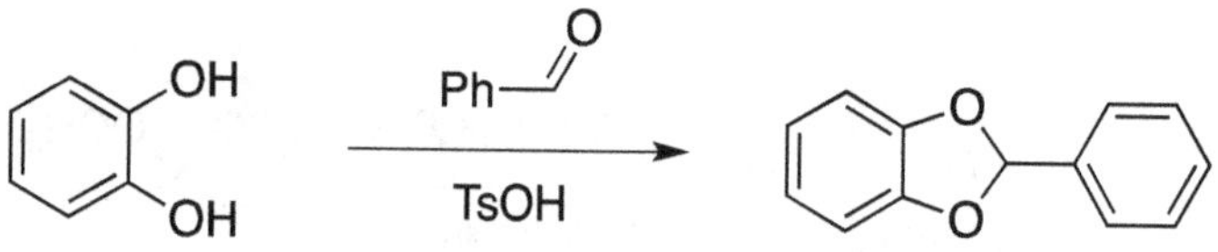

b)

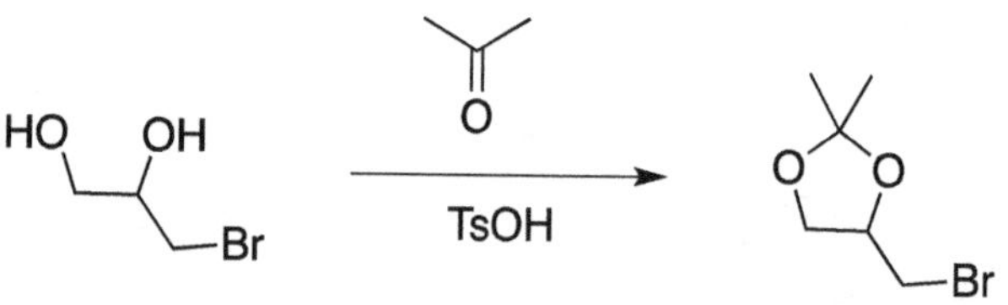

Problem 11.16. Provide the major products in the following reactions:

a)

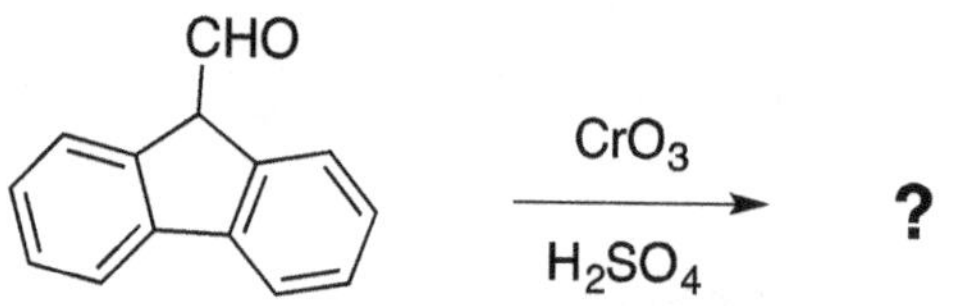

b)

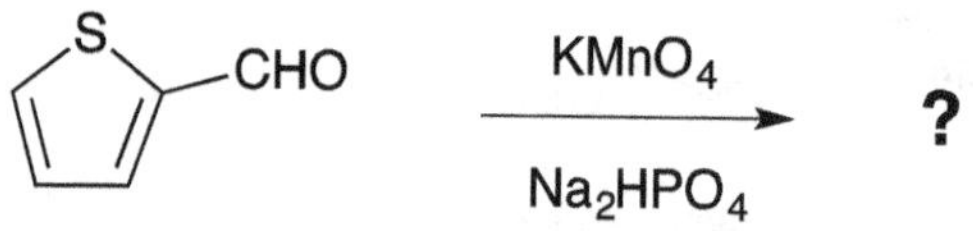

Both CrO_3 and $KMnO_4$ belong to the group of strong oxidants that produce carboxylic acids in the reaction with aldehydes:

a)

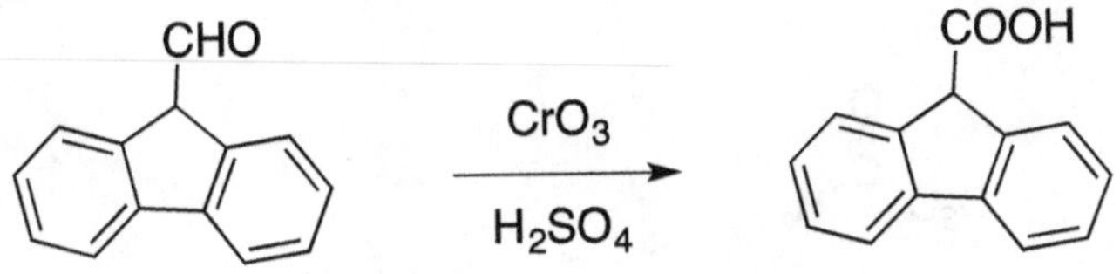

b)

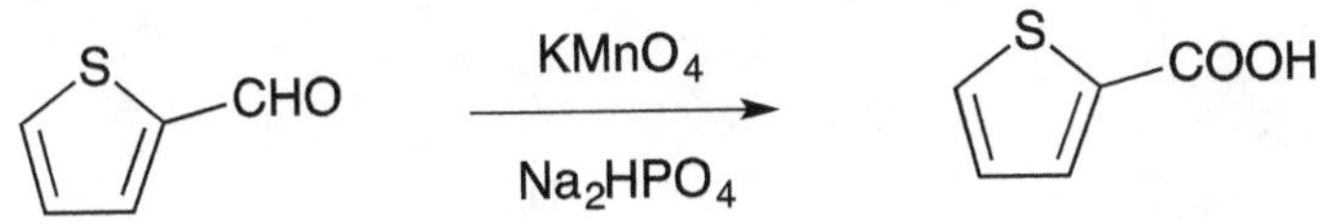

Problem 11.17. Suggest mechanisms of acid-catalyzed enolizations for 2-methylcyclopentanone.

Solution:

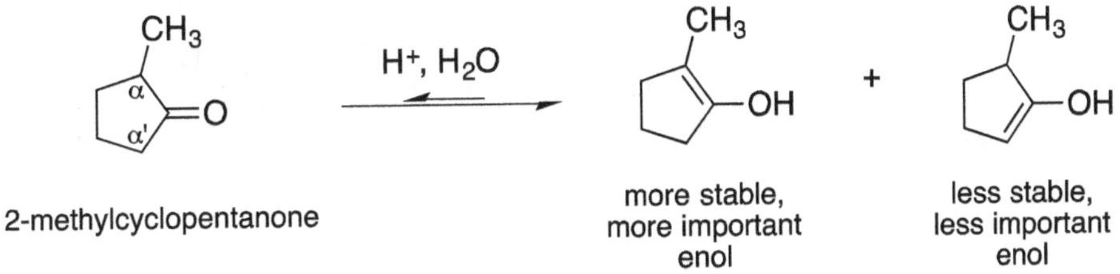

2-methylcyclopentanone

more stable,
more important
enol

+

less stable,
less important
enol

Mechanism of acid-catalyzed keto-enol tautomerization:

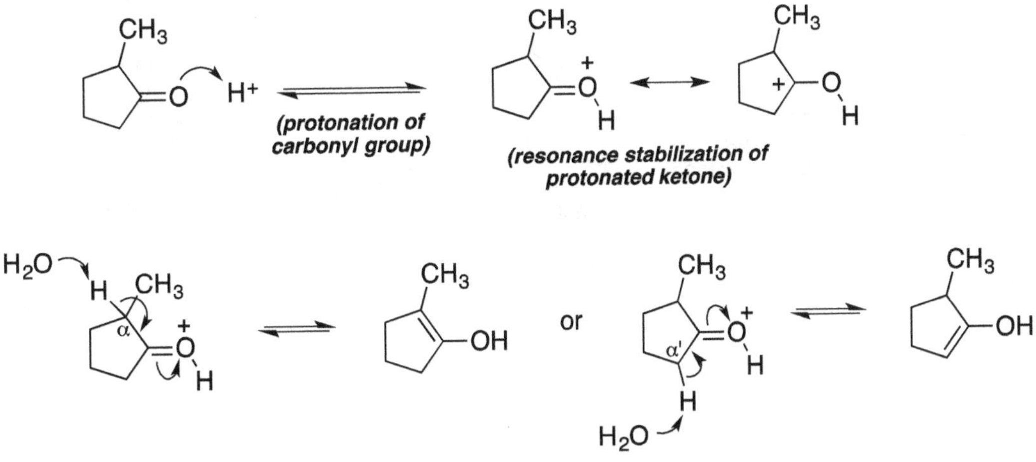

(protonation of
carbonyl group)

(resonance stabilization of
protonated ketone)

or

Problem 11.18. Write detailed mechanism for deuterium exchange of α-hydrogens in acetaldehyde.

Solution:

Deuterium exchange:

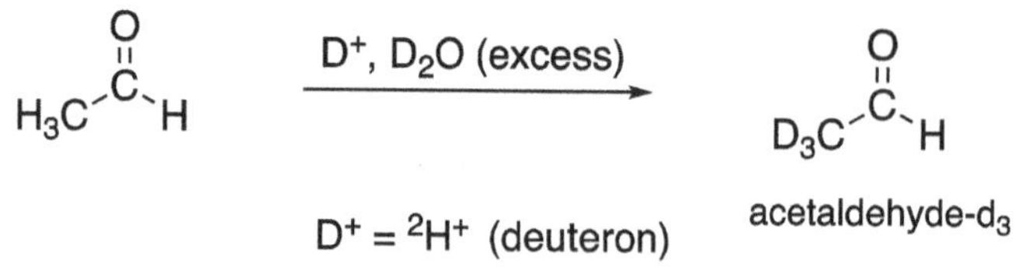

$D^+ = {}^2H^+$ (deuteron)

acetaldehyde-d₃

Mechanism:

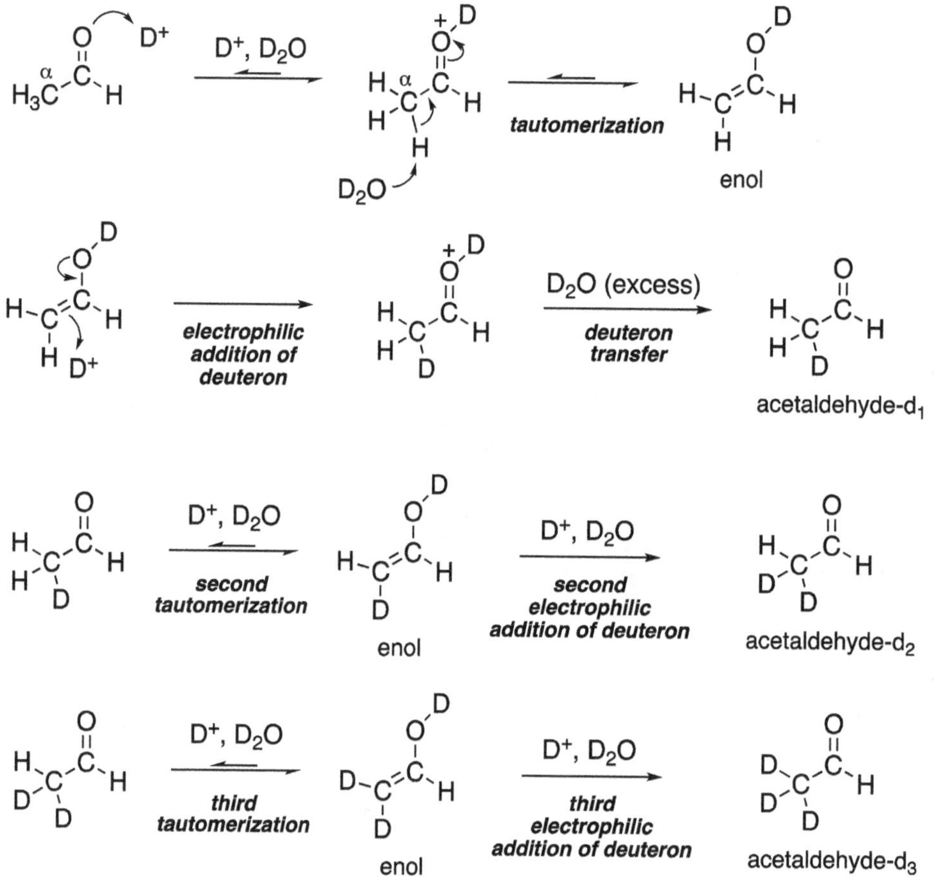

Problem 11.19. Explain the difference in the acidity of α-hydrogens in CH_3COCH_3 ($pK_a = 30$) and $CH_3COCH_2COCH_3$ ($pK_a = 9$).

Solution:
Dimethyl malonate is more acidic because its enolate anion is more stable owing to the additional resonance delocalization:

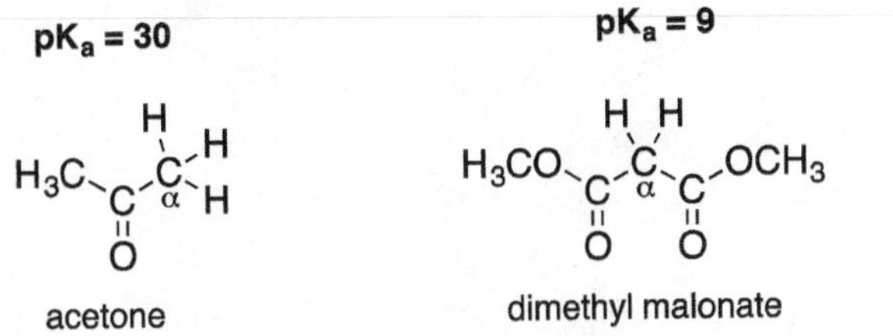

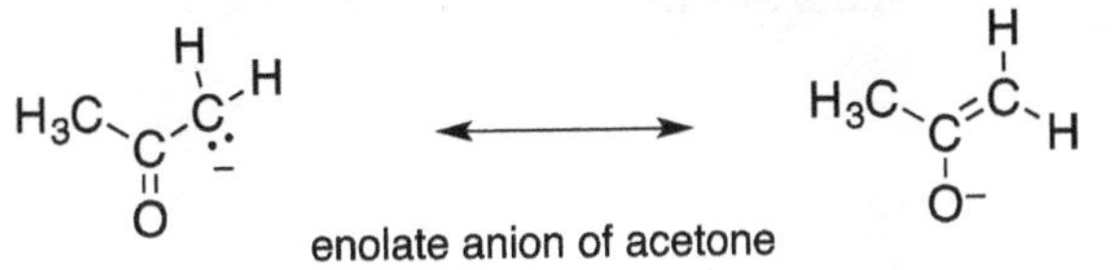

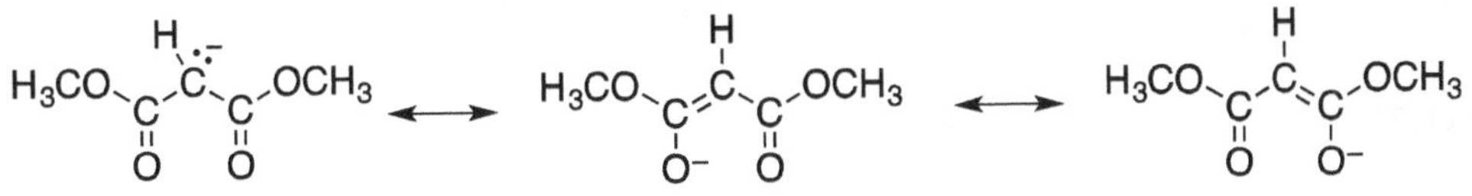

enolate anion of dimethyl malonate is more stable because of additional resonance delocalization

Problem 11.20. Write detailed mechanisms for the reactions shown in Figure 11.17.

Solution:

Reaction 1:

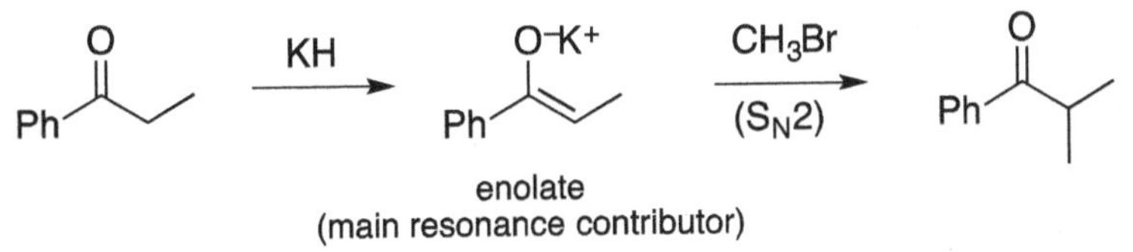

enolate
(main resonance contributor)

Mechanism:

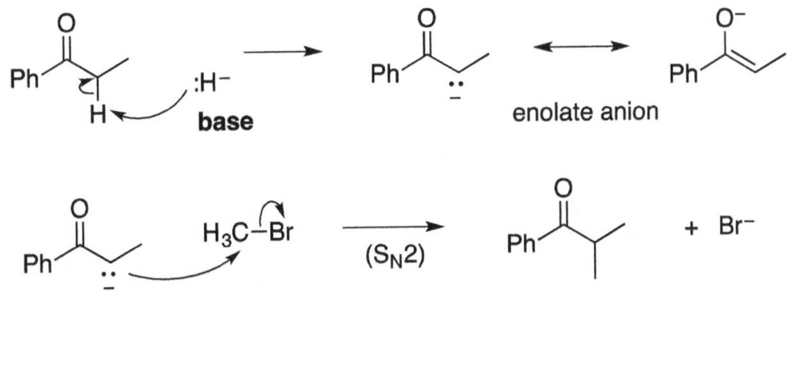

Reaction 2:

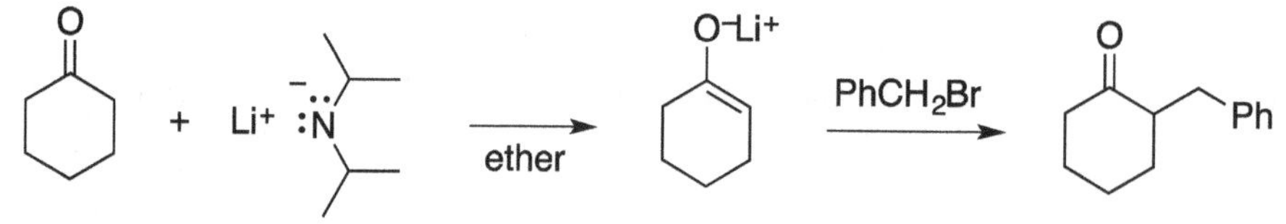

Mechanism:

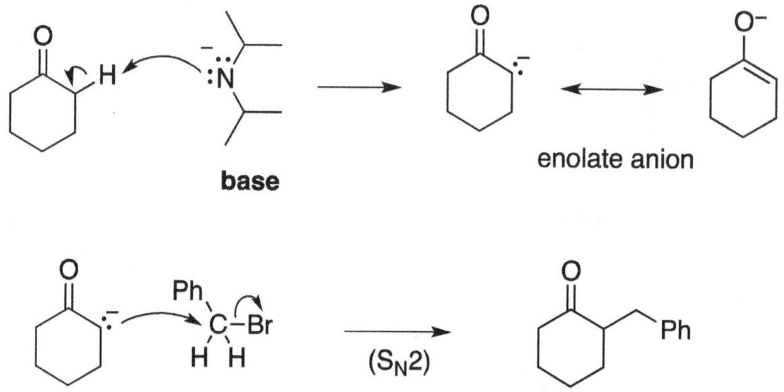

enolate anion

base

(S_N2)

Problem 11.21. Write detailed mechanisms for reactions shown in Figure 11.18.

Solution:

Reaction 1:

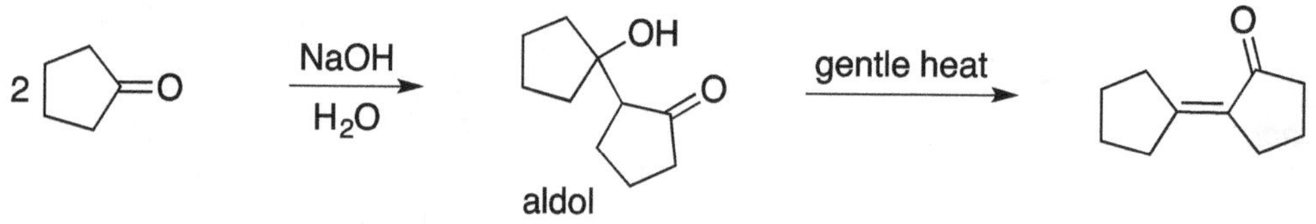

aldol

Mechanism:

deprotonation

enolate

nucleophilic
addition

proton
transfer

aldol

H^+, H_2O, heat

**(dehydration,
see Section 8.5)**

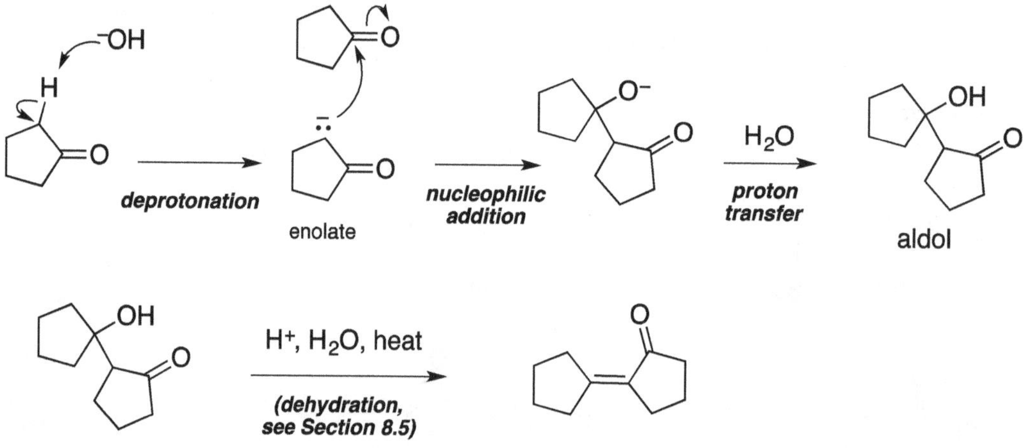

Reaction 2:

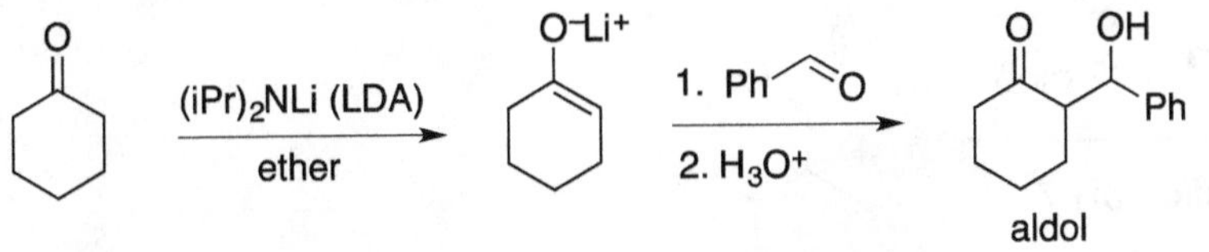

Mechanism:

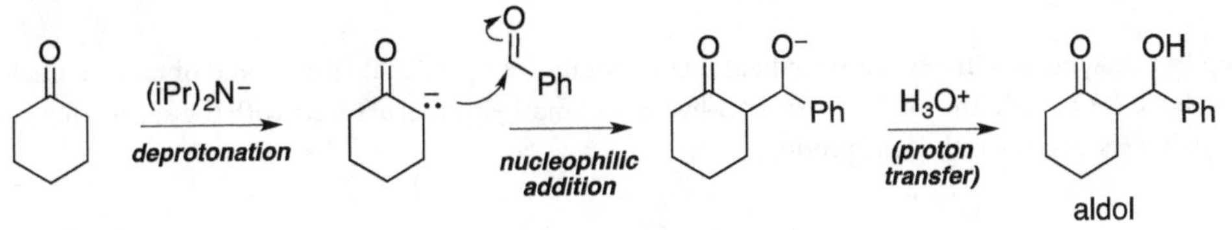

Reaction 3:

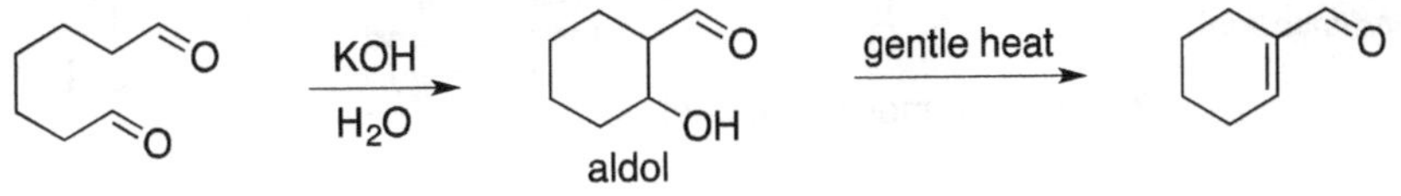

Mechanism:

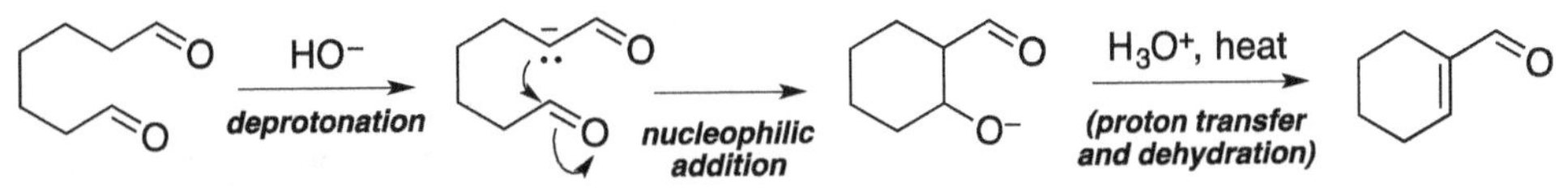

Problem 11.22. Which of the following compounds are able to undergo self-condensation by aldol reaction? Draw the products of these condensation reactions.

  a) formaldehyde   b) acetaldehyde   c) benzaldehyde   d) acetone

Solution:

The presence of α-hydrogens in a molecule of carbonyl compound is required for a self-condensation reaction. Formaldehyde ($H_2C=O$) and benzaldehyde ($PhHC=O$) do not have α-hydrogens and are not able to undergo self-condensation. The self-condensation reactions of acetaldehyde and acetone are shown below:

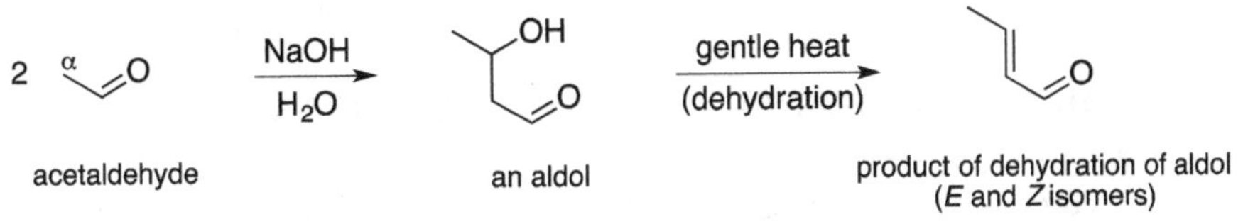

acetaldehyde   an aldol   product of dehydration of aldol
(E and Z isomers)

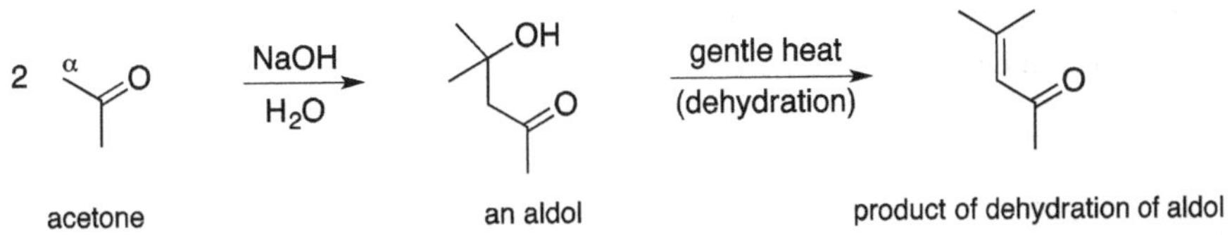

acetone   an aldol   product of dehydration of aldol

Problem 11.23. The synthesis of the product involves a mixed aldol reaction followed by an acetal formation. What is the structure of the reactant?

Solution:

The first step in this synthesis involves a mixed aldol condensation of propanal (the source of enolate nucleophile) with formaldehyde ($H_2C=O$). The initially formed 3-hydroxy-2-methylpropanal reacts with the second formaldehyde molecule to yield cyclic acetal as the final product.

Problem 11.24. Why are α-hydrogens in aldehydes more acidic than the hydrogen atom directly attached to the carbon of the carbonyl group?

Solution:

The α-hydrogens in aldehydes are more acidic because the enolate anions are more stable due to resonance delocalization. Deprotonation of the hydrogen atom directly attached to the carbon of the carbonyl group forms anion of aldehyde that does not have any resonance stabilization:

11.2. Additional Problems for Chapter 11 (for answers see Ch 17)

Problem 11.25. Select one compound from the given set that fits **all** of the following descriptions:

a) has the molecular formula C_8H_{14}, and
b) absorbs 1 mole of H_2 when exposed to excess H_2 and Pt, and
c) produces **two different ketones** upon ozonolysis.

a)

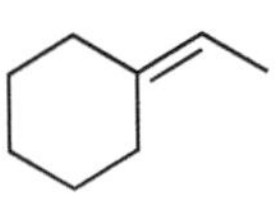

b)

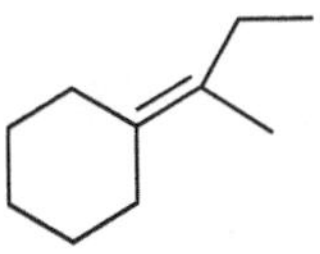

c)

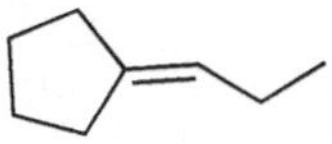

d)

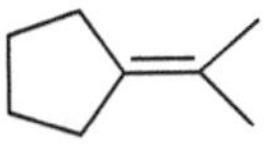

e)

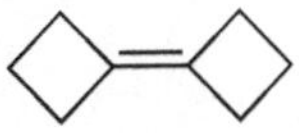

Problem 11.26. Provide the product(s) in the following reaction.

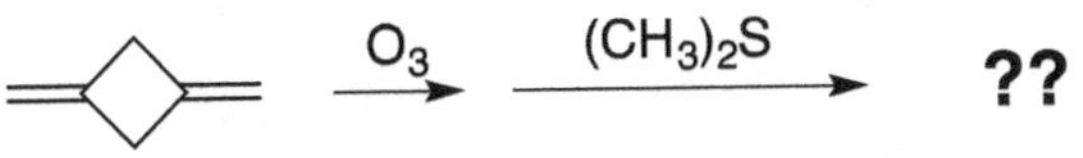

$$ \text{(structure)} \quad \xrightarrow{O_3} \quad \xrightarrow{(CH_3)_2S} \quad \textbf{??} $$

Problem 11.27. Provide structures of A, B, C, and D based on the following details. Compound **A**, molecular formula C_6H_{10}, absorbs one equivalent of H_2 to form **B**, molecular formula C_6H_{12}. Ozonolysis of A yields cyclopentanone and formaldehyde:

A $\xrightarrow{H_2,\ Pd}$ B

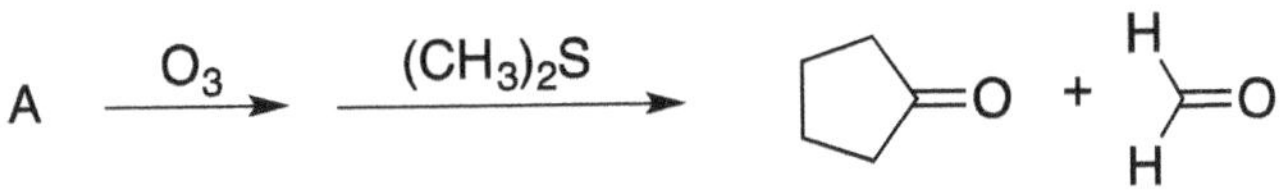

A $\xrightarrow{O_3} \xrightarrow{(CH_3)_2S}$

A also reacts with HBr to form **C**, molecular formula $C_6H_{11}Br$.

A $\xrightarrow[CH_2Cl_2]{HBr}$ C

C undergoes elimination to produce **D**, molecular formula C_6H_{10}.

C $\xrightarrow[\text{ethanol-}H_2O]{KOH}$ D

D undergoes cleavage upon ozonolysis to yield the keto-aldehyde shown below.

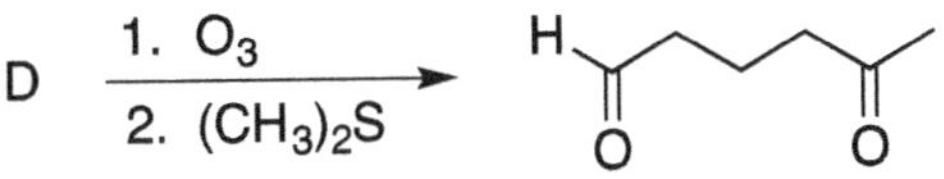

D $\xrightarrow[\text{2. }(CH_3)_2S]{\text{1. }O_3}$

CHAPTER 12

Carboxylic Acids and Their Derivatives

12.1. Chapter 12 Problems and Solutions

Problem 12.1. Provide the IUPAC names:

a) 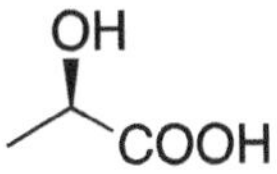

b) 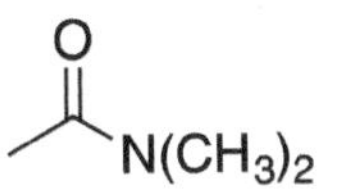

c) 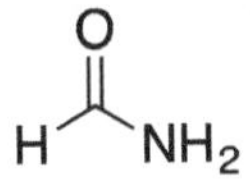

d) 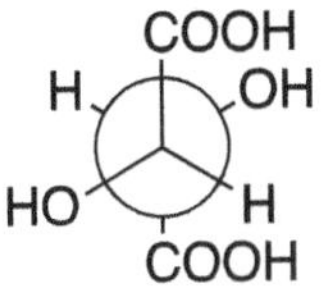

e) 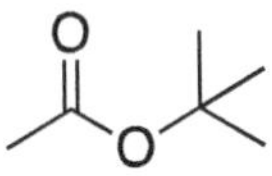

f) 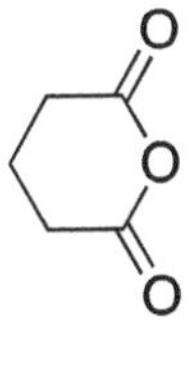

g) 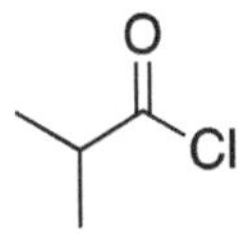

h) 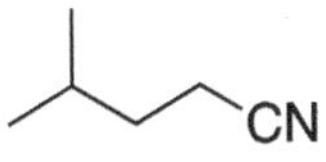

Solution:

a) 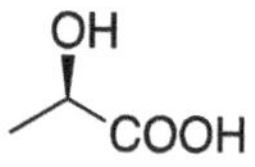
OH
\|
COOH

(*R*)-2-hydroxypropanoic acid

b) 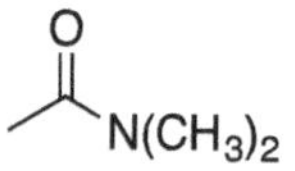
O
‖
N(CH₃)₂

N,N-dimethylacetamide

c) 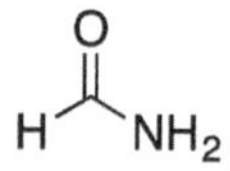
O
‖
H   NH₂

formamide

d) 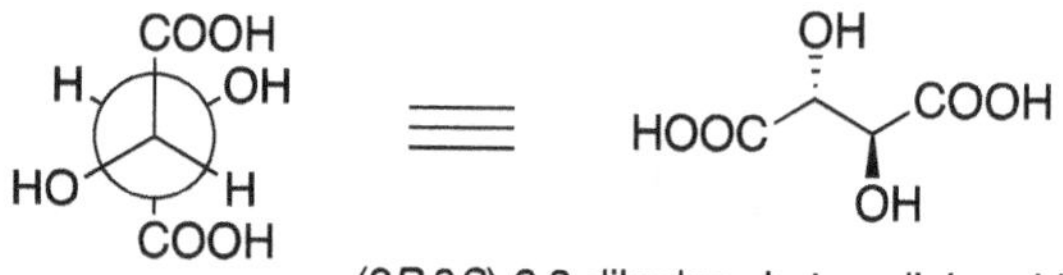
COOH
H   OH
HO   H
COOH

≡

OH
HOOC   COOH
OH

(2*R*,3*S*)-2,3-dihydroxybutanedioic acid

e) 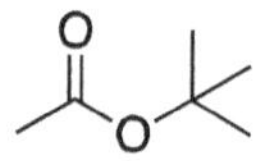
O
‖
O

tert-butyl acetate

f) 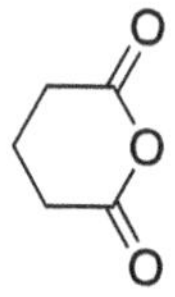
O
O
O

pentanedioic anhydride

g) 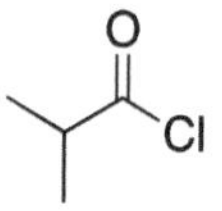
O
‖
Cl

2-methylpropanoyl chloride

h) 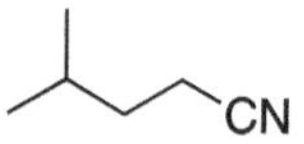
CN

4-methylpentanenitrile

Problem 12.2. The following compounds are listed as ingredients on the labels of cosmetics and household chemicals. Use web-based resources to determine the structures of these compounds.

a) glyceryl stearate   b) ethyl acetate   c) citric acid   d) cocamide MEA

Solution:

Glyceryl stearate:

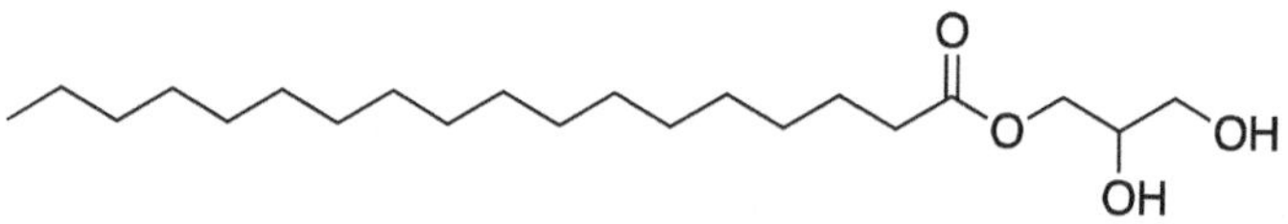

Ethyl acetate:

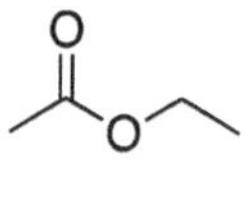

Citric acid:

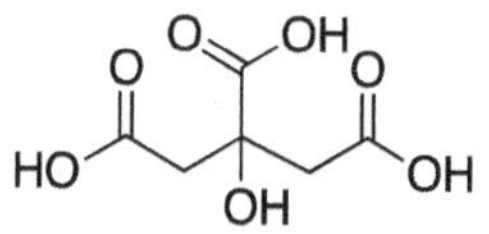

Cocamide MEA:

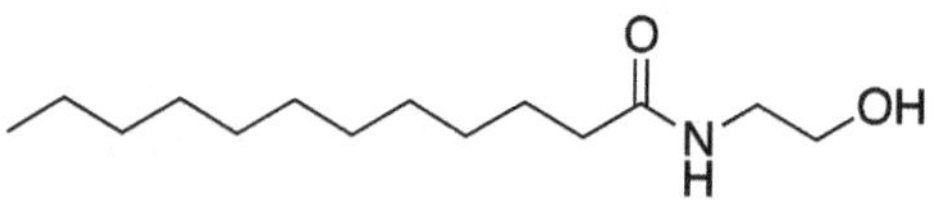

Problem 12.3. Sort the following compounds according to increasing boiling points.

(I)

(II)

(III)

(IV)

Solution:
Carboxylic acids (**II** and **IV**) have higher boiling points (bp) than alcohols (**III**) and alkanes (**I**) of comparable size because of their high polarity and the presence of strong hydrogen bonding between molecules. The presence of two carboxylic groups in compound (**IV**) leads to further increase of the bp. An alkane (**I**) has the lowest bp due to the lack of attraction between nonpolar molecules.

(**I**) (lowest bp) < (**III**) < (**II**) < (**IV**) (highest bp)

Problem 12.4. Rank these anions according to increasing basicity:

$ClCH_2COO^-$ FCH_2COO^- $CH_3CH_2COO^-$ CH_3COO^-

Solution:
The basicity of these anions correlates with the acidity of the corresponding carboxylic acids in agreement with inductive effects of substituents (see Section 2.3 of the textbook). The conjugate base of the strongest acid (i.e., FCH_2COO^-) has the weakest basicity, and the conjugate base of the weakest acid (i.e., $CH_3CH_2COO^-$) has the strongest basicity:

FCH_2COOH (strongest acid) > $ClCH_2COOH$ > CH_3COOH > CH_3CH_2COOH (weakest acid)

FCH_2COO^- (weakest base) < $ClCH_2COO^-$ < CH_3COO^- < $CH_3CH_2COO^-$ (strongest base)

Problem 12.5. Sort the following carboxylic acids according to increasing acidity:

Solution:
Acidity of carboxylic acids depends on the inductive effects of substituents (see Section 2.3 of the textbook). The presence of the electron-withdrawing fluorine atom stabilizes the anion and increases acidity. In contrast, the presence of the electron-donating alkyl groups leads to the lower acidity. Longer alkyl chain or several alkyl substituents will have a stronger electron-donating effect.

strongest acid   **weakest acid**

Problem 12.6. Provide the resonance contributor that explains why *N,N*-dimethylformamide (DMF) shows three signals in the ^{13}C NMR.

Solution:

The amide bond in DMF has a partial double-bond character due to the important resonance contributor shown below. Because of the restricted rotation about this bond, the methyl groups are not equal and show different signals in NMR spectra. There are three signals in the ^{13}C NMR spectrum of DMF corresponding to the carbons **a**, **b**, and **c** in the actual molecule which is best represented by the resonance hybrid:

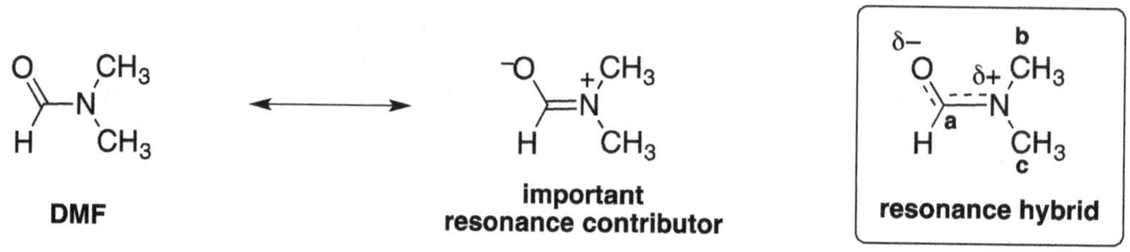

DMF

important resonance contributor

resonance hybrid

Problem 12.7. Sort these compounds according to their relative reactivity toward the nucleophilic acyl substitution:

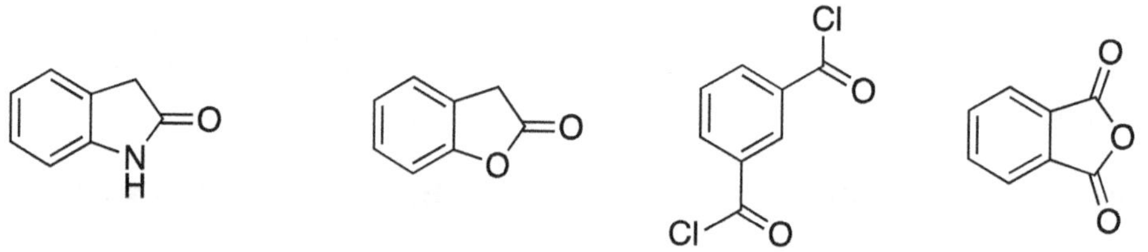

Solution:

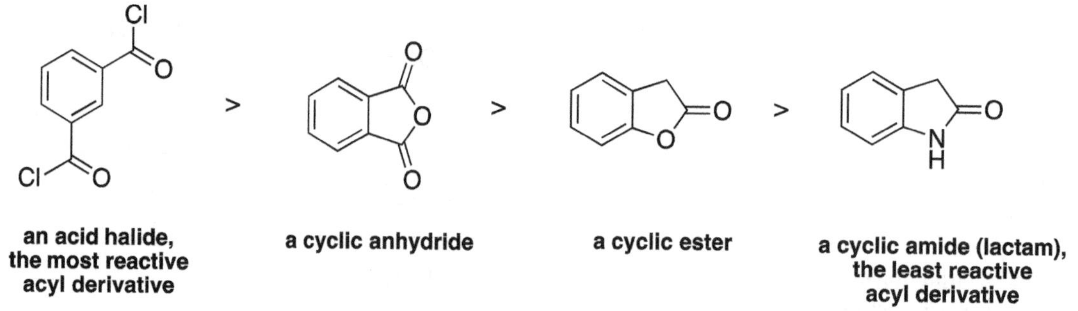

an acid halide, the most reactive acyl derivative > **a cyclic anhydride** > **a cyclic ester** > **a cyclic amide (lactam), the least reactive acyl derivative**

Problem 12.8. Propose mechanisms for reactions shown in Figure 12.9.

Solution:
Abbreviated mechanisms of these reactions are shown below:

Hydrolysis:

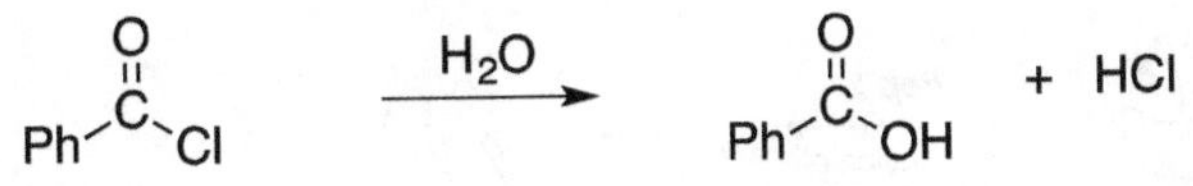

Mechanism:

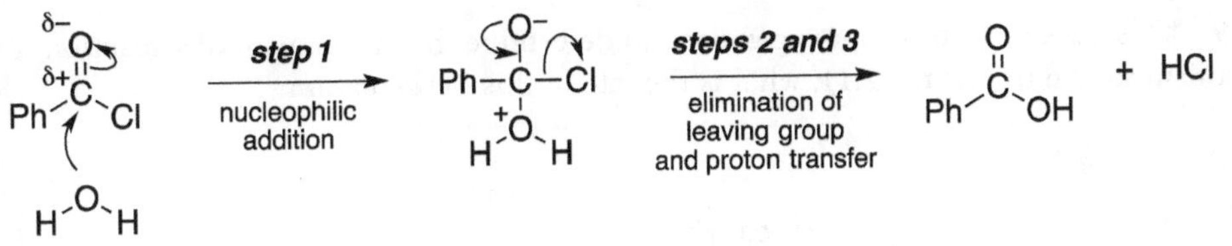

Formation of esters:

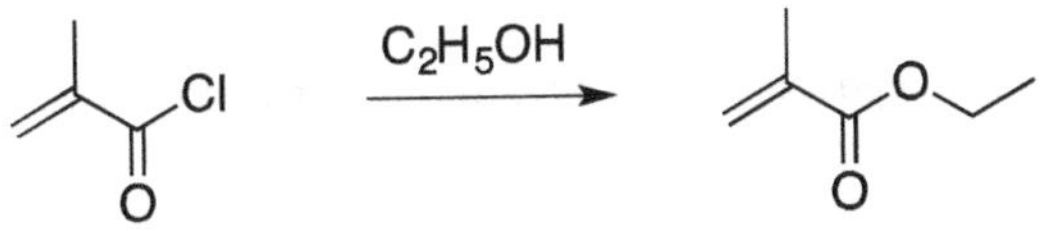

Mechanism:

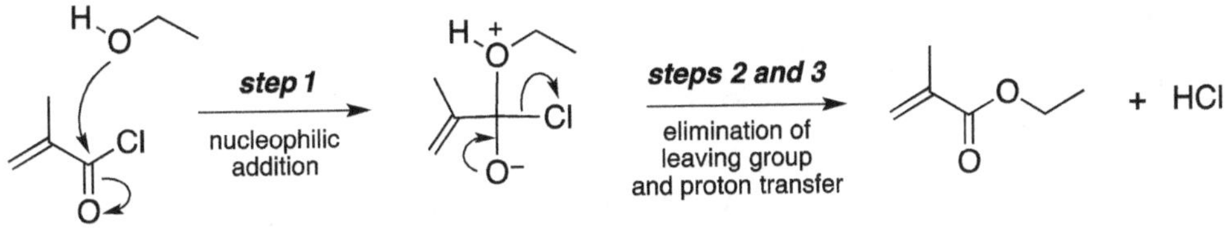

Formation of amides:

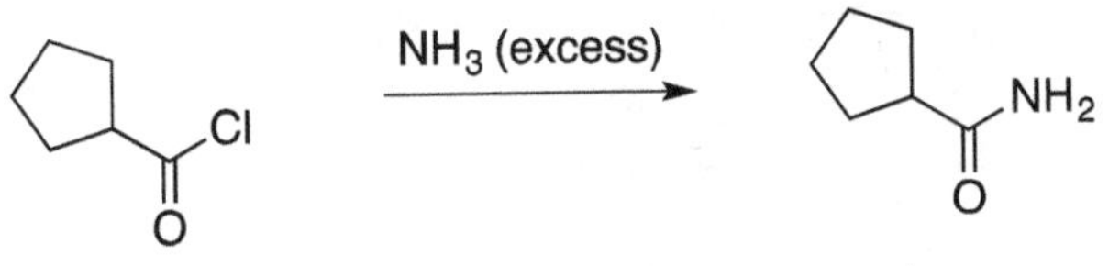

Mechanism:

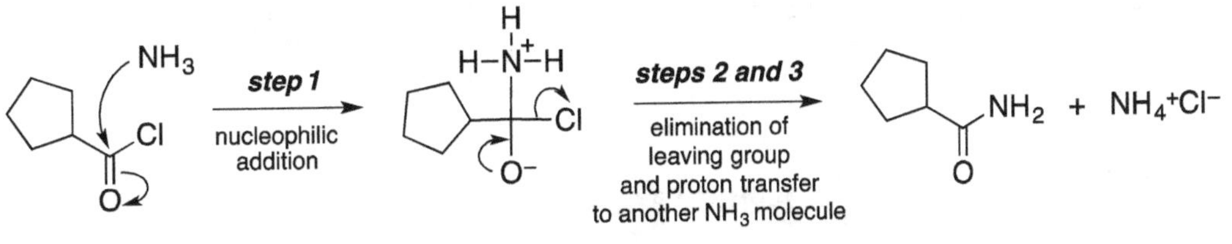

Coupling with lithium diorganocuprates:

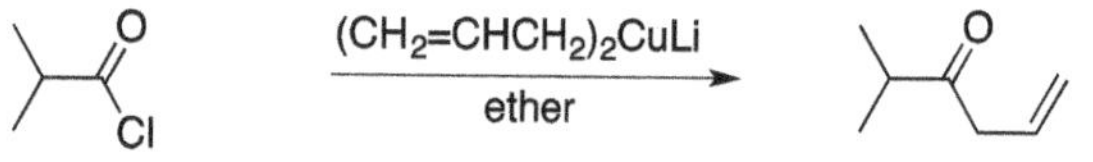

Mechanism:

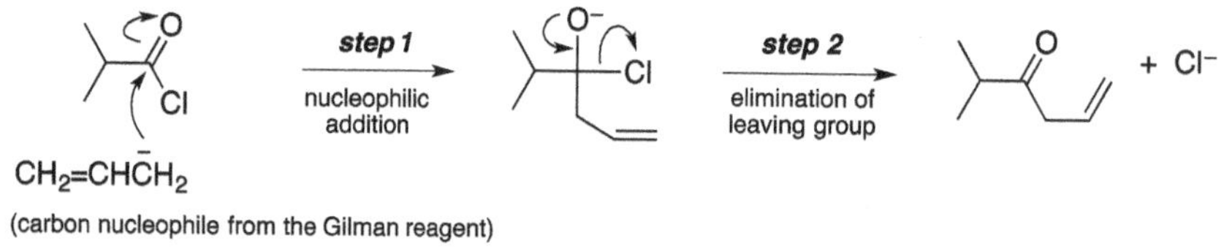

CH₂=CH$\overset{-}{\text{C}}$H₂

(carbon nucleophile from the Gilman reagent)

Problem 12.9. ^{18}O is a heavy isotope of oxygen used to determine the mechanism of a reaction. Based on the mechanism shown in Figure 12.11, what is the fate of this oxygen atom?

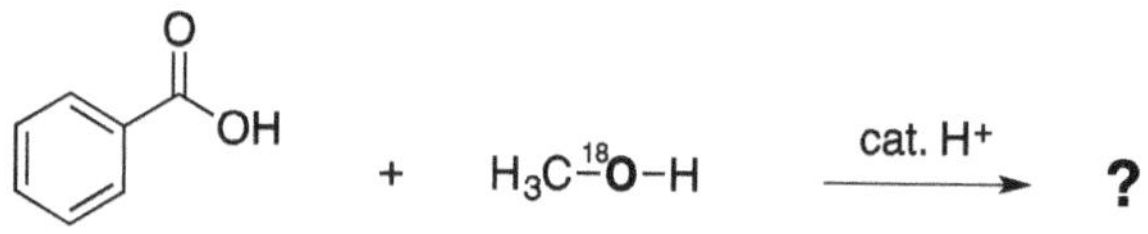

Solution:

A detailed mechanism of the esterification reaction showing the position of the oxygen label is shown below:

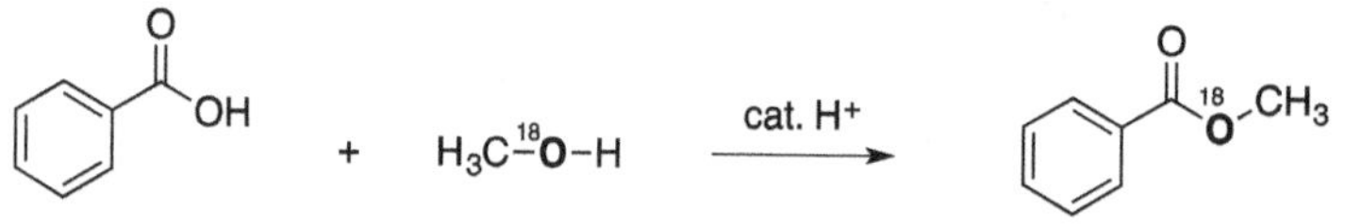

Mechanism:

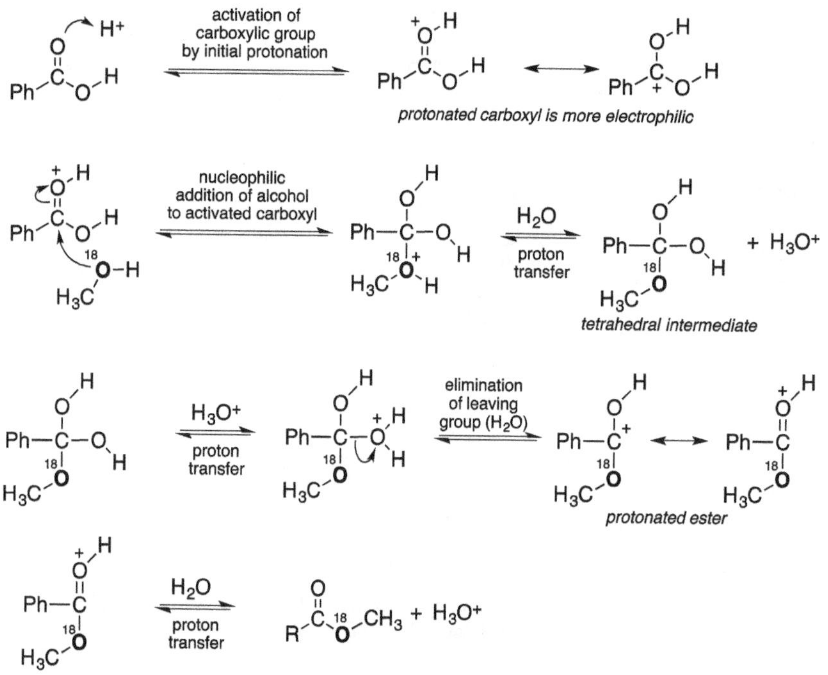

Problem 12.10. Use the Fischer esterification to prepare the following esters:

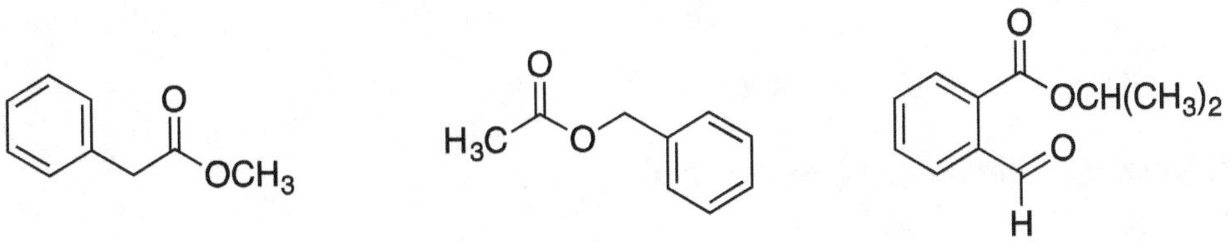

Solution:

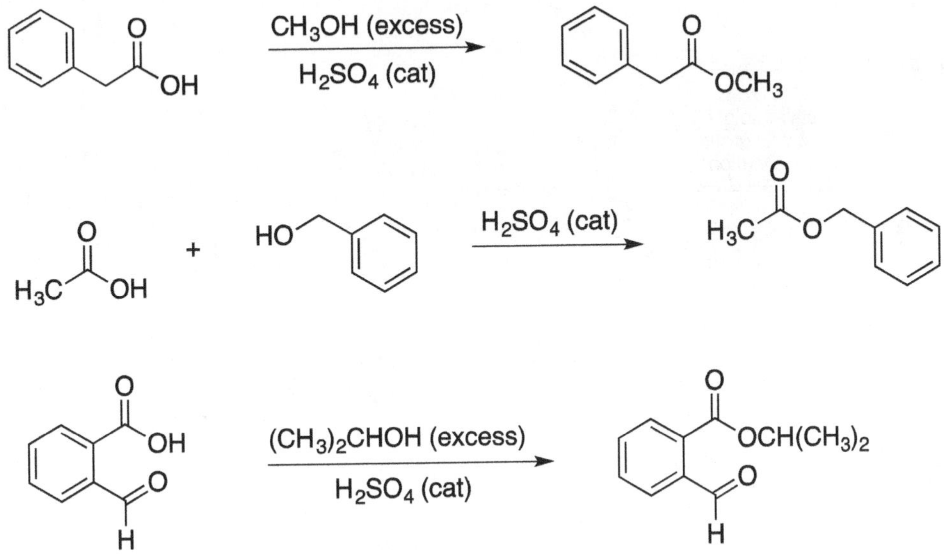

Problem 12.11. Esters can be hydrolyzed under acidic as well as under basic condition. Why is the hydrolysis under basic conditions irreversible, while under acidic conditions it is reversible?

Solution:
Each step in the mechanism of the acid-catalyzed hydrolysis is an equilibrium (see Figure 12.11 in the textbook) and the entire reaction is an equilibrium. In the mechanism of the basic hydrolysis, the last step (proton transfer from acid to alkoxide, Figure 12.12 in the textbook) is almost completely irreversible because of the large difference in the pK_a of carboxylic acid and alcohol. The produced in this step carboxylate anion is unreactive in nucleophilic acyl substitution.

Problem 12.12. Propose mechanisms for reactions shown in Figure 12.14.

Solution:

Abbreviated mechanisms for amide hydrolysis are shown below:

Hydrolysis of an amide by aqueous acid:

Mechanism:

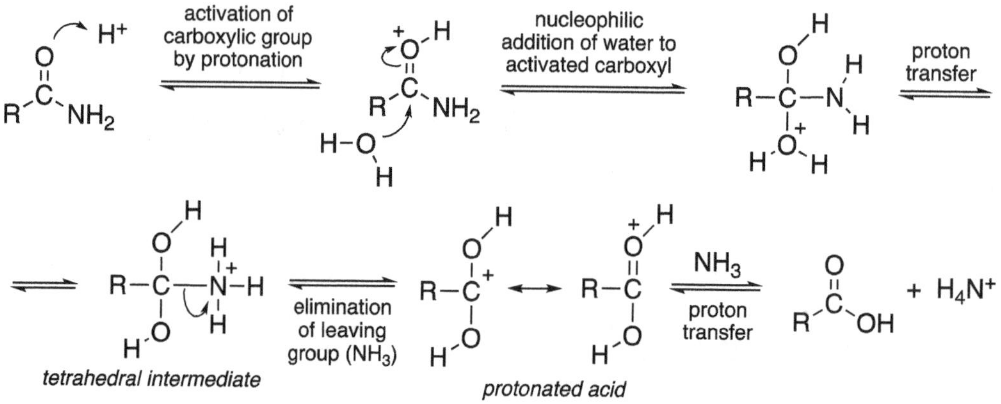

Hydrolysis of an amide by aqueous base:

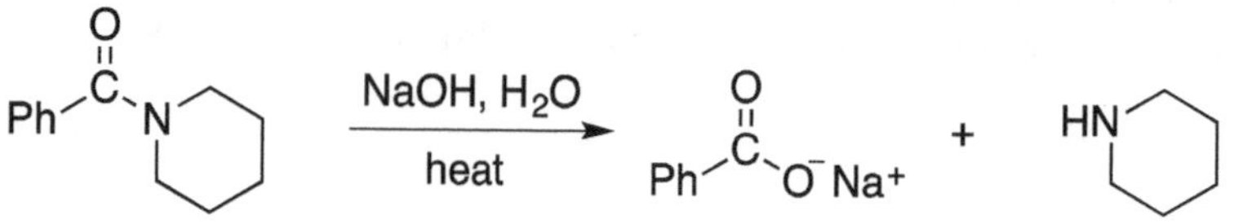

Mechanism:

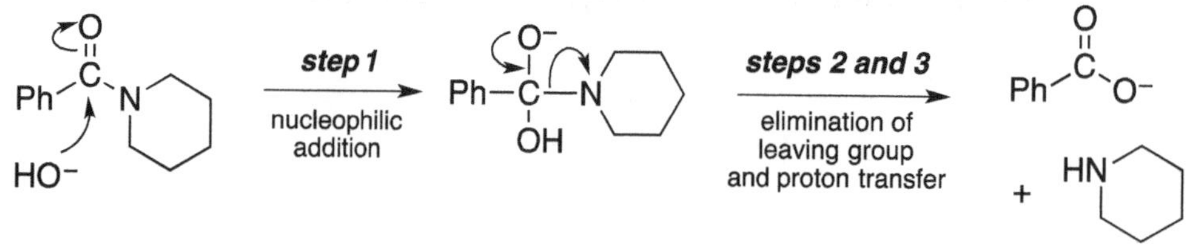

Problem 12.13. Under acidic conditions amides are protonated. For example:

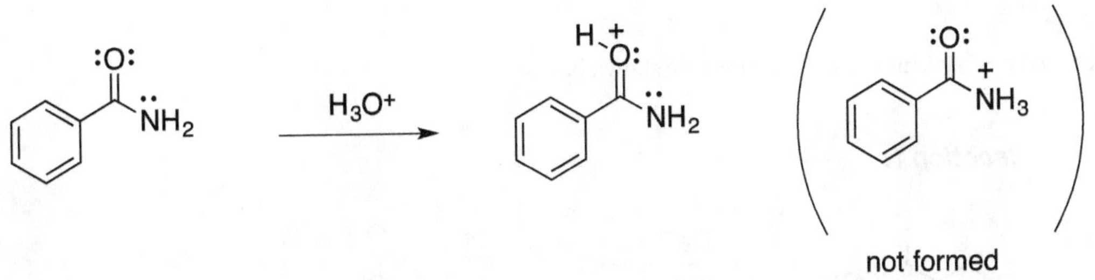

not formed

Using resonance structures, explain why the protonation of an amide occurs on the carbonyl group and not on the nitrogen atom.

Solution:

No resonance stabilization is possible for the N-protonated species as explained below:

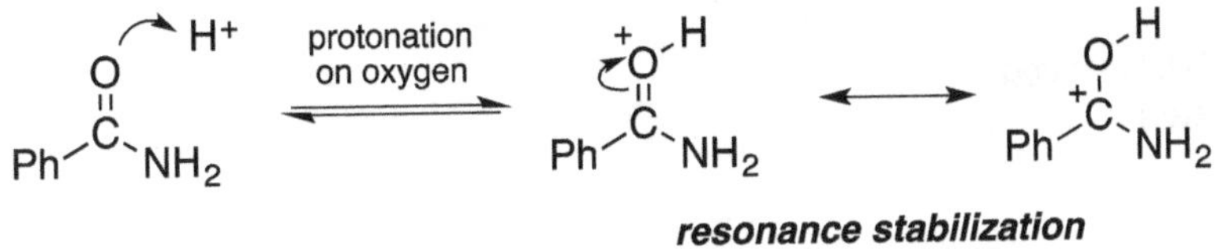

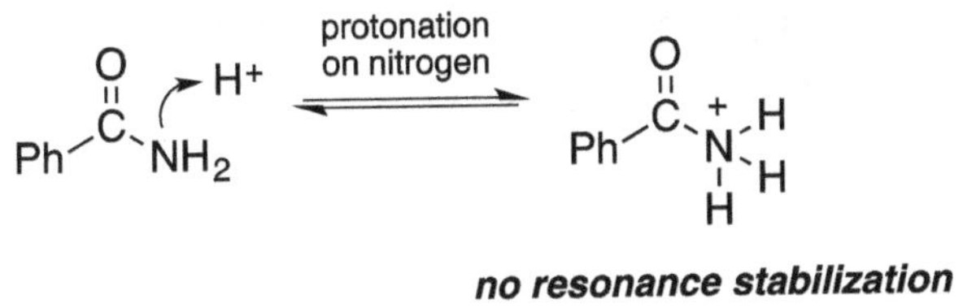

resonance stabilization

no resonance stabilization

Problem 12.14. Both esters and amides can be hydrolyzed to form carboxylic acid under acidic conditions. While the mechanisms of these reactions are very similar, the hydrolysis of amides under these conditions require at least an equimolar amount of acid; while for the hydrolysis of esters, a catalytical amount is fully sufficient. Explain.

Solution:

Acid is released in the final step of ester hydrolysis (see Scheme 12.11 of the textbook) and therefore this is a catalytic reaction. In the case of the amide hydrolysis (see solution to Problem 12.12), the acid is consumed in the process of the protonation of ammonia or amine released as the leaving group.

Problem 12.15. Propose mechanisms for the reactions shown in Figure 12.18.

Solution:

Abbreviated mechanisms of these reactions are shown below:

Reaction 1:

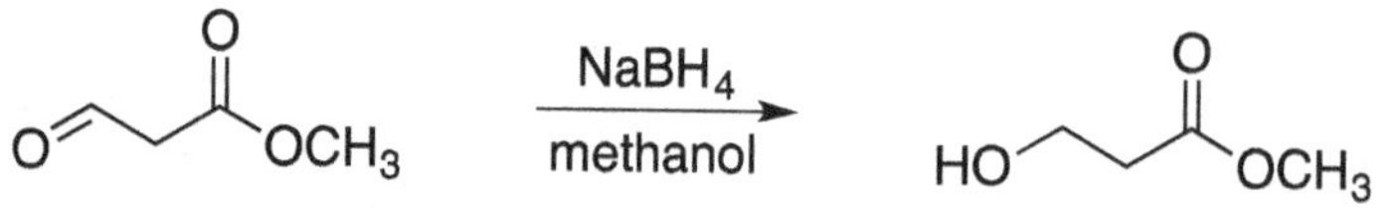

methyl 3-oxopropanoate

NaBH$_4$
methanol

methyl 3-hydroxypropanoate

Mechanism:

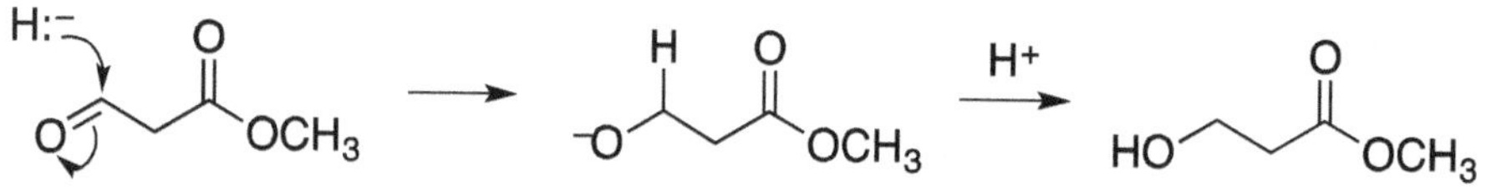

(NaBH$_4$ is the source of H:$^-$ reacting with aldehyde but not ester)

Reaction 2:

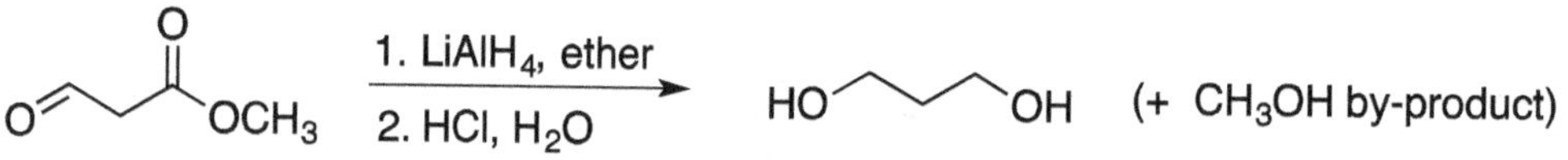

1. LiAlH$_4$, ether
2. HCl, H$_2$O

1,3-propanediol   (+ CH$_3$OH by-product)

Mechanism:

addition   elimination

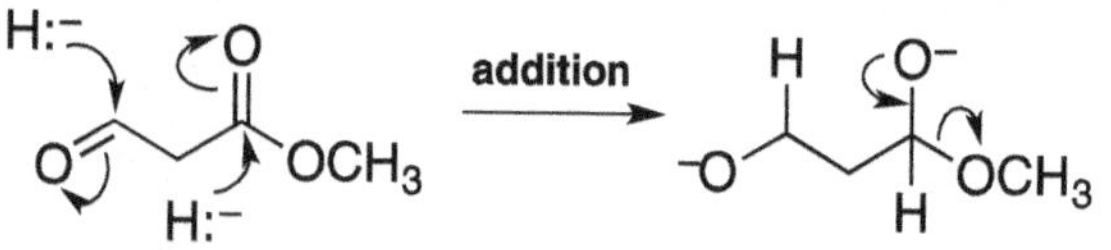

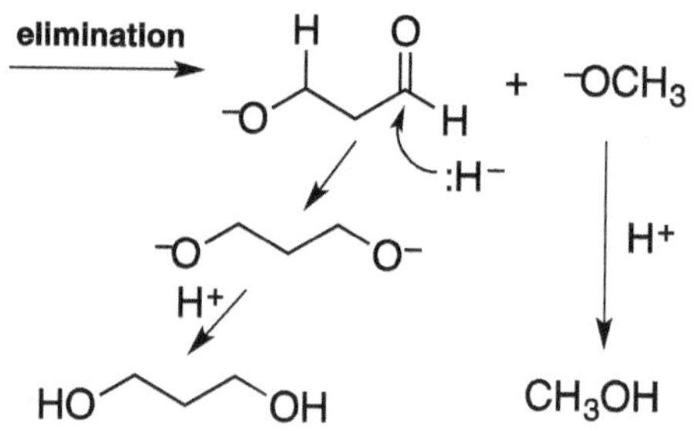

(LiAlH$_4$ is the more effective source of H:$^-$ reacting with both aldehyde and ester)

Reaction 3:

HOCH$_2$CH$_2$OH, H$^+$
(protection step)

LiAlH$_4$, ether
(reduction of an ester)

H$^+$, excess H$_2$O
(deprotection step and protonation)

3-hydroxypropanal

Mechanism of protection and deprotection:
(the deprotection follows the reversed order of steps)

hemiacetal
formation
(Section 11.7)

a hemiacetal

acetal
formation
(Section 11.7)

an acetal

For the mechanism of the ester reduction with LiAlH$_4$, see Figure 12.16 in the textbook

Problem 12.16. When isatin is reacted with LiAlH$_4$, both carbonyl groups are reduced. Treatment of the reaction mixture with diluted HCl results in the elimination of water and the formation of indole as major product. What is the structure of the product of the first step in this reaction sequence? What would be the expected outcome if you were to protect the ketone functional group?

LiAlH$_4$, ether

?

diluted HCl, heat

isatin

indole

Solution:

Isatin has two different carbonyl groups: a ketone and an amide. The reaction of isatin with LiAlH$_4$ produces indolin-3-ol as an intermediate product via reduction of ketone to hydroxyl group (see Section 11.4 of the textbook) and reduction of amide to the cyclic amine. Dehydration of indolin-3-ol forms indole as the final product. The reduction of protected isatin yields indolin-3-one, as shown below:

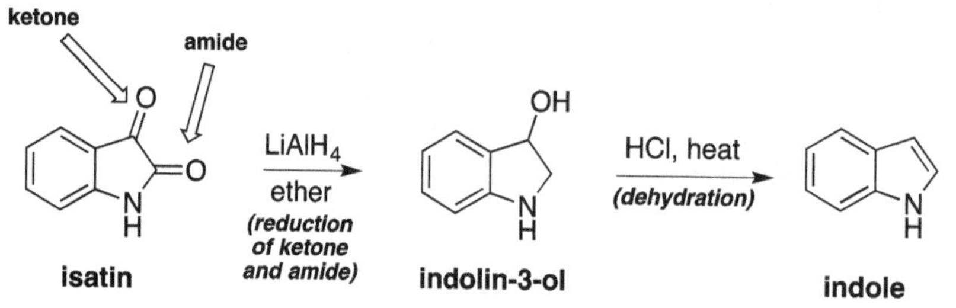

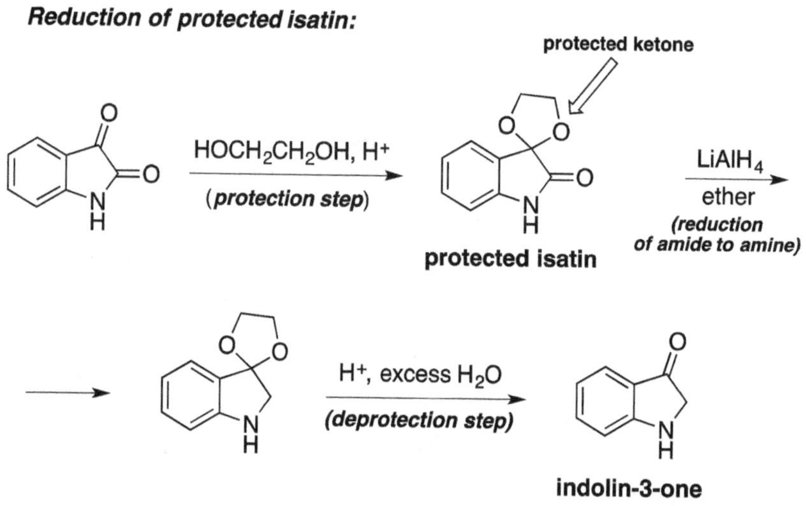

Reduction of protected isatin:

Problem 12.17. Provide either the starting material or the major products of the following sequence of reactions, as indicated:

a)

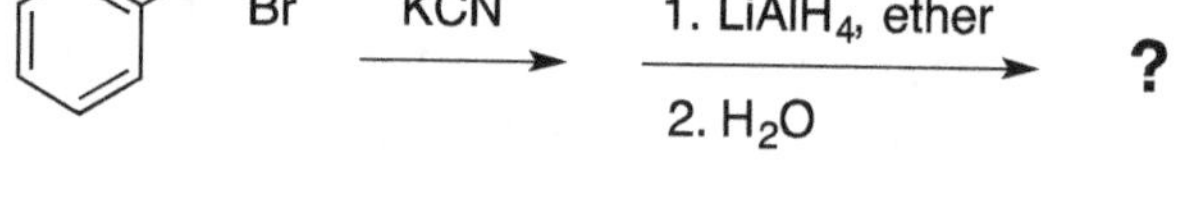

b)

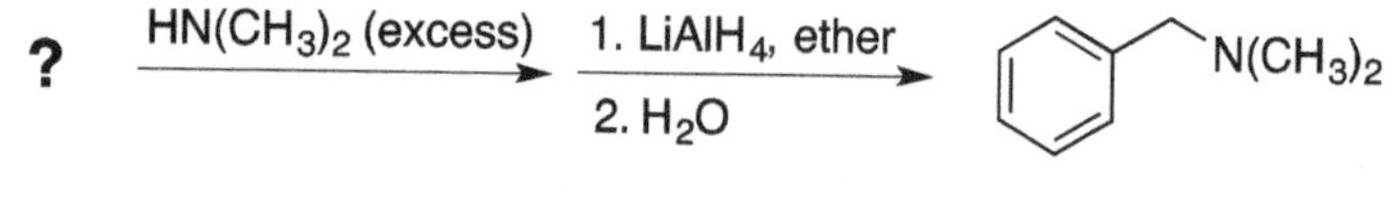

c)

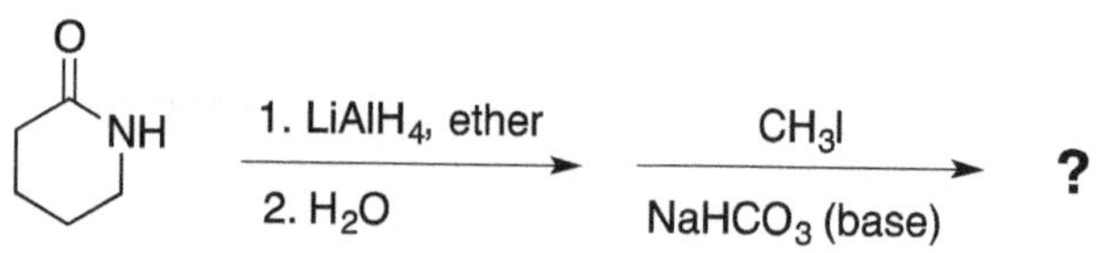

Solution:

a)

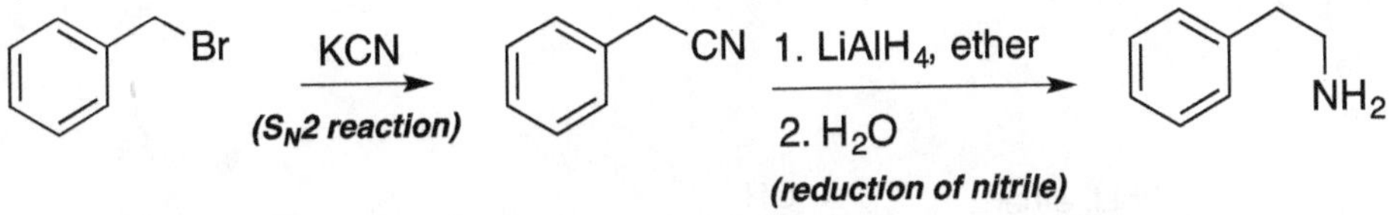

b)

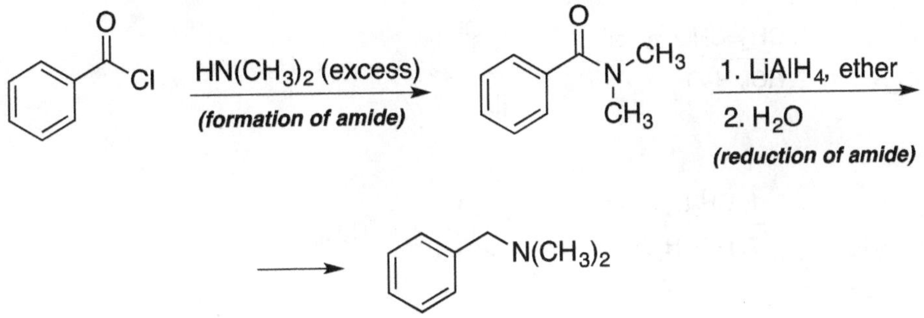

c)

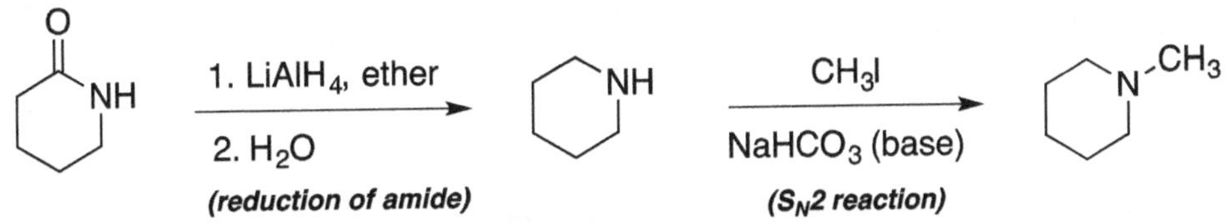

Problem 12.18. Which of the following molecules *cannot* be prepared by treating ethyl acetate with a Grignard or organolithium reagent?

Solution:

The first three molecules can be prepared by treating ethyl acetate with a Grignard or organolithium reagent as illustrated below. The last molecule has two methyl groups and one ethyl group and can be prepared only starting from an ester of propanoic acid:

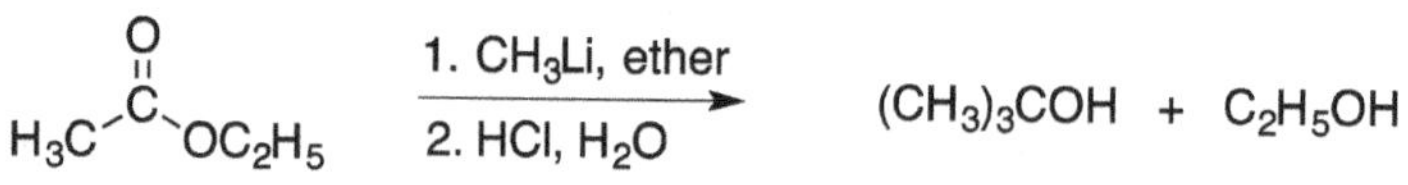

H_3C—C(=O)—OC_2H_5 ethyl acetate

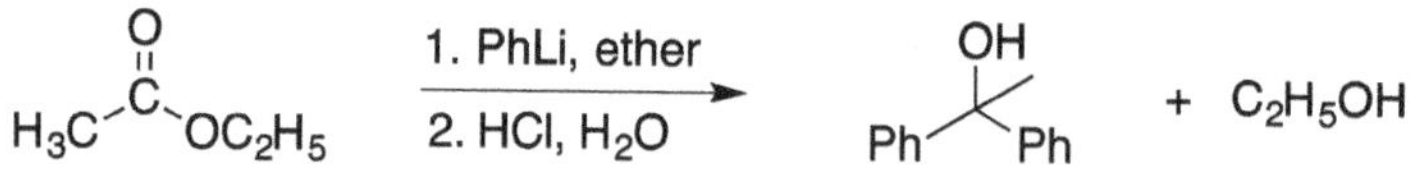

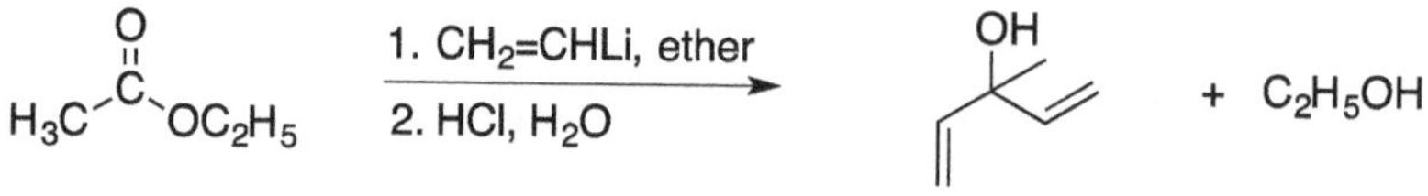

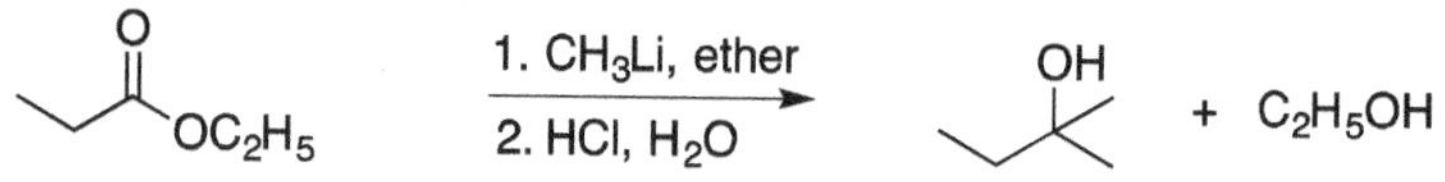

1. CH_3Li, ether
2. HCl, H_2O
→ $(CH_3)_3COH$ + C_2H_5OH

H_3C—C(=O)—OC_2H_5

1. $PhLi$, ether
2. HCl, H_2O
→ Ph—C(OH)—Ph + C_2H_5OH

H_3C—C(=O)—OC_2H_5

1. CH_2=$CHLi$, ether
2. HCl, H_2O
→ (OH, divinyl carbinol) + C_2H_5OH

(ester of propanoic acid) —C(=O)—OC_2H_5

1. CH_3Li, ether
2. HCl, H_2O
→ (OH tertiary alcohol) + C_2H_5OH

Problem 12.19. A common procedure for the preparation of carboxylic acids (RCOOH) consists of the treatment of Grignard reagents (RMgBr) with carbon dioxide (CO_2), followed by the addition of a strong acid (aqueous HCl or H_2SO_4). Propose a mechanism for this reaction.

Solution:

Preparation of carboxylic acids from carbon dioxide:

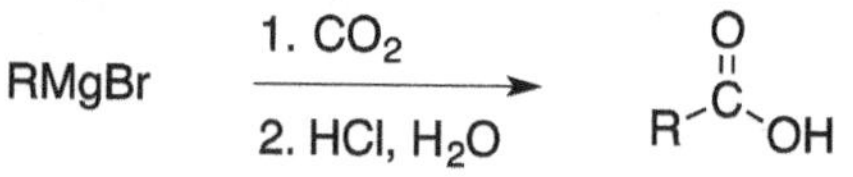

RMgBr
1. CO_2
2. HCl, H_2O
→ R—C(=O)—OH

Mechanism:

O=C=O
R:⁻
(carbanion from RMgBr)
→ *(nucleophilic addition to carbonyl)* →
R—C(=O)—O^-
→ HCl, H_2O *(protonation of carboxylate anion)* →
R—C(=O)—OH

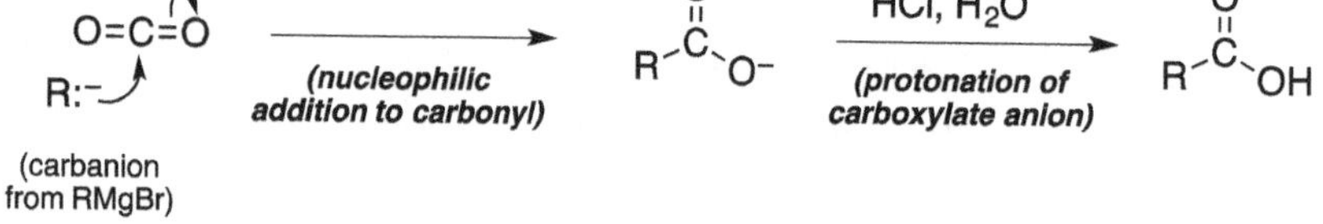

Problem 12.20. Provide the product of the following reaction:

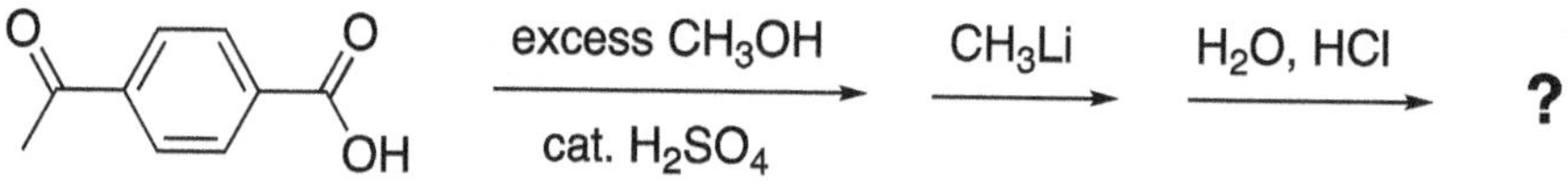

(4-acetylbenzoic acid structure) —C(=O)—OH
excess CH_3OH
cat. H_2SO_4
→ CH_3Li → H_2O, HCl → **?**

Solution:

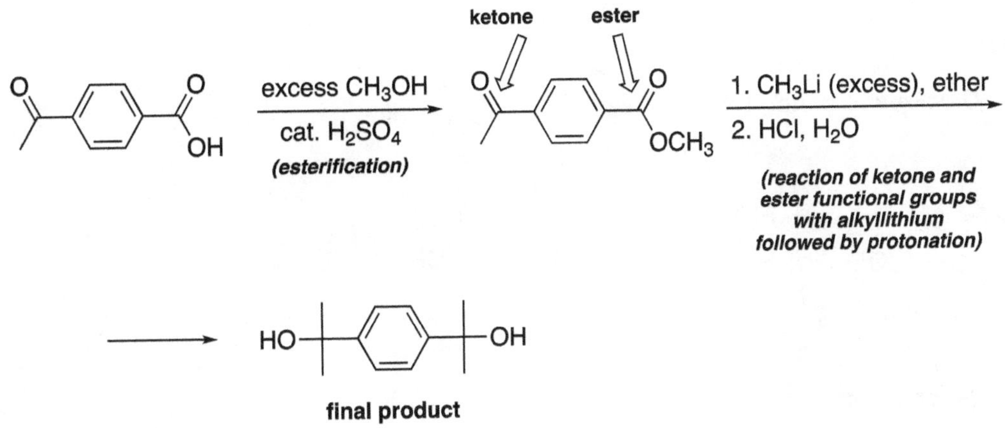

Problem 12.21. Gilman reagents are less reactive than Grignard or organolithium reagents toward nucleophilic acyl substitution. In general, only acid chlorides react with these reagents and ketones are formed as products. For example:

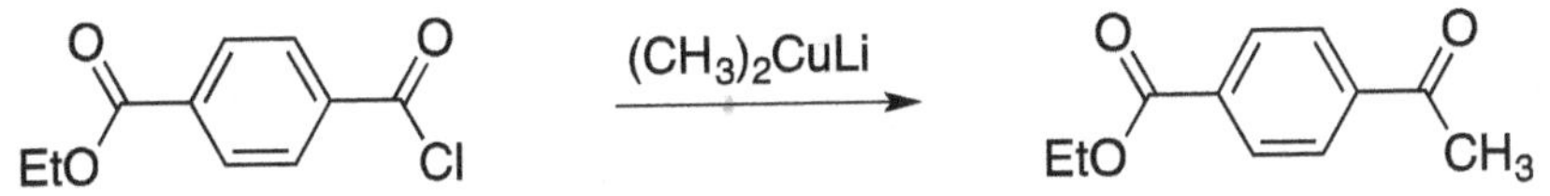

For each of the following compounds propose a synthesis from an acid chloride and a Gilman reagent:

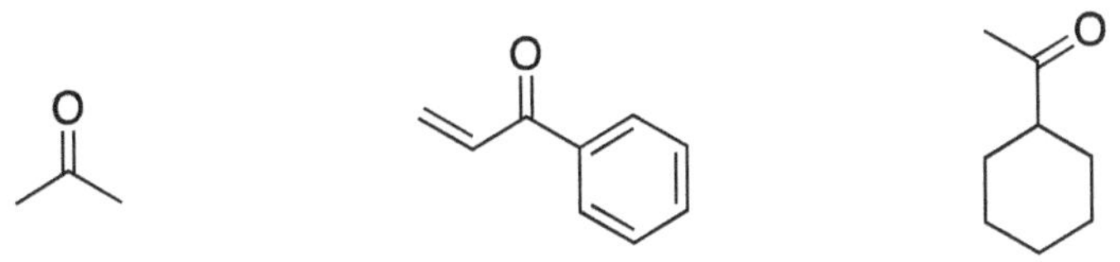

Solution:

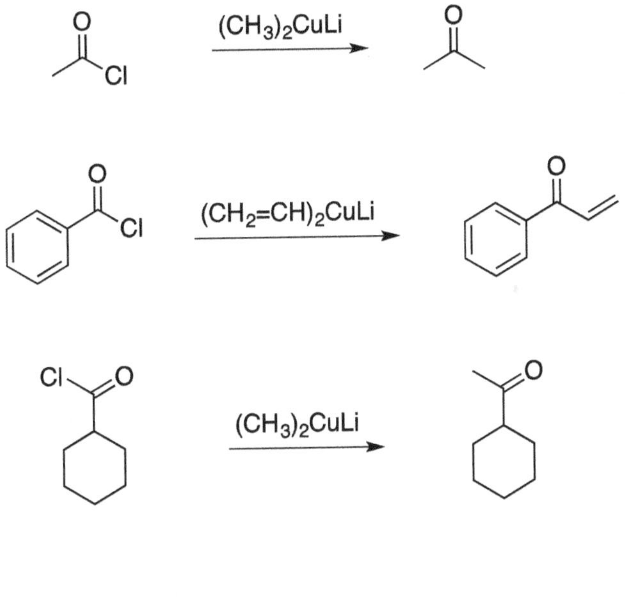

Problem 12.22. Write detailed mechanism for the Dieckmann condensation (Figure 12.20).

Solution:

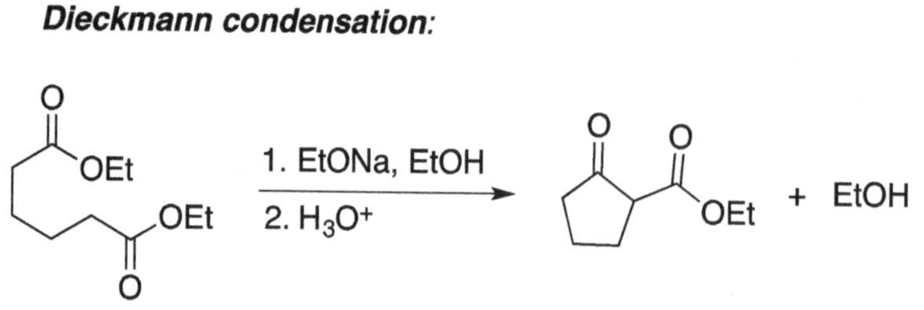

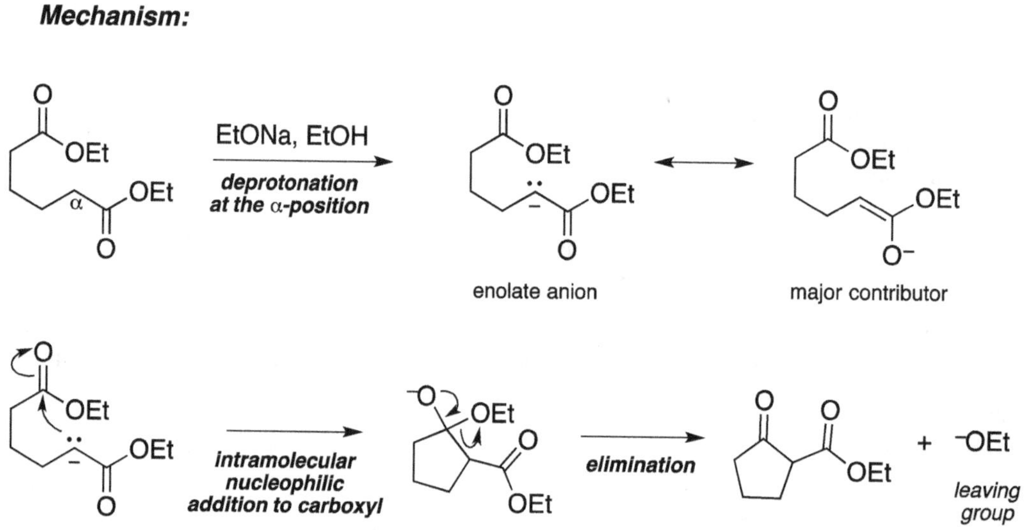

Dieckmann condensation:

Mechanism:

Problem 12.23. Write detailed mechanisms for the reactions shown in Figure 12.22.

Solution:

Acetoacetic ester synthesis:

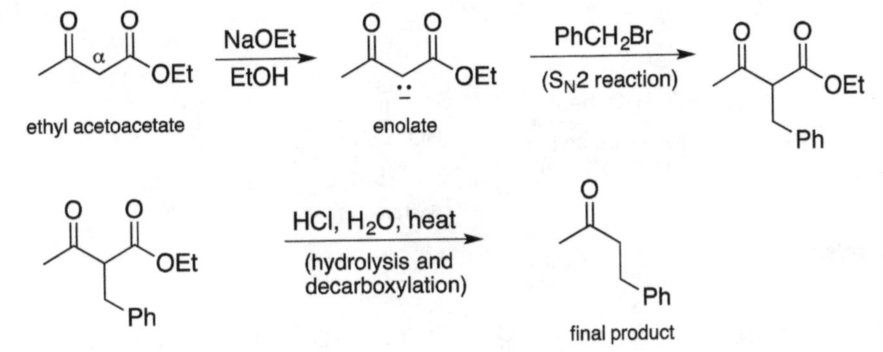

ethyl acetoacetate   enolate

final product

Mechanism:

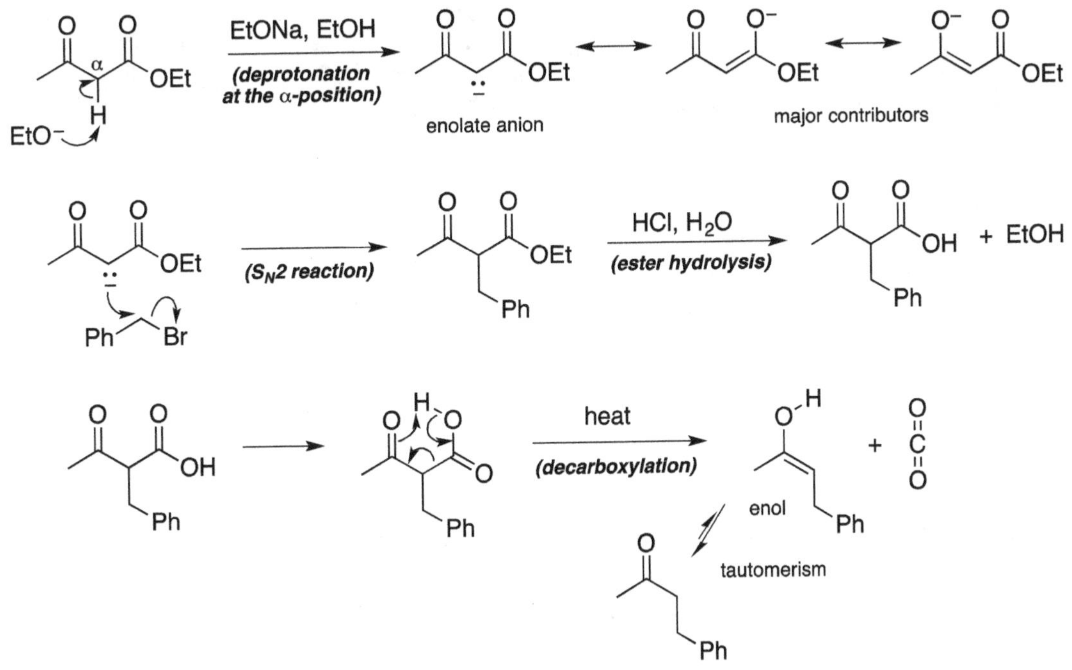

enolate anion   major contributors

Malonic ester synthesis:

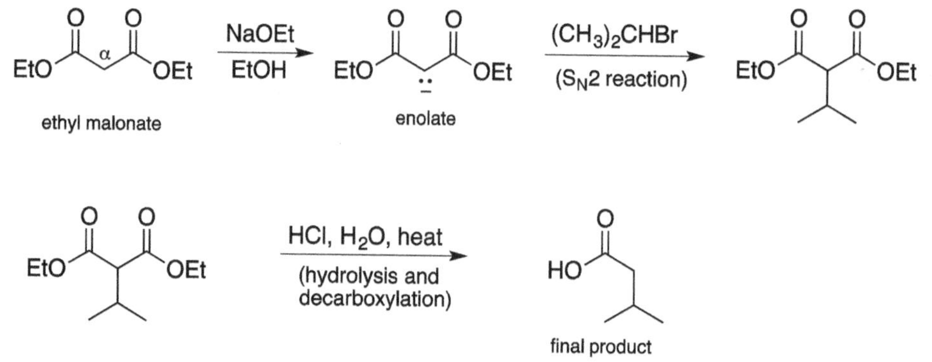

ethyl malonate → enolate → (CH₃)₂CHBr (Sₙ2 reaction)

HCl, H₂O, heat
(hydrolysis and
decarboxylation)

final product

Mechanism:

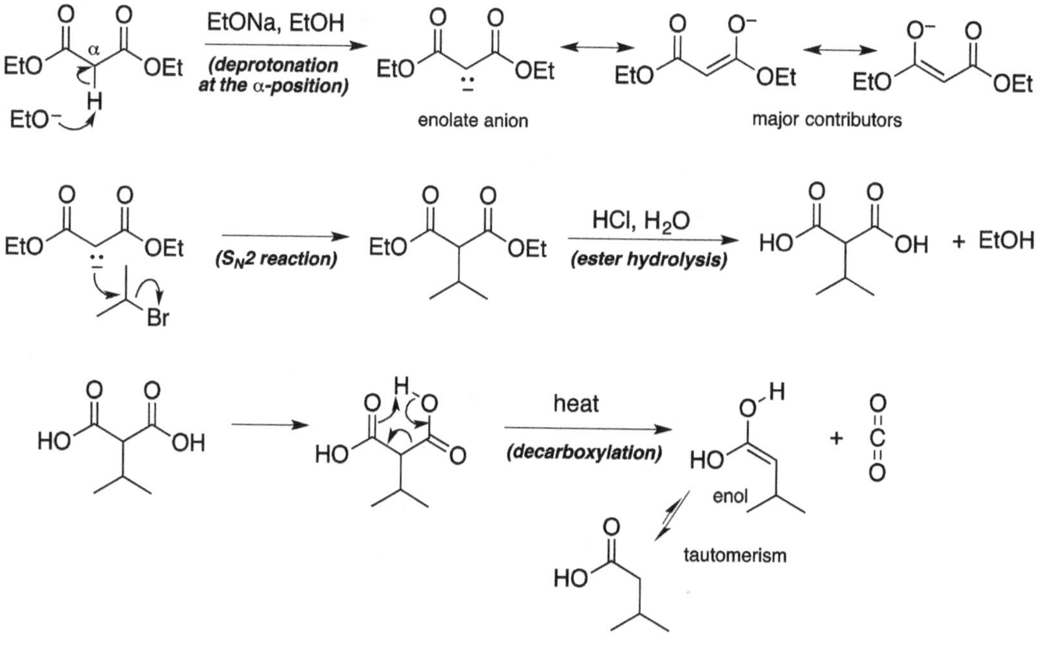

EtONa, EtOH
(deprotonation
at the α-position)

enolate anion

major contributors

(Sₙ2 reaction)

HCl, H₂O
(ester hydrolysis)

+ EtOH

heat
(decarboxylation)

enol

+ O=C=O

tautomerism

Problem 12.24. Provide the major products of the following reactions:

a)

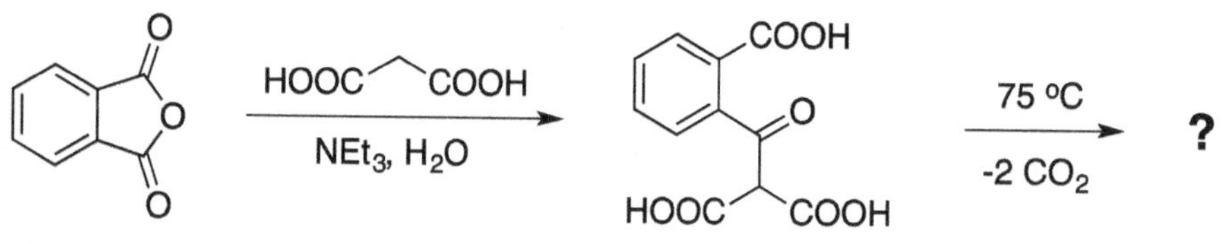

HOOC⌒COOH

NEt₃, H₂O

75 °C
-2 CO₂

?

b)

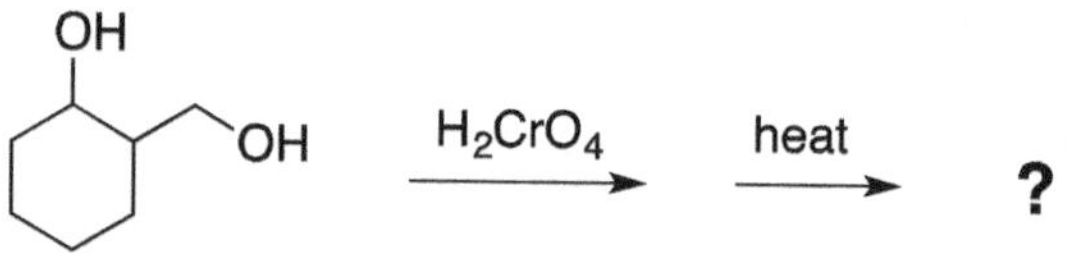

H₂CrO₄ heat

?

c)

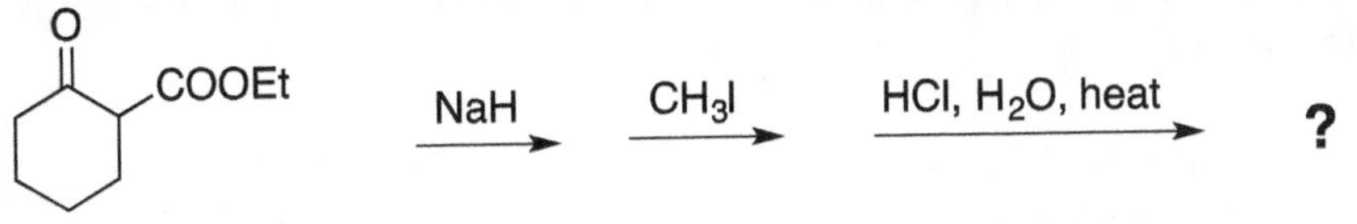

NaH → CH$_3$I → HCl, H$_2$O, heat → **?**

Solution:

a)

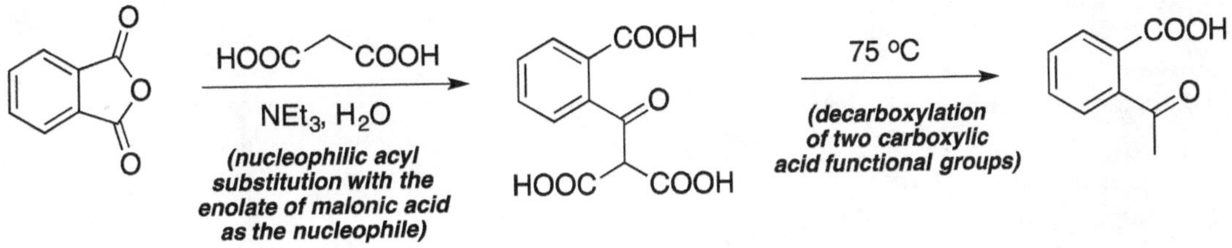

HOOC COOH

NEt$_3$, H$_2$O

(nucleophilic acyl substitution with the enolate of malonic acid as the nucleophile)

75 °C

(decarboxylation of two carboxylic acid functional groups)

b)

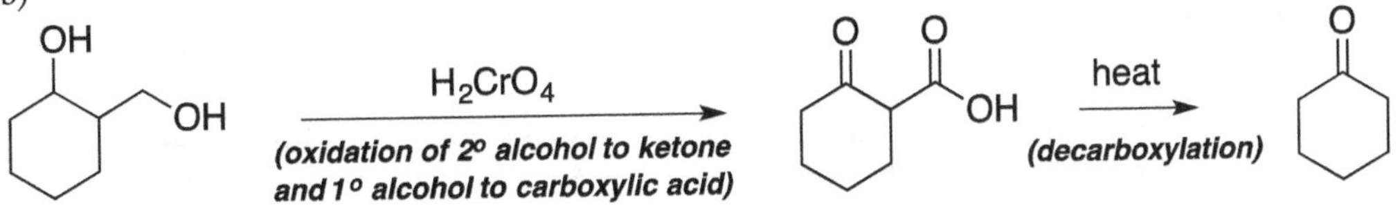

H$_2$CrO$_4$

(oxidation of 2° alcohol to ketone and 1° alcohol to carboxylic acid)

heat

(decarboxylation)

c)

H:$^-$ (strong base)

(deprotonation at the α-position)

CH$_3$I

(S$_N$2 reaction)

HCl, H$_2$O, heat

(hydrolysis and decarboxylation)

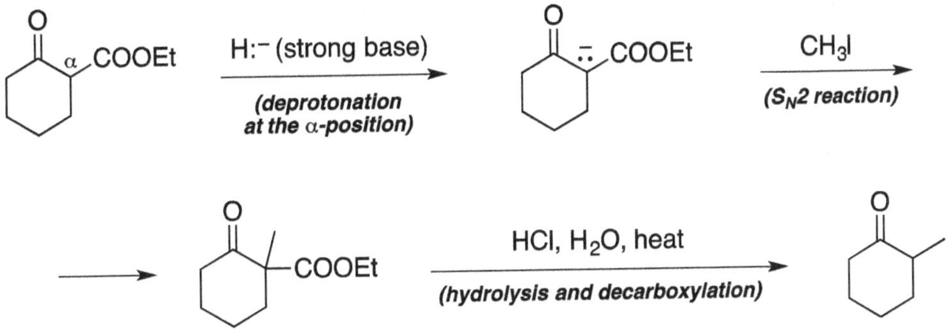

Problem 12.25. Battery acid is a 30% solution of H$_2$SO$_4$ in water. Why is it not recommended to use a PET bottle for long-term storage of this acid?

Solution:

Strong acid will hydrolyze the ester links in PET, eventually destroying the polymer as shown below:

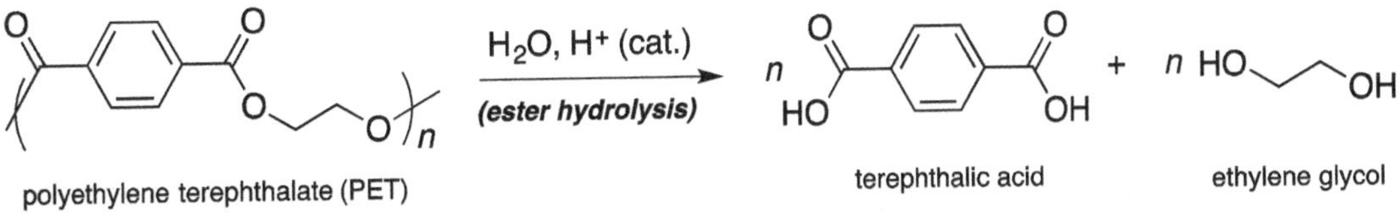

polyethylene terephthalate (PET)

H$_2$O, H$^+$ (cat.)

(ester hydrolysis)

n

terephthalic acid

+ n HO OH

ethylene glycol

Problem 12.26. When ε-caprolactam is heated to about 260°C in an inert atmosphere, ring opening occurs and a polymeric material (nylon 6, also known as Perlon or Capron) is produced. Propose a general structure for the resulting polymer.

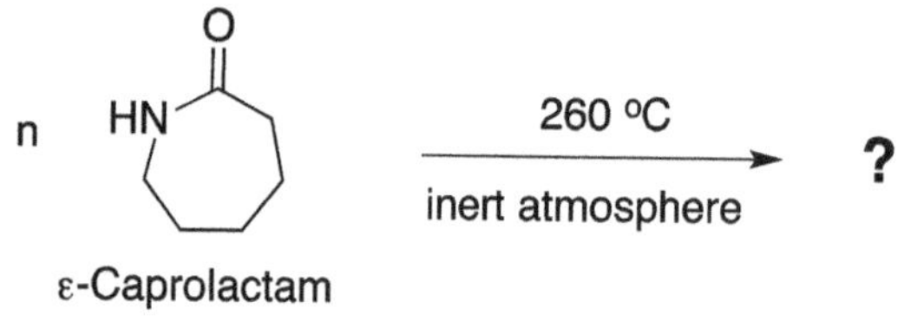

ε-Caprolactam

Solution:
The structure of nylon 6 is shown below:

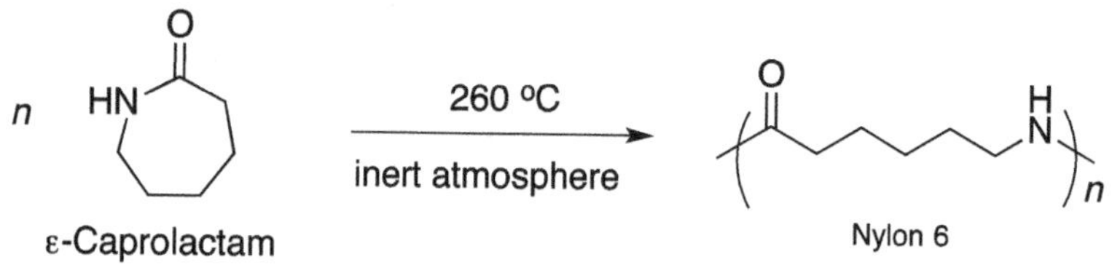

ε-Caprolactam   Nylon 6

Problem 12.27. Kevlar is a polymeric material that is five times stronger than steel. Based on its general structure, which compounds would you use to synthesize Kevlar in high yield?

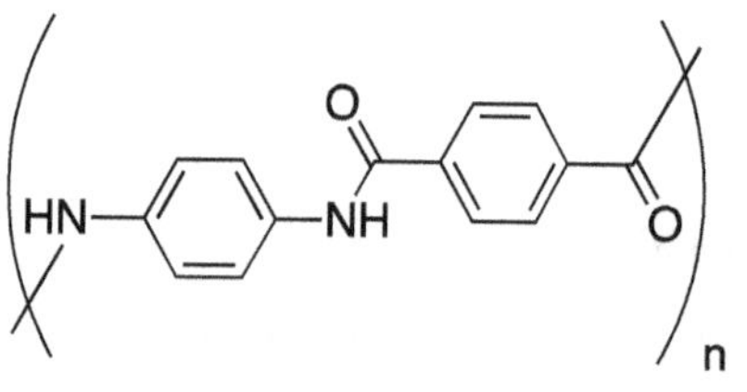

General structure of Kevlar

Solution:
Kevlar is prepared by polycondensation of 1,4-phenylenediamine with terephthaloyl chloride:

1,4-phenylenediamine   terephthaloyl chloride

heat

Kevlar

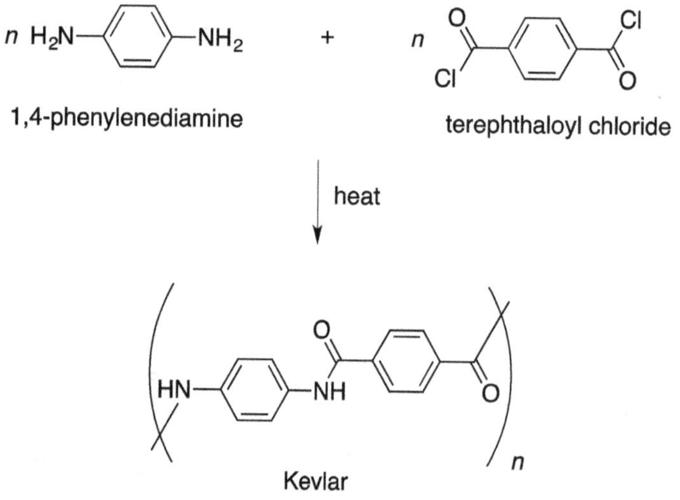

Problem 12.28. When sodium 2-chloroacetate is heated to about 160 °C in an inert atmosphere, a polymer called polyglucolide and sodium chloride are produced. What is the general structure of this polymer?

sodium 2-chloroacetate

Solution:
Polyglucolide is prepared by the solid-state polycondensation of sodium 2-chloroacetate:

polyglucolide

12.2. Additional Problems for Chapter 12 (for answers see Ch 17)

Problem 12.29. Structures A and B undergo decarboxylation readily under mild thermal condition compared to structure C.

A   B   C

Identify the factor(s) that facilitate thermal decarboxylation in structures A and B. Also, provide the mechanism to account for this process.

Problem 12.30. Provide the structure of products obtained via thermal decarboxylation of A and B in the above problem.

Problem 12.31. Determine the appropriate reducing agent for each reaction that can be used to selectively obtain the indicated product in high yield.

Problem 12.32. Provide the structures of unknowns A, B, C, D, E in the following reaction scheme.

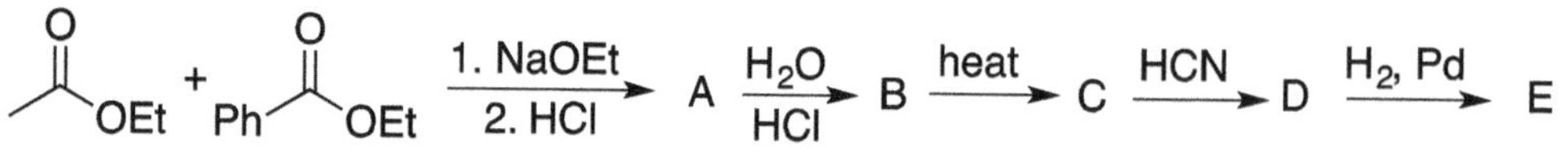

Noncyclic Conjugated Systems

13.1. Chapter 13 Problems and Solutions

Problem 13.1. The selected spectroscopic data of propenal (acrolein) are compared to compounds with similar structural features.

Explain these data. Why is the terminal alkene carbon in propenal in ^{13}C NMR shifted downfield by 22 ppm, compared to the corresponding carbon in propene? Why does the carbonyl group of propenal absorb IR irradiation at lower wavenumber compared to propanal?

Solution:
The actual structure of propenal is best described by its resonance hybrid (see the structure below). The β-carbon in the hybrid has a partial positive charge and, therefore, is deshielded and shifted downfield in the ^{13}C NMR spectrum (see Section 9.2.2D of the textbook) compared to the regular double bond carbon in propene. The C–O bond in the resonance hybrid has a partial single bond character. Normally, the C=O stretching vibration is found at about 1740 cm^{-1}, while the C–O bond stretching occurs at 1030 cm^{-1}. The observed stretching frequency at 1696 cm^{-1} is due to the partial single bond character of the carbonyl group in propenal.

Resonance contributors of propenal:

Problem 13.2. Provide the products of the following conjugate electrophilic addition reactions.

a)

1 mol HBr

b)

1 mol Br$_2$

Solution:

a)

1 mol HBr

a mixture of *cis* and *trans* isomers

b)

1 mol Br$_2$

a mixture of *cis* and *trans* isomers

Problem 13.3. Quite often the outcome of the conjugate electrophilic addition is temperature dependent, due to both the kinetics and the relative stability of the products. In the case of the addition of HCl to 1,3-butadiene (Figure 13.4) at –78 °C, the least stable isomer is formed as a major product (chemists say the reaction is kinetically controlled), while at room temperature, the most stable isomer is formed as a major product (thermodynamic control). Based on this information, which isomer is the major product at –78 °C and room temperature?

Solution:

A double bond with a greater number of alkyl substituents has higher thermodynamic stability compared to the less substituted double bond (see Section 6.5.4 of the textbook). The product of 1,2-addition has only one alkyl substituent and three hydrogens at the double bond, while the product of 1,4-addition has two alkyl substituent and two hydrogens at the double bond and therefore is more stable.

HCl (1 mol)

product of 1,2-addition is
the major product at –78 °C

**less stable
(1 substituent
at double bond)**

+

product of 1,4-addition is the
major product at room temperature

**more stable
(2 substituents
at double bond)**

Problem 13.4. What are products of the following transformations?

a)

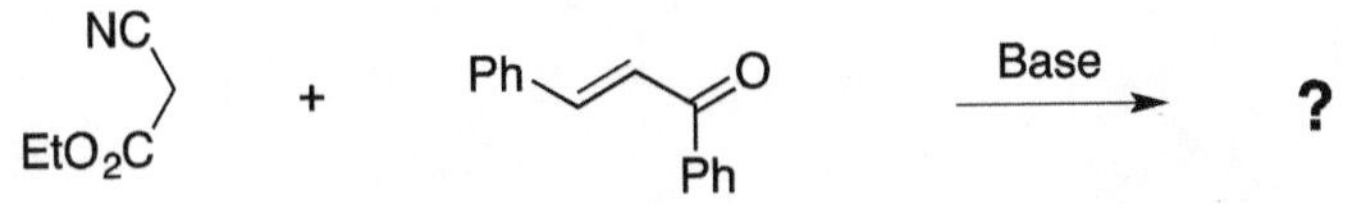

b)

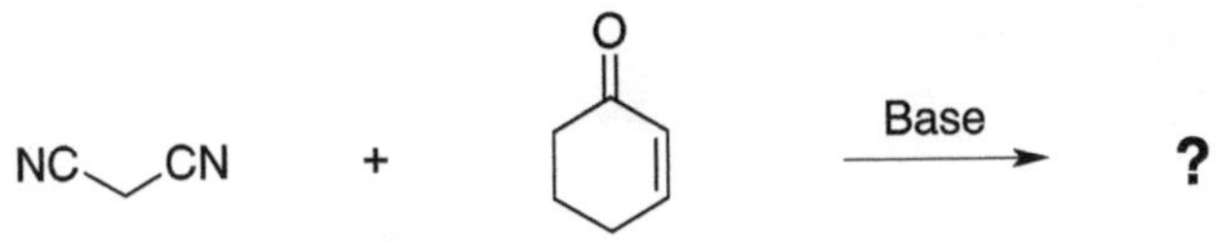

c)

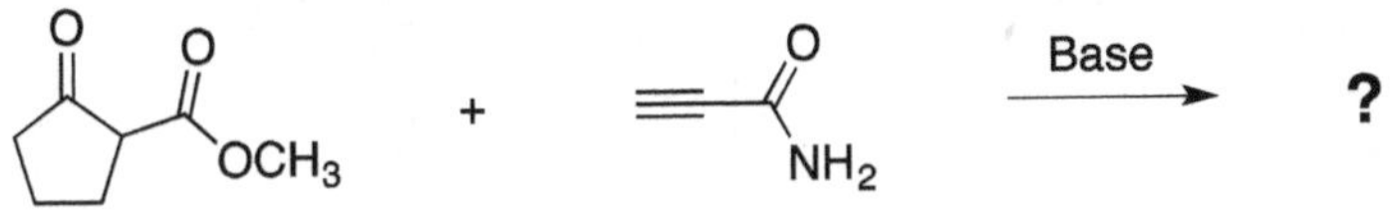

Solution:
All these reactions proceed as the Michael addition reactions of the enolate anions with the α,β-unsaturated carbonyl compounds as shown below:

a)

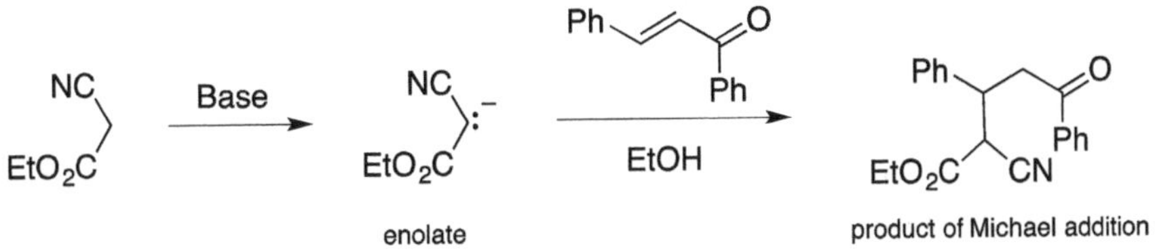

b)

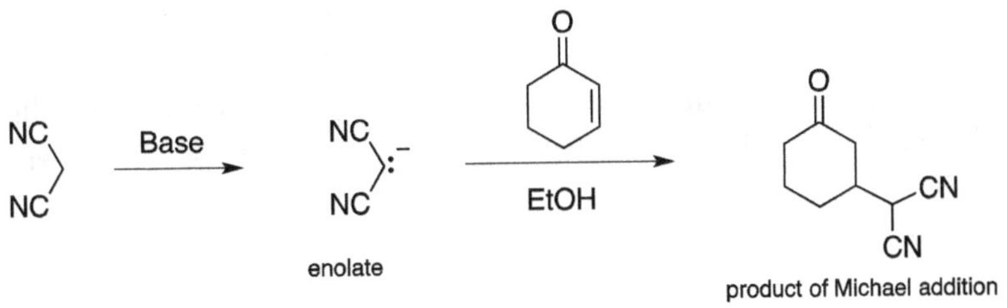

c)

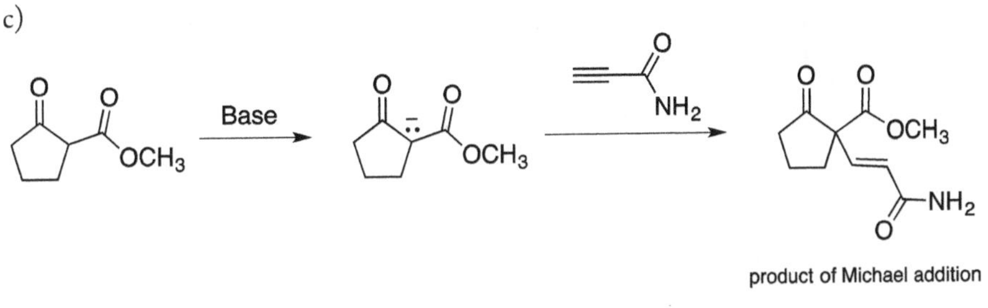

Problem 13.5. For each of the following molecules, propose a synthesis that involves the reaction of an α,β-unsaturated ketone with a Gilman reagent.

a)

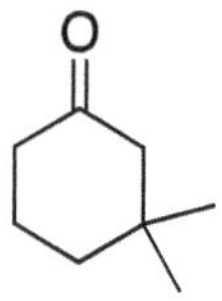

b)

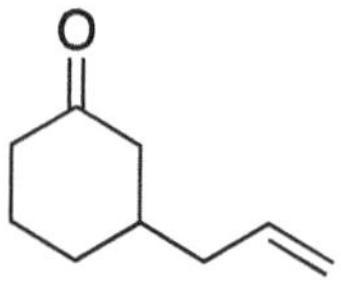

Solution:

a)

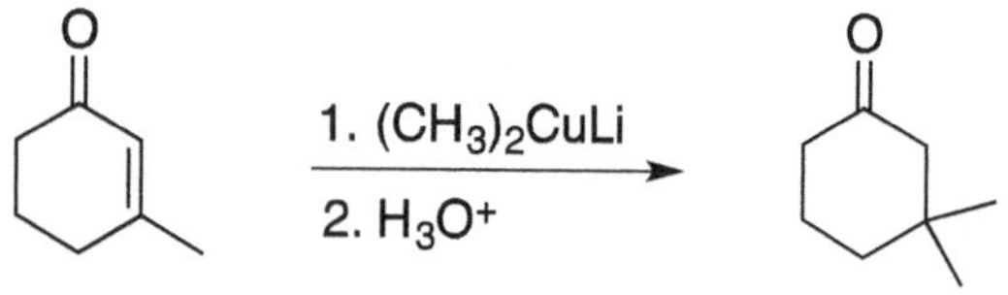

1. (CH₃)₂CuLi
2. H₃O⁺

b)

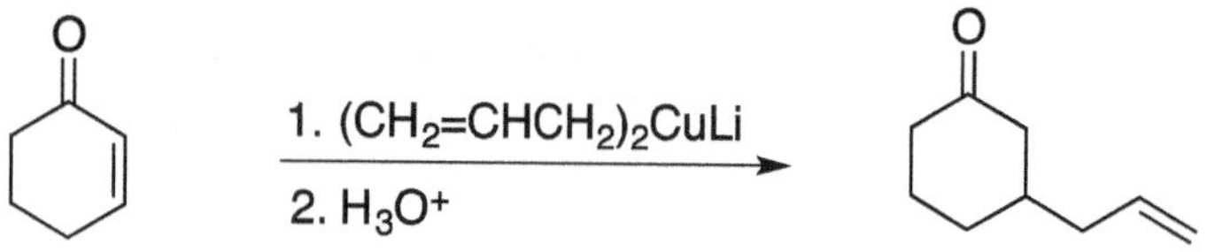

1. (CH₂=CHCH₂)₂CuLi
2. H₃O⁺

Problem 13.6. The formation of a bicyclic product involves a stepwise sequence of reactions. The first step is a Michael addition, which is followed by an aldol reaction, and finally an elimination step. Draw the structures of the intermediates.

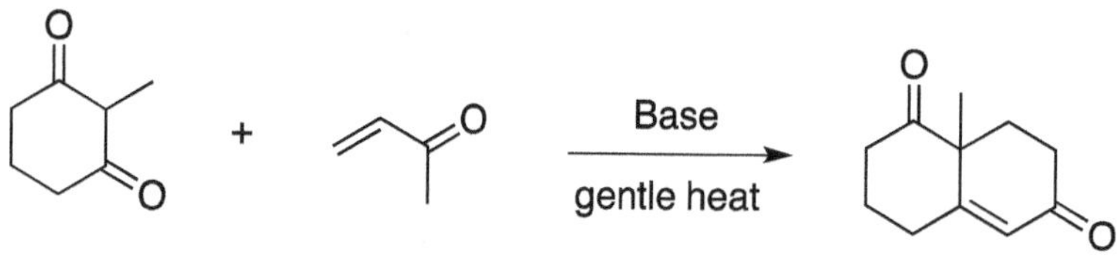

Base

gentle heat

Solution:

Step 1. Michael addition:

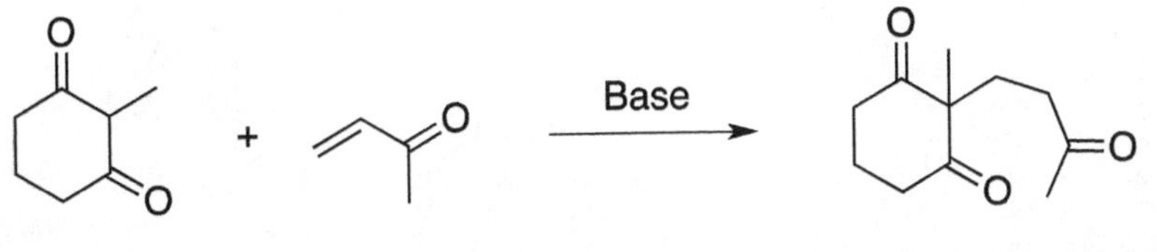

product of Michael addition

Step 2. Aldol condensation (Section 11.10):

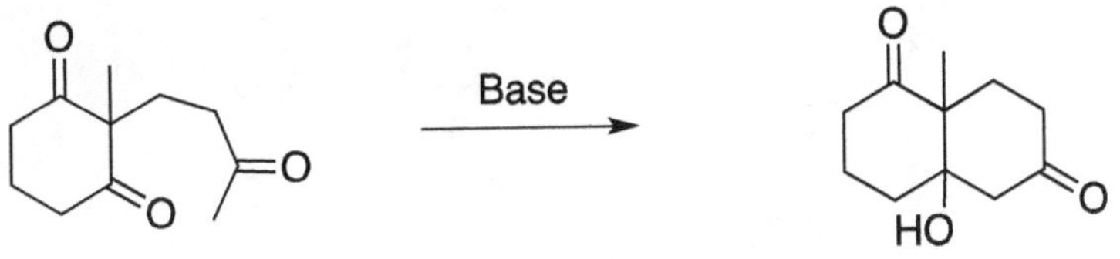

aldol

Step 3. Dehydration of aldol (Section 11.10):

gentle heat

Problem 13.7. What are the products of the following transformations?

a)

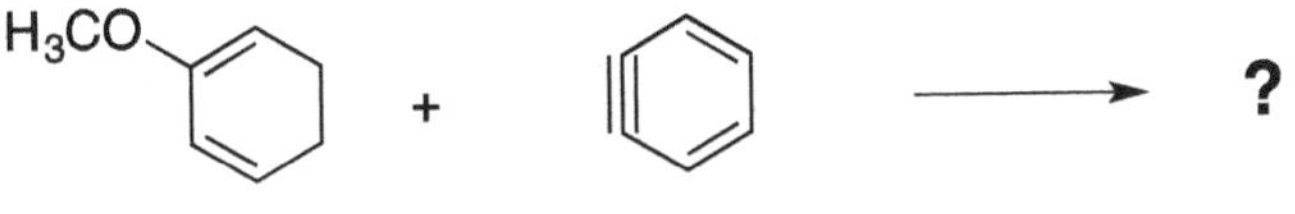

benzyne

b)

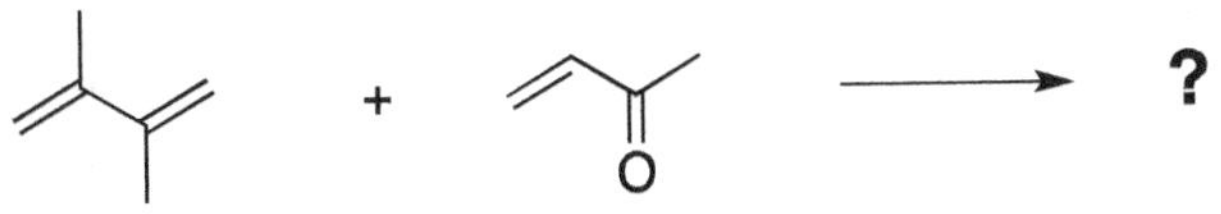

c)

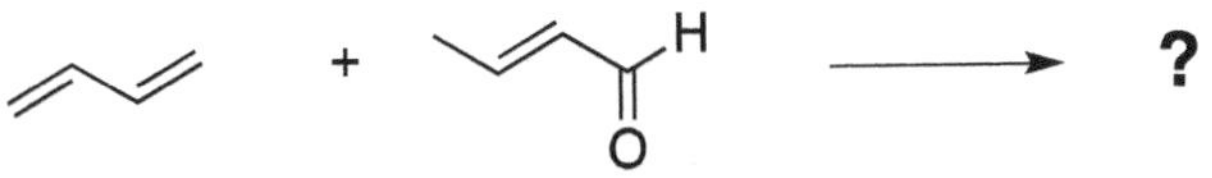

Solution:

All these are Diels–Alder reactions of dienes with dienophiles:

a)

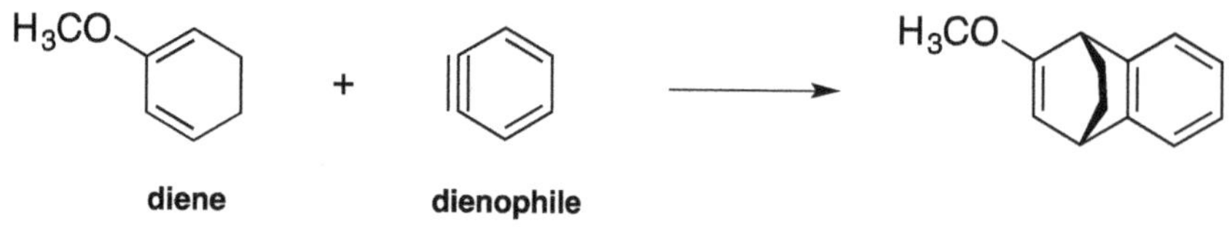

diene   dienophile

b)

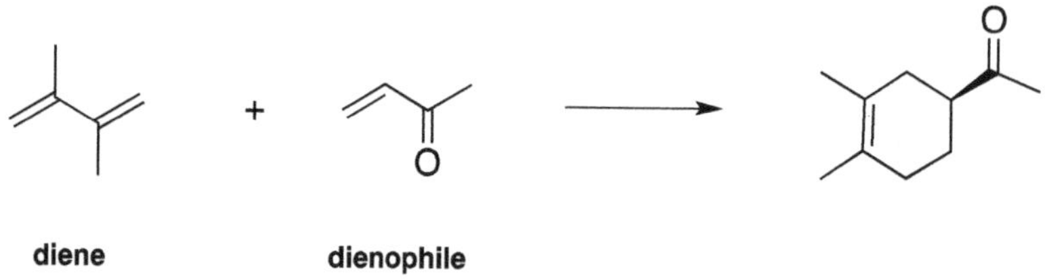

diene   dienophile

c)

diene   dienophile

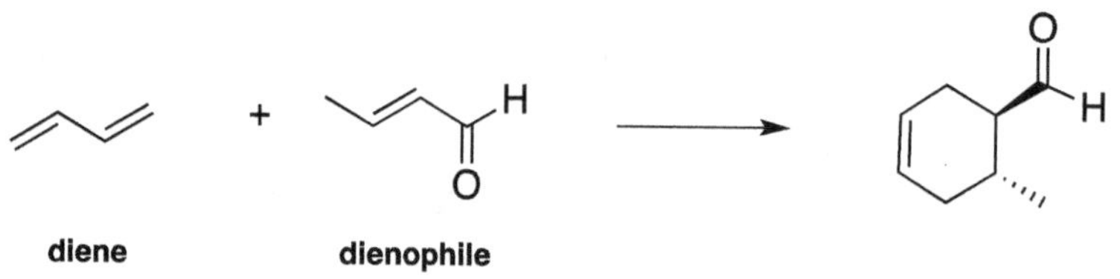

Problem 13.8. Suggest dienes and dienophiles required for the synthesis of the following compounds via Diels–Alder reaction.

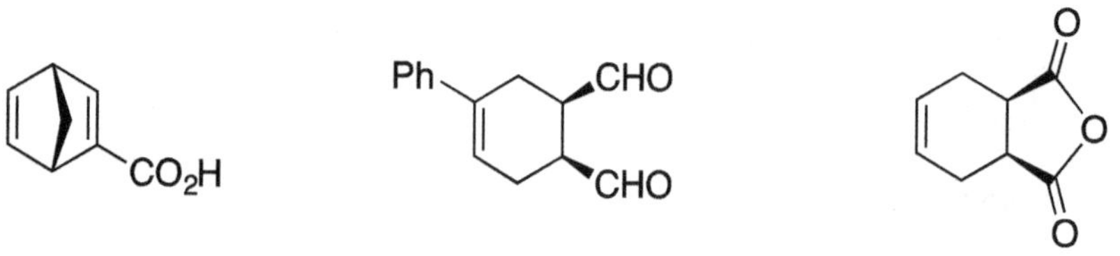

Solution:

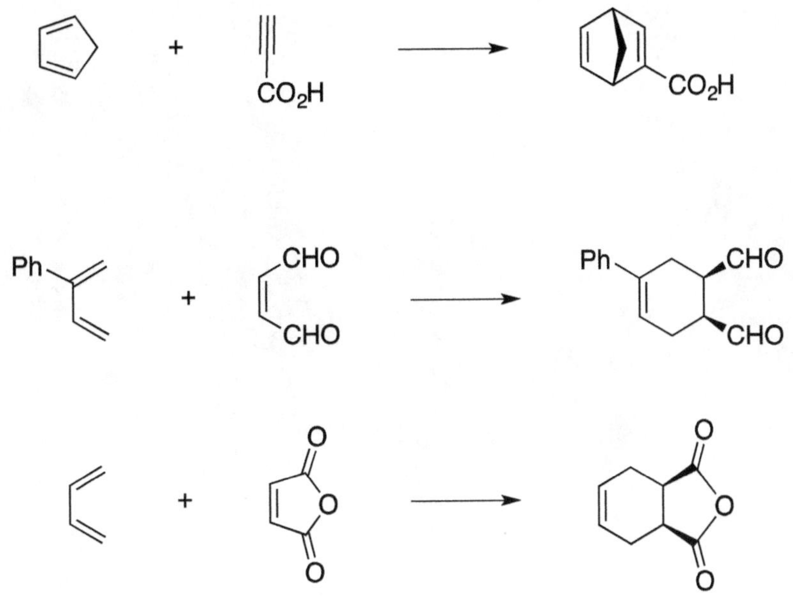

13.2. Additional Problems for Chapter 13 (for answers see Ch 17)

Problem 13.9. Consider the addition of one mole of HBr to 1,3-butadiene to answer the following questions a–c.

a) Provide the reaction mechanism and structures of 1,2- and 1,4-addition products formed in this reaction.
b) Which is more stable, the 1,2- or 1,4-addition product?
c) Which addition product in the above reaction will be the major product when the reaction is under thermodynamic control? Explain your reasoning.

Problem 13.10. Determine if the following dienes will react with a dienophile in a Diels–Alder reaction.

a) 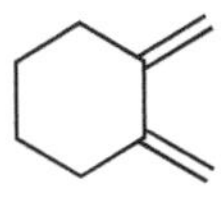   b) 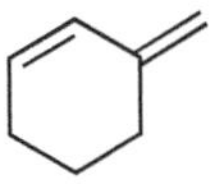   c)

d)    e)

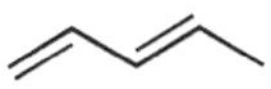

Problem 13.11. Identify the diene and dienophile that can be used to synthesize the following compound using a Diels–Alder reaction.

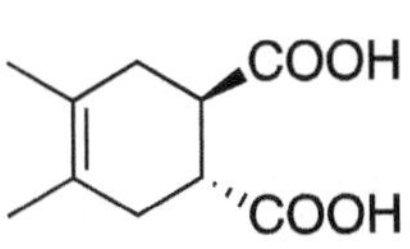

Benzene and Aromatic Compounds

14.1. Chapter 14 Problems and Solutions

Problem 14.1. Draw all possible resonance contributors for cycloheptatrienyl cation, pyridine, pyrrole, furan, and thiophene.

Solution:

Cycloheptatrienyl cation:

Pyridine:

Pyrrole:

Furan:

Thiophene:

Problem 14.2. In ground state, the central double bond of pentaheptafulvalene is polarized with a partial negative charge on the carbon atom of the pentagon carbon ring, and a partial positive charge on the carbon atom of the heptagon carbon ring. Explain this using resonance structures.

pentaheptafulvalene

Solution:

Moving a pair of π electrons to the five-membered ring, as shown below by resonance, results in two aromatic rings, the cyclopentadienyl anion and the cycloheptatrienyl cation linked together. Since both rings have aromatic stabilization (see Figure 14.3 of the textbook), this major contributor will be responsible for the observed dipolar structure of pentaheptafulvalene.

**major contributor
(both rings are aromatic)**

**resonance
hybrid**

Problem 14.3. Pyridine is commonly used as a base in organic synthesis. Explain why pyrrole cannot be used for the same purpose.

pyridine

pyrrole

Solution:

The lone pair of electrons on the nitrogen of pyridine is available for protonation, and the protonated pyridine (pyridinium cation) retains aromatic stability as illustrated below by the resonance. In contrast, the lone pair of electrons in pyrrole is an essential part of the aromatic sextet (see the solution of Problem 14.1). Pyrrole is not a base because protonation of the nitrogen atom would destroy the aromatic system as shown below.

pyridinium cation (protonated pyridine) has aromatic stabilization as illustrated by the resonance

protonated pyrrole is not aromatic since the sp³ hybridized nitrogen cannot participate in the resonance

Problem 14.4. Explain: 2,4-cyclopentadienone is unstable and cannot be isolated; 2,4,6-cycloheptatrienone, on the other hand, is quite stable and can readily be isolated.

2,4-cyclopentadienone   2,4,6-cycloheptatrienone

Solution:

The carbonyl group is generally characterized by the presence of an important resonance contributor with a negative charge on the electronegative oxygen atom (Section 11.2 of the textbook). In the case of 2,4-cyclopentadienone, such a contributor will have the antiaromatic, extremely unstable five-membered ring occupied by 4π electrons. In contrast, the major resonance contributor of 2,4,6-cycloheptatrienone will have a significant aromatic stabilization due to the presence of seven-membered cyclic conjugated system occupied by a sextet of π electrons as illustrated below.

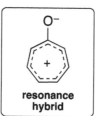

**a highly unfavorable contributor
(4 π electons in a conjugated ring is an
antiaromatic system)**

**major resonance contributor
(the seven-membered ring
has aromatic stabilization)**

**resonance
hybrid**

Problem 14.5. What are the IUPAC names of the following compounds?

a)

b)

c)

Solution:

a) 1-fluoro-3-isopropylbenzene

b) 4-bromo-1-ethyl-2-iodobenzene

c) 2-chloro-3-phenyl-1-propene

Problem 14.6. What are the IUPAC names of the major products of the following reactions?

a)

$H_2C=PPh_3$

?

b)

H_2CrO_4

?

Solution:

a)

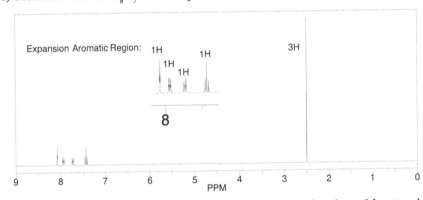

$H_2C=PPh_3$

(the Wittig reaction, Section 11.5)

vinyl benzene
(common name: styrene)

b)

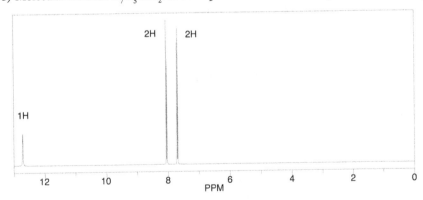

H_2CrO_4

(oxidation od aldehyde, Section 11.8)

3-methoxybenzoic acid

Problem 14.7. Provide the IUPAC names of the compounds on the basis of their NMR spectra.

a) Molecular formula: C_8H_7BrO. Compound contains ketone functional group.

Expansion Aromatic Region: 1H   1H
1H
1H

3H

8

9 8 7 6 5 4 3 2 1 0
PPM

b) Molecular formula: $C_7H_5ClO_2$. The compound contains a carboxylic acid functional group.

2H   2H

1H

12   10   8   6   4   2   0
PPM

c) Molecular formula: C_8H_8O. The compound contains an aldehyde functional group.

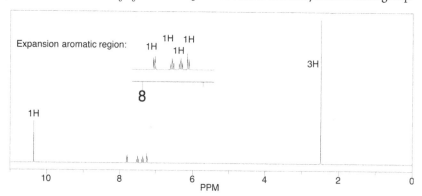

Solution:

a) This molecule has four signals (1H each) in the aromatic region of NMR spectrum, which is in agreement with a benzene ring bearing two substituents. One of these substituents is a carbonyl group with methyl attached (a singlet of 3H at 2.5 ppm) and the second is bromine in the meta position relative to the carbonyl. The signal at 8.1 ppm does not have any significant signal splitting (see Section 9.2.2C of the textbook), which is in agreement with its position between the two substituents in the benzene ring. The signal at 7.4 ppm is a triplet due to the splitting on the two nonequivalent protons at the adjacent carbons. This spectrum is in agreement with the structure of 1-(3-bromophenyl)ethan-1-one as explained below:

1-(3-bromophenyl)ethan-1-one
(common name: *m*-bromoacetophenone)

a: 1H at 8.1 ppm
b: 1H (doublet) at about 7.7 ppm
c: 1H (triplet) at about 7.4 ppm
d: 1H (doublet) at about 7.9 ppm
e: 3H (singlet) at about 2.5 ppm

b) This spectrum is in agreement with the structure of *p*-chlorobenzoic acid as explained below:

p-chlorobenzoic acid

a: 2H (doublet) at 7.7 ppm
b: 2H (doublet) at about 8.1 ppm
c: 1H (singlet) at about 12.7 ppm

c) This spectrum is in agreement with the structure of *o*-methylbenzaldehyde as explained below:

o-methylbenzaldehyde

a: 1H (doublet) at 7.2 ppm
b: 1H (triplet) at about 7.4 ppm
c: 1H (triplet) at about 7.5 ppm
d: 1H (doublet) at about 7.8 ppm
e: 1H (singlet) at about 10.4 ppm
f: 3H (singlet) at about 2.5 ppm

Problem 14.8. Propose mechanisms for reactions shown in Figures 14.17 and 14.19.

Solution:
Abbreviated mechanisms for Figure 14.17:

Reaction 3:

Abbreviated mechanisms for Figure 14.19:

Reaction 1:

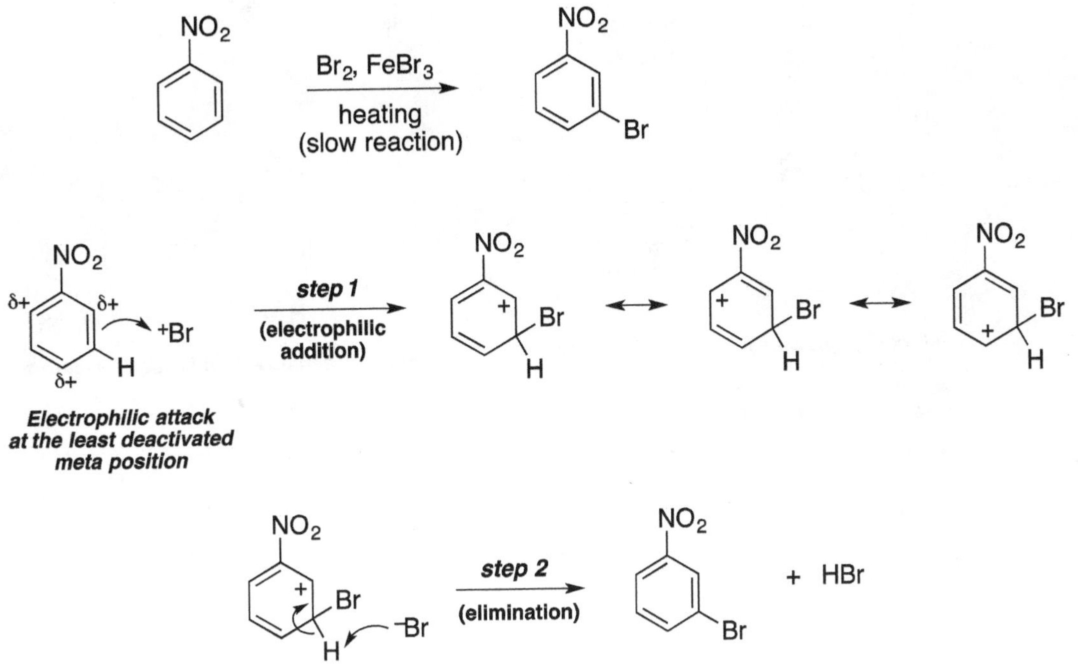

NO2
Br2, FeBr3
heating
(slow reaction)
NO2
Br
NO2
δ+
δ+
δ+
+Br
H
step 1
(electrophilic addition)
Br
H
Electrophilic attack at the least deactivated meta position
step 2
(elimination)
-Br
+ HBr

Reaction 2:

Cl−
+N(CH3)3
Br2, FeBr3
heating
Br
δ+
δ+
δ+
+Br
H
step 1
(electrophilic addition)
Electrophilic attack at the least deactivated meta position
step 2
(elimination)
-Br
+ HBr

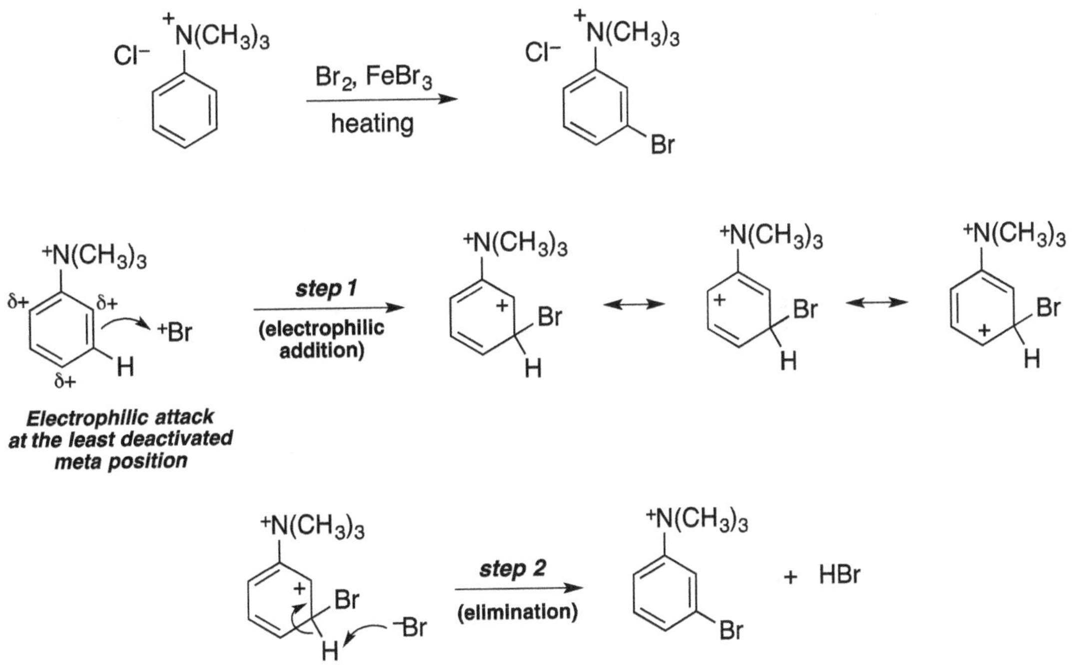

Reaction 3:

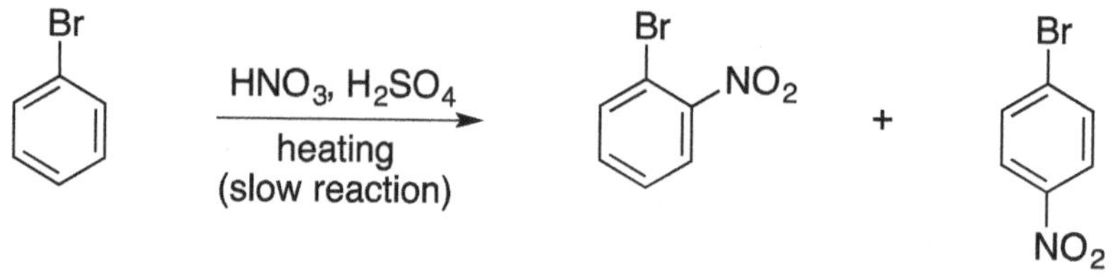

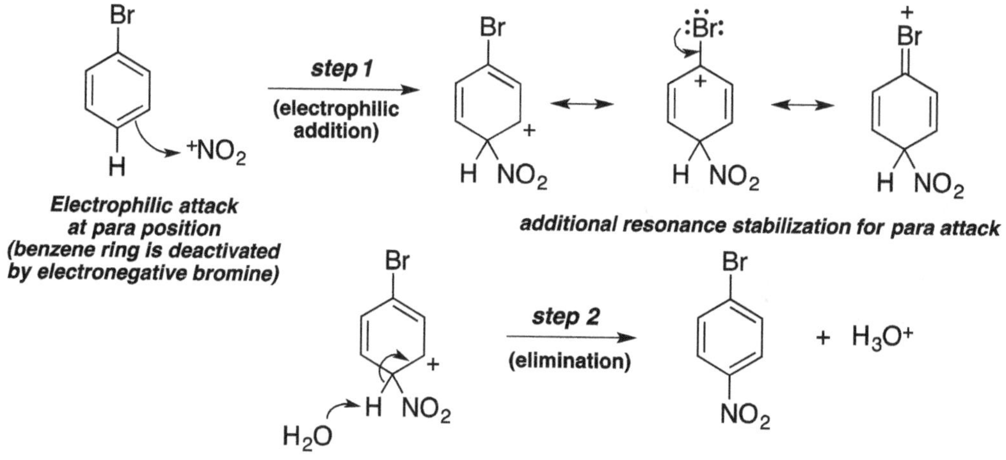

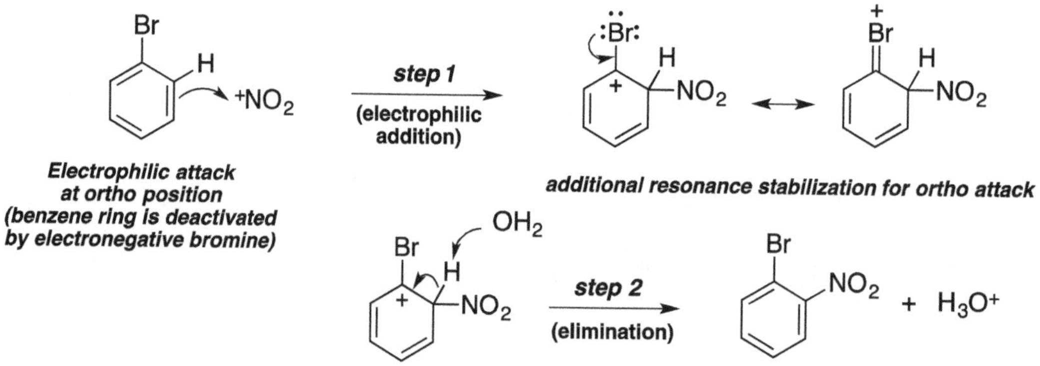

Problem 14.9. Provide the major products of the following transformations.

a)

b)

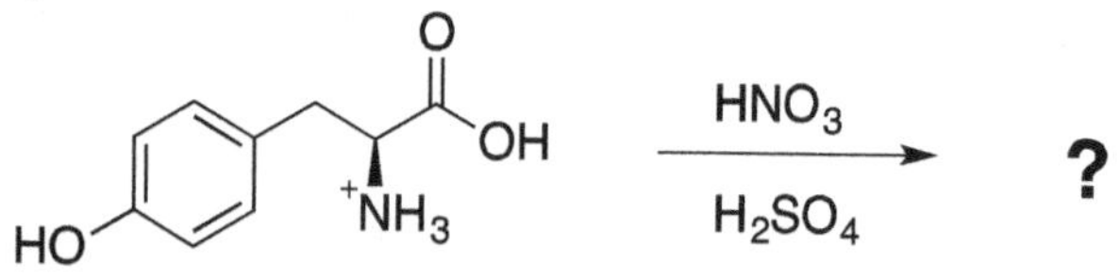

c)

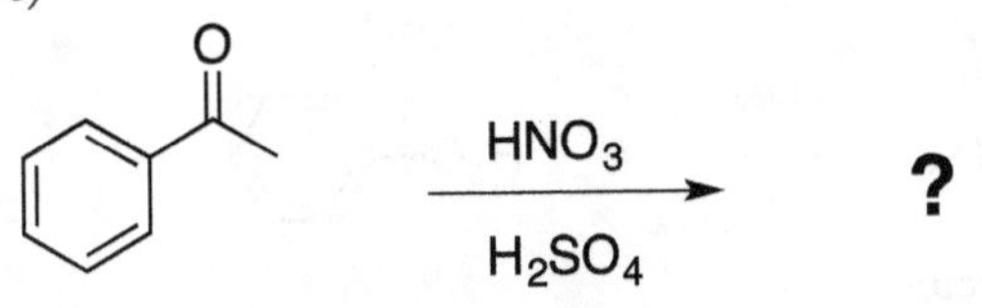

$$\xrightarrow[\text{H}_2\text{SO}_4]{\text{HNO}_3}$$

?

d)

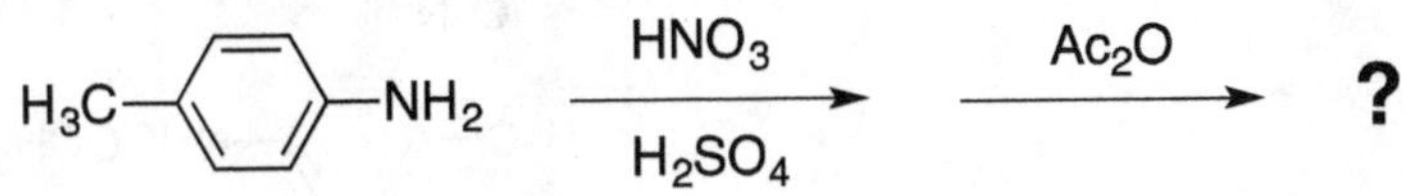

H$_3$C — ⬡ — NH$_2$

$$\xrightarrow[\text{H}_2\text{SO}_4]{\text{HNO}_3}$$ $$\xrightarrow{\text{Ac}_2\text{O}}$$

?

e)

H$_3$C — ⬡ — NH$_2$

$$\xrightarrow{\text{Ac}_2\text{O}}$$ $$\xrightarrow[\text{H}_2\text{SO}_4]{\text{HNO}_3}$$

?

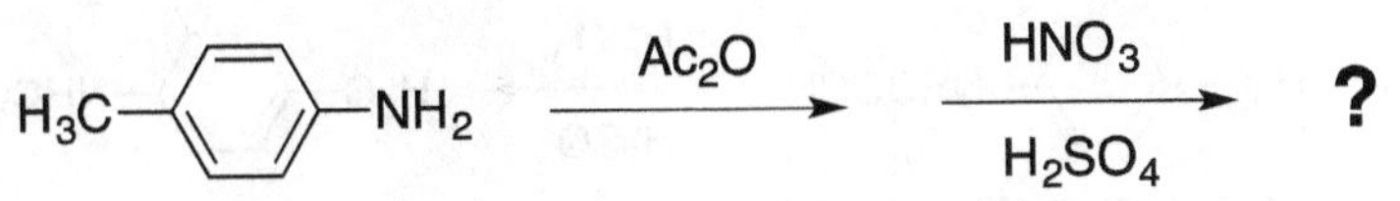

Solution:

a)

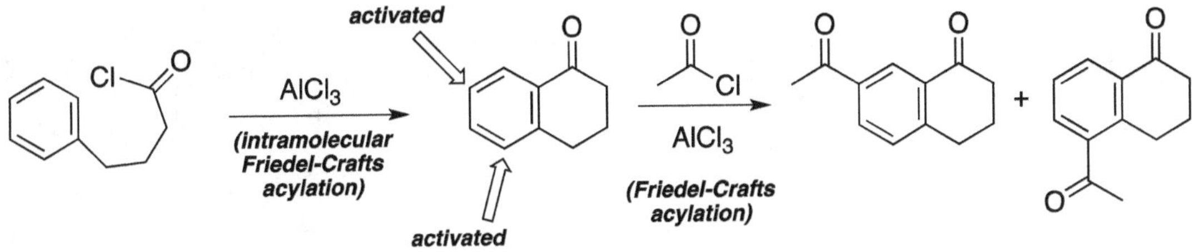

b)

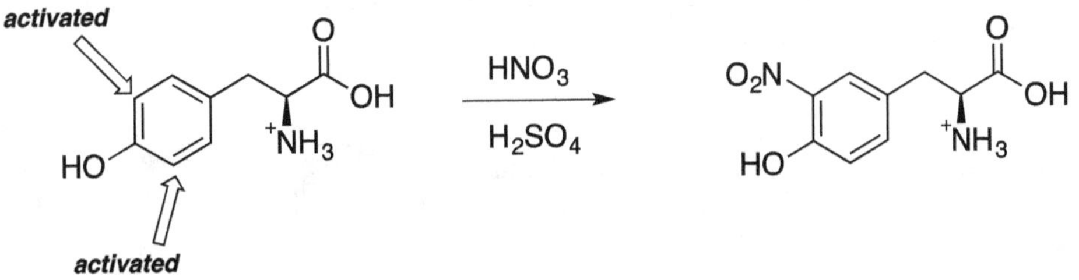

c)

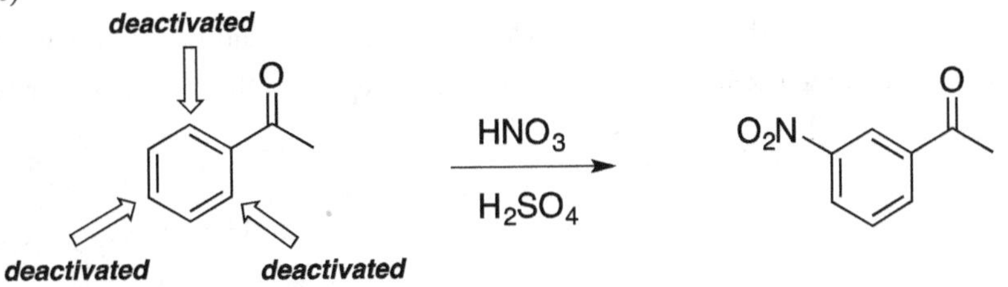

d)

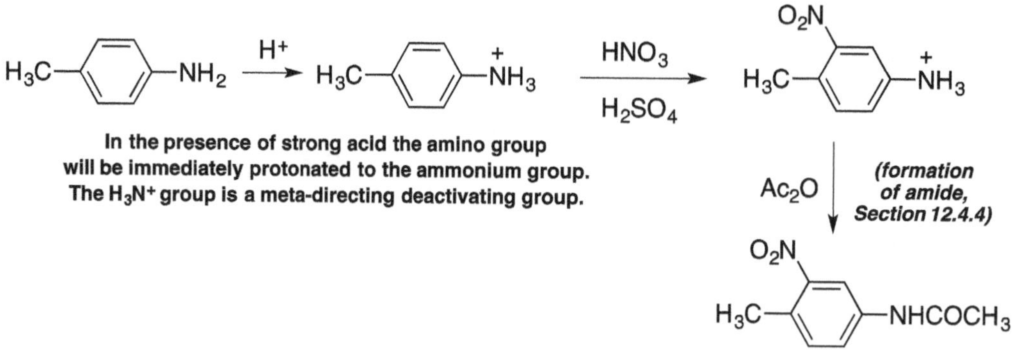

H+
HNO3
H2SO4
In the presence of strong acid the amino group
will be immediately protonated to the ammonium group.
The H3N+ group is a meta-directing deactivating group.
Ac2O
(formation
of amide,
Section 12.4.4)

e)

Ac2O
HNO3
H2SO4
Amido group is o-,p-directing activating group.
Amides are not basic and cannot be protonated.

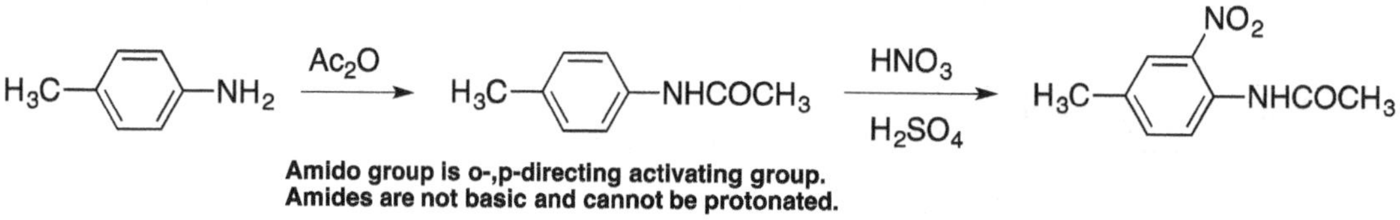

Problem 14.10. The following synthesis involves three elementary steps: 1. a transesterfication; 2. an electrophilic aromatic substitution; 3. a dehydration. Draw the intermediates.

acid catalyst
heat

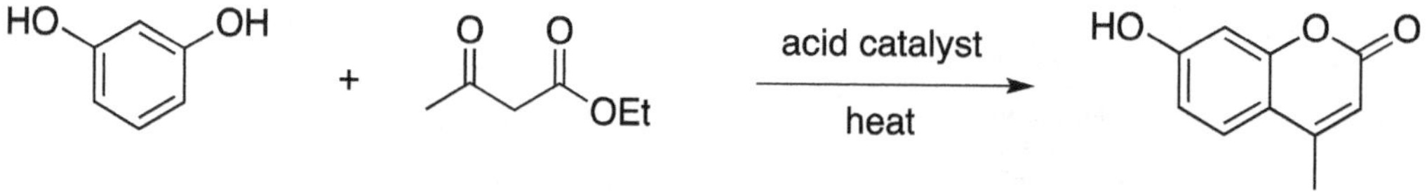

Solution:

Step 1: Transesterification. At this step, the exchange of the alcohol fragments in acetoacetic ester occurs according to the general nucleophilic acyl substitution mechanism (see Section 12.3).

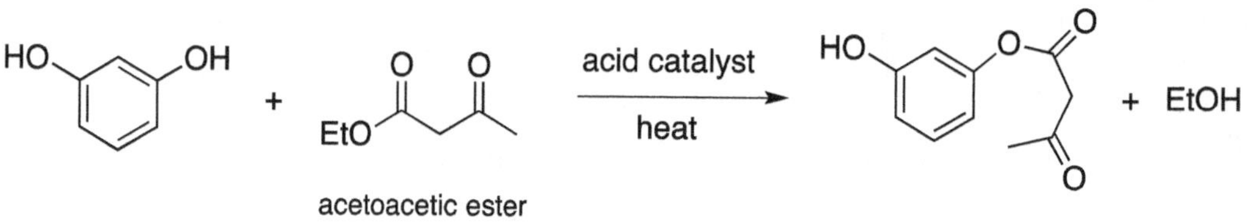

acid catalyst
heat
+ EtOH
acetoacetic ester

Step 2: An electrophilic aromatic substitution. The intramolecular electrophilic aromatic substitution occurs with the electrophile generated by protonation of the ketone carbonyl. This step is analogous to the intramolecular Friedel–Crafts reaction (see Problem 14.9a).

H+

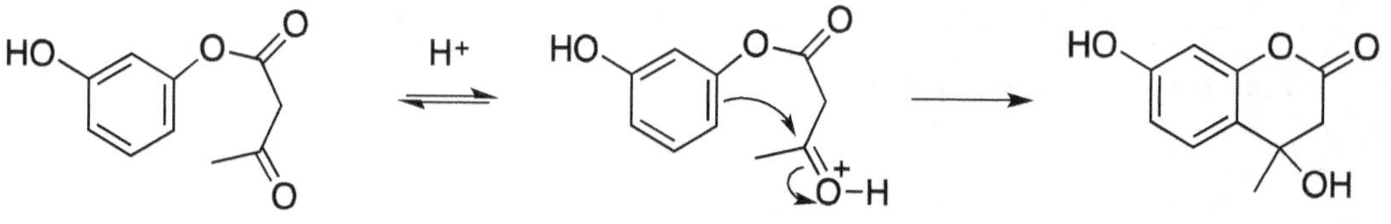

Step 3: Dehydration. Acid-catalyzed dehydration of tertiary alcohol (see Section 8.5) yields the final product:

Problem 14.11. The following two reactions result in the same product. Explain.

Solution:
Both reactions involve the same tertiary carbocation as the electrophile in electrophilic aromatic substitution. In the second reaction, the 3° carbocation is formed by 1,2-hydride shift from the less stable 2° carbocation (see Figure 5.9 and the related text in Chapter 5).

Problem 14.12. Propose mechanisms for the reactions shown in Figure 14.24.

Solution:

Abbreviated mechanisms for Figure 14.24:

Reaction 1:

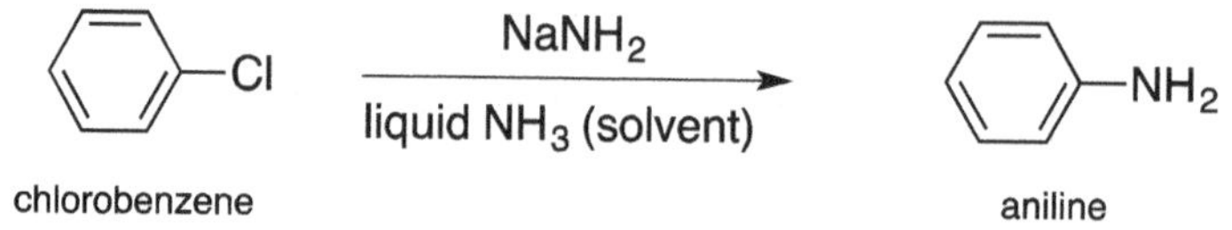

chlorobenzene

aniline

Mechanism:

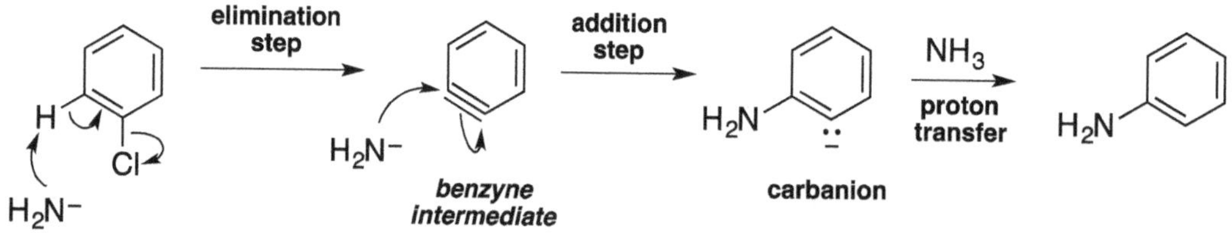

benzyne
intermediate

carbanion

Reaction 2:

o-chlorotoluene

o-toluidine

m-toluidine

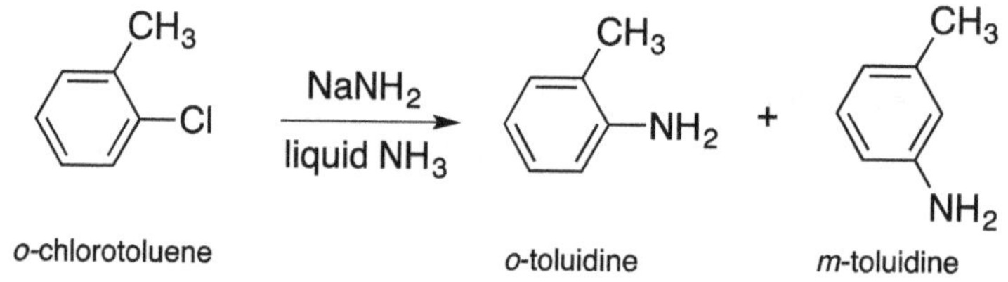

Mechanism:

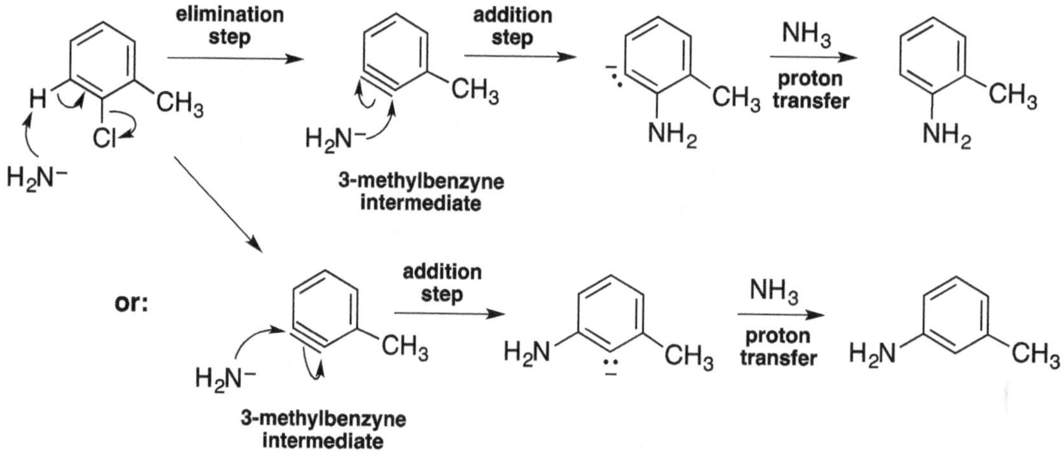

3-methylbenzyne
intermediate

or:

3-methylbenzyne
intermediate

Problem 14.13. What are the major products of the following reactions?

a)

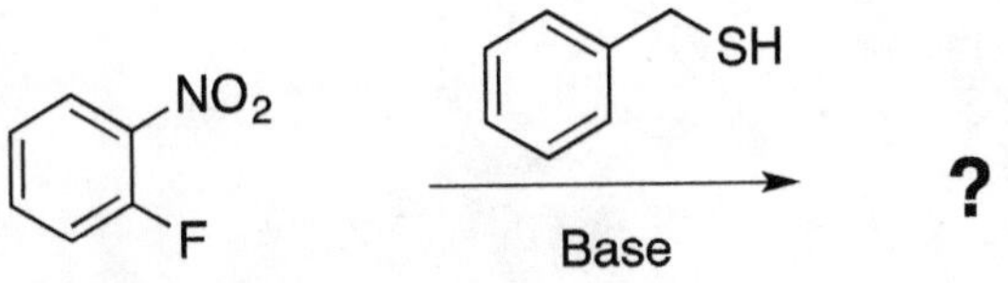

b)

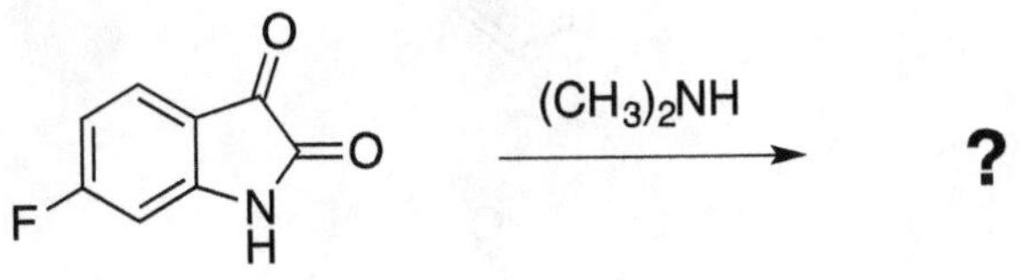

c)

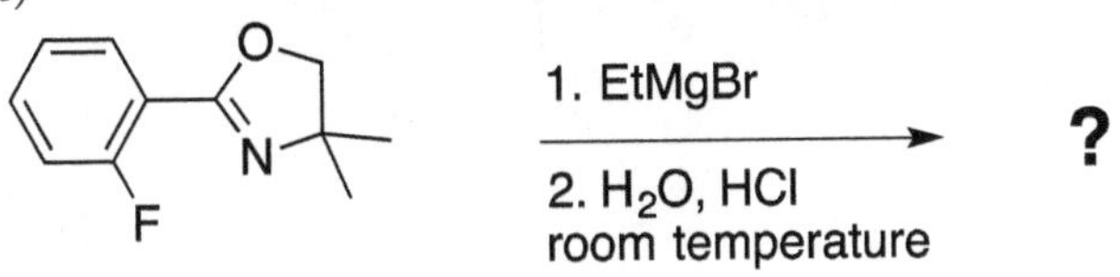

d)

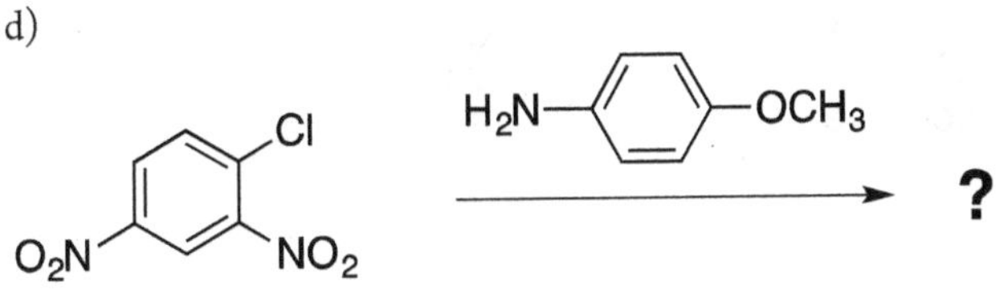

e)

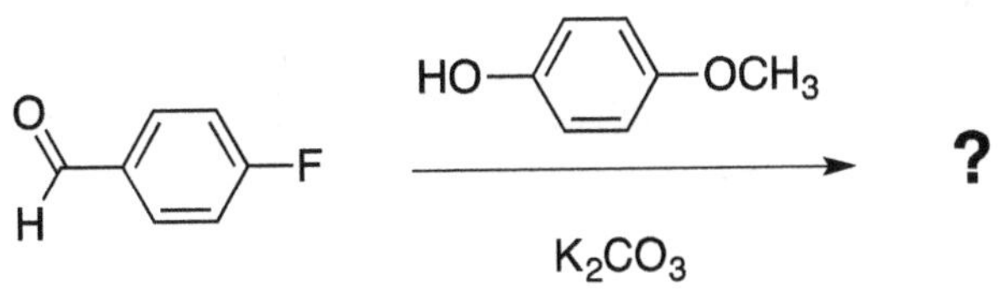

Solution:

All these reactions involve nucleophilic aromatic substitution of halogen in the benzene ring with the corresponding nucleophile according to the addition/elimination mechanism (Section 14.5.1):

a)

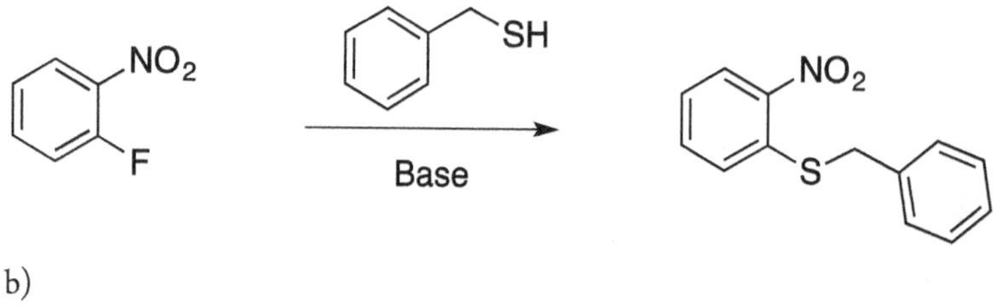

b)

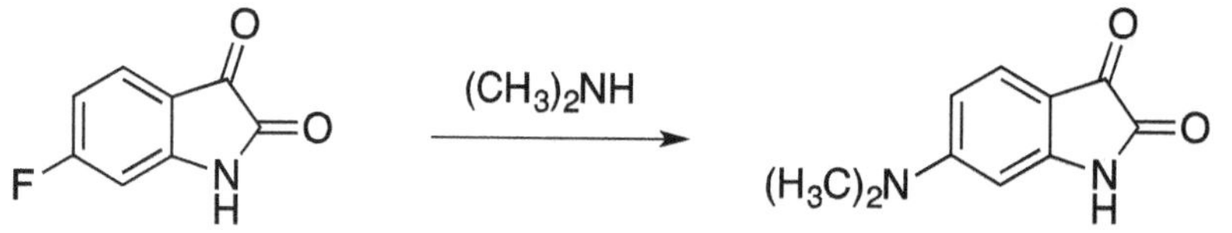

c)

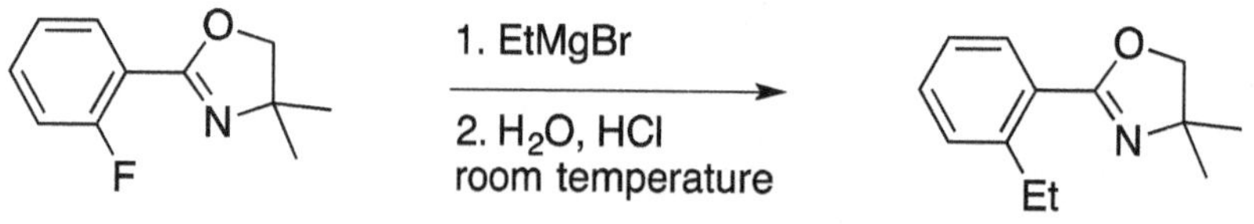

d)

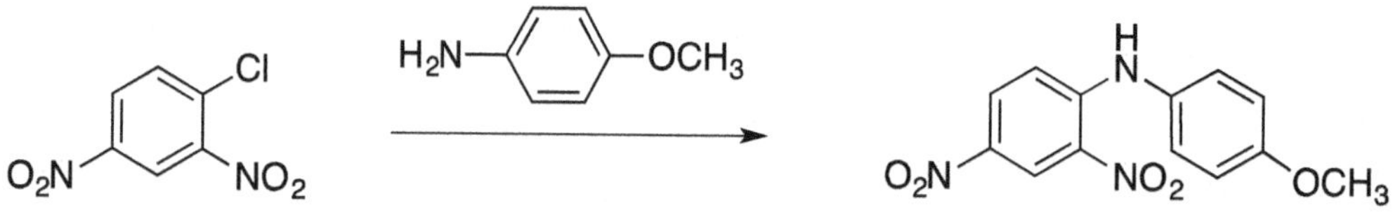

e)

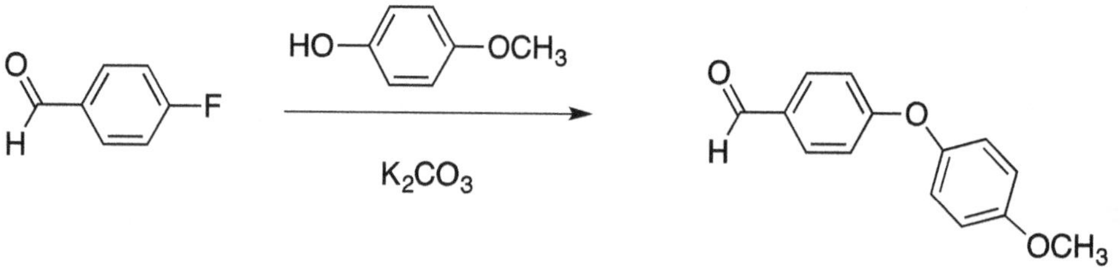

Problem 14.14. Propose a detailed mechanism (i.e., initiation, propagation, and termination steps) for the radical chlorination of ethylbenzene.

Solution:

See Section 3.6 for the radical chain mechanism of chlorination reaction.

$$PhCH_2CH_3 + Cl_2 \xrightarrow{\text{heat or light}} PhCHClCH_3 + HCl$$

Initiation:

$$Cl-Cl \xrightarrow{\text{heat or light}} Cl\cdot + \cdot Cl$$

chlorine radicals

Chain Propagation:

Ph—C(H)(CH₃)—H + ·Cl ⟶ Ph—C·(CH₃) + H—Cl

benzylic radical

Ph—C·(H)(CH₃) + Cl—Cl ⟶ Ph—C(H)(CH₃)—Cl + ·Cl

regenerated chlorine radical

Chain Termination:

Cl· + ·Cl ⟶ Cl—Cl

Ph—C·(H)(CH₃) + ·Cl ⟶ Ph—C(H)(CH₃)—Cl

Ph—C·(H)(CH₃) + ·C(H)(CH₃)—Ph ⟶ PhCH₂CH₂Ph

Problem 14.15. What are the major products of the following transformations?

a)

PhCH₃ $\xrightarrow[\text{DMSO (solvent)}]{\text{IBX, 80 °C}}$ $\xrightarrow{CH_2=PPh_3}$ **?**

b)

PhCH₃ $\xrightarrow[\text{light or heat}]{\text{NBS}}$ $\xrightarrow{\text{KCN}}$ $\xrightarrow[H_2SO_4]{H_2O}$ **?**

Solution:

a)

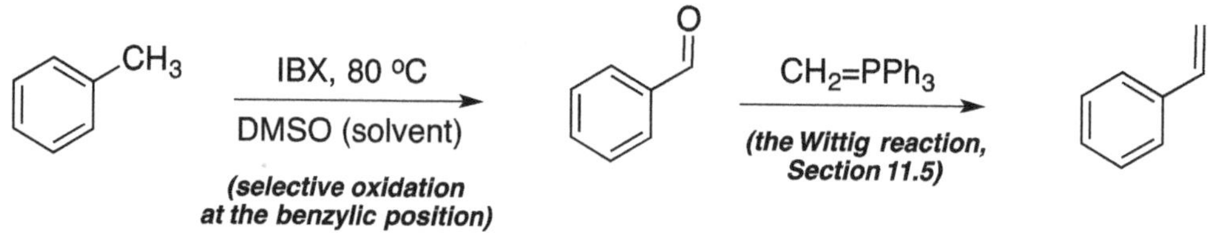

CH₃ → **IBX, 80 °C** / **DMSO (solvent)** *(selective oxidation at the benzylic position)* → (benzaldehyde) → **CH₂=PPh₃** *(the Wittig reaction, Section 11.5)* → (styrene)

b)

CH₃ → **NBS** / **light or heat** *(radical bromination at the benzylic position)* → CH₂Br → **KCN** *(nucleophilic substitution, Section 5.1)* → CH₂CN →

→ **H₂O** / **H₂SO₄** *(hydrolysis of nitriles, Section 12.4.4)* → CH₂CO₂H

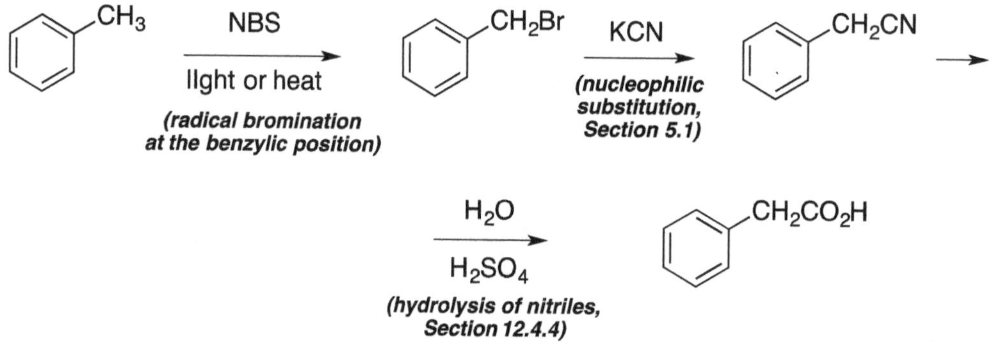

Problem 14.16. Benzyl bromide is a primary halide. In nucleophilic substitution reactions, why does this compound react via S$_N$1 and S$_N$2 reaction mechanisms, dependent on the reaction conditions?

Solution:

As a primary halide, benzyl bromide is a good substrate for the S$_N$2 reaction, especially in polar aprotic solvents (e.g., acetone, acetonitrile, and DMSO) as explained in Section 5.2.1 of the textbook. In protic solvents (water and alcohols), which are the best solvents for the unimolecular reactions, it reacts via S$_N$1 mechanism because of the resonance stabilization of the benzylic carbocation (Section 5.2.2 of the textbook).

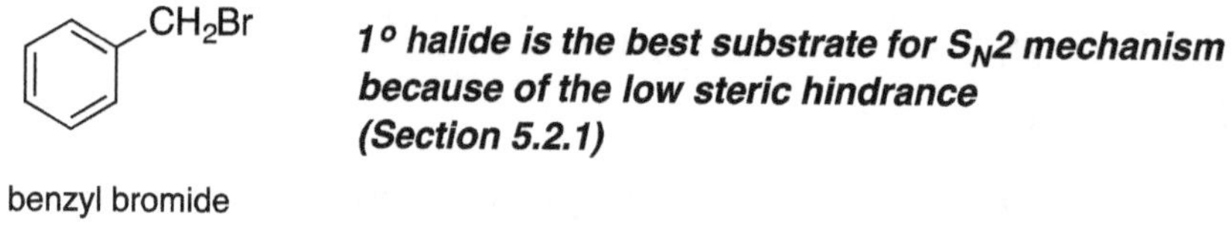

CH₂Br

benzyl bromide

1° halide is the best substrate for S$_N$2 mechanism because of the low steric hindrance (Section 5.2.1)

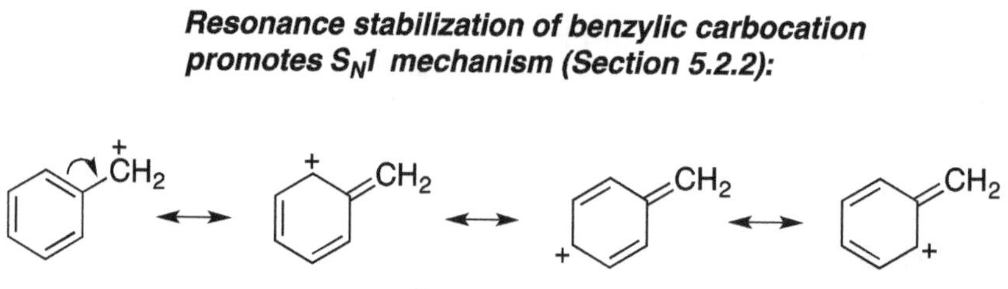

Resonance stabilization of benzylic carbocation promotes S$_N$1 mechanism (Section 5.2.2):

Problem 14.17. What are the major products of the following transformations?

a)

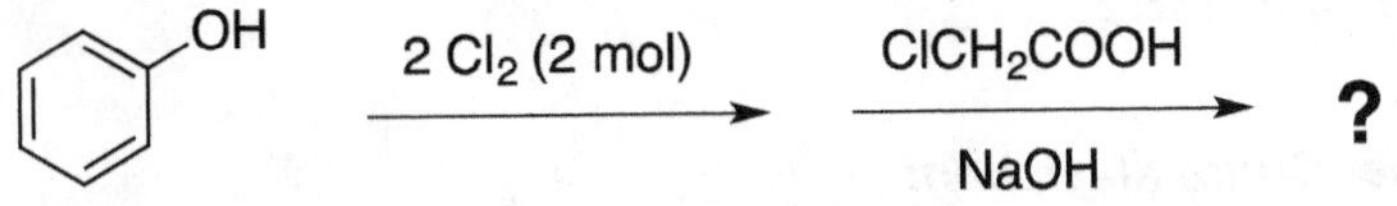

b)

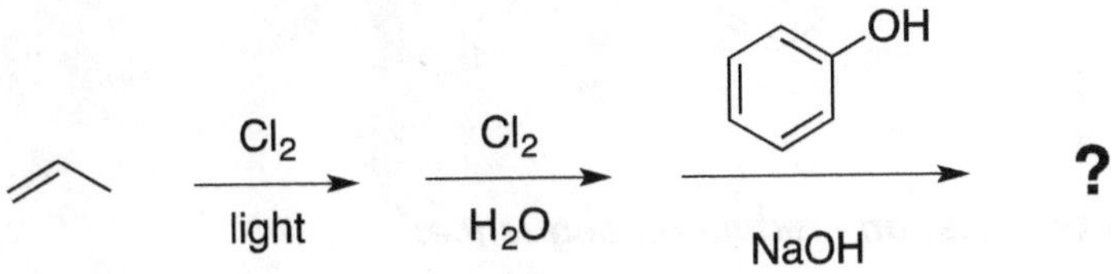

Solution:

a)

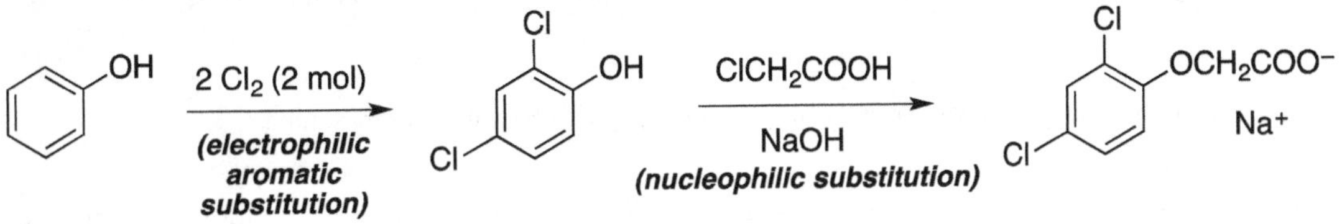

b)

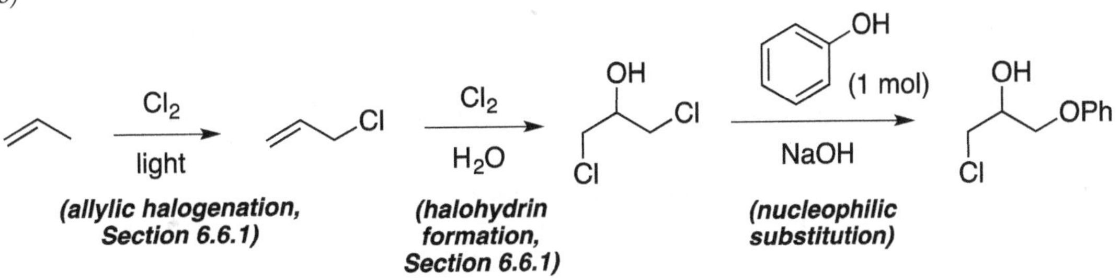

14.2. Additional Problems for Chapter 14 (for answers see Ch 17)

Problem 14.18. Imidazole is a biologically important molecule and a commonly used base in organic synthesis. The structure of this heterocyclic aromatic amine is provided below for your reference. Explain why the reaction of imidazole with an acid always involves the N atom at the C=N in preference to the other N atom in the structure.

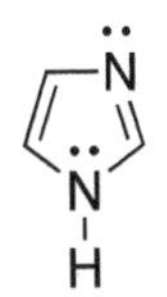

Imidazole

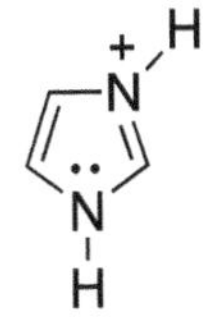

Conjugate Acid

Problem 14.19. n-Butylbenzene can be prepared from benzene *directly* via Friedel–Crafts alkylation or *indirectly* via Friedel–Crafts acylation followed by subsequent reduction of the carbonyl group in the acylated product as shown in the following scheme.

Direct synthesis via Friedel-Crafts alkylation:

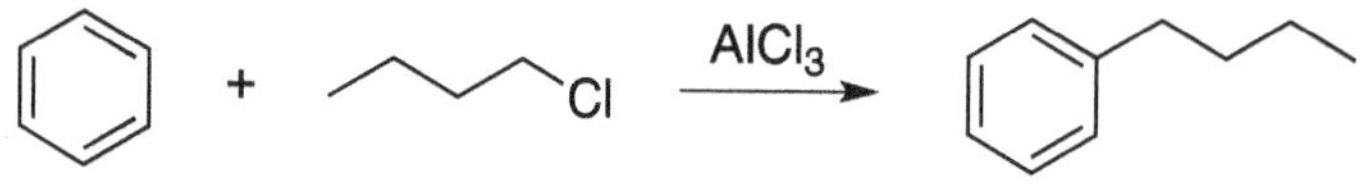

Synthesis via Friedel-Crafts acylation - reduction sequence:

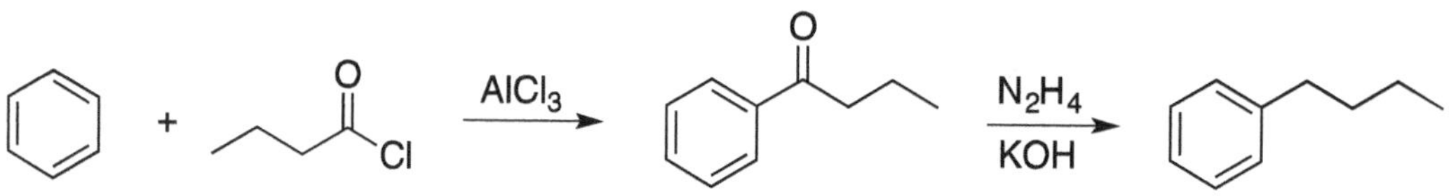

Which synthetic strategy will yield n-butylbenzene in high yield? Explain your reasoning.

Problem 14.20. Provide reagent(s) that can be used to convert toluene to the following aromatic compounds:

a) benzyl bromide   b) *o*-bromotoluene   c) benzoic acid

Problem 14.21. Provide a route for the conversion of benzene to the following compounds:

a) aniline   b) styrene (vinylbenzene)
c) *m*-chlorobenzoic acid   d) *m*-bromonitrobenzene

Amines

15.1. Chapter 15 Problems and Solutions

Problem 15.1. Draw structures and provide names for all amines with the molecular formula $C_4H_{11}N$. Classify these amines as primary, secondary, and tertiary.

Solution:

Isomeric amines with the molecular formula $C_4H_{11}N$ are shown below:

Primary (1°) amines:

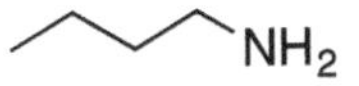

| 1-butanamine | 2-butanamine | 2-methyl-1-propanamine | 2-methyl-2-propanamine |

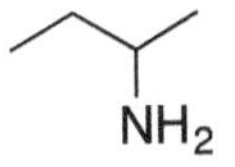

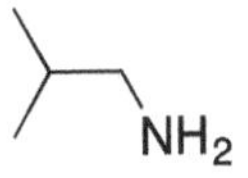

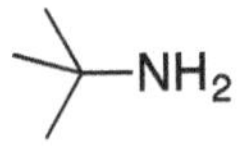

Secondary (2°) amines:

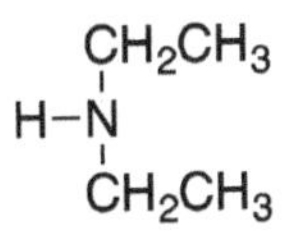

diethylamine 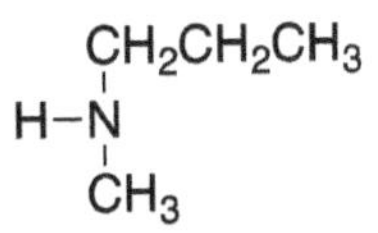   *N*-methyl-1-propanamine 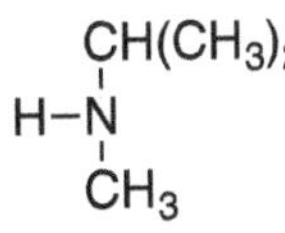   *N*-methyl-2-propanamine

Tertiary (3°) amine:

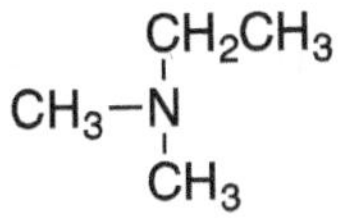

N,N-dimethylethanamine

Problem 15.2. Provide the IUPAC name and the common name for the amines with the following ¹H NMR spectra.

a) The amine is a secondary amine.

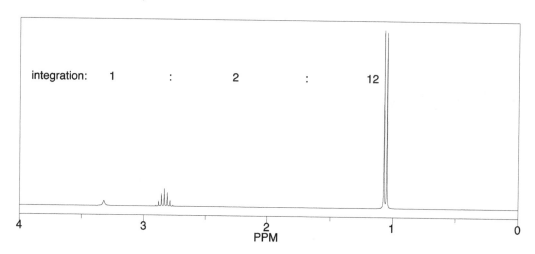

b) The amine is a derivative of aniline.

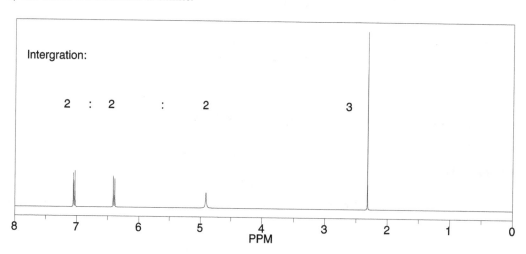

Solution:

a) The broad signal of one hydrogen at about 3.7 ppm belongs to the NH proton. The septet at 2.8 ppm belongs a hydrogen (CH) coupled on two CH_3 groups. The doublet at 1.1 ppm corresponds to a CH_3 group coupled on the CH, which is a combination signals typical of the isopropyl group, $(CH_3)_2CH$. Further analysis of the integration leads to the structure of diisopropylamine (a common name, which is also adopted by IUPAC) shown below:

a: 12H (doublet) at about 1.1 ppm
b: 2H (septet) at about 2.8 ppm
c: 1H (broad singlet) at about 3.3 ppm

diisopropylamine

Note that the coupling of the NH protons on the neighboring CH protons is not present in amines, and the NH (as well as the NH_2) protons are usually displayed as broad singlets.

b) This spectrum is in agreement with the molecule of *p*-toluidine (a common name, which is also adopted by IUPAC) as explained below:

p-toluidine

a: 3H at about 2.3 ppm
b: 2H (doublet) at about 7.0 ppm
c: 2H (doublet) at about 6.4 ppm
d: 2H (broad singlet) at about 4.9 ppm

Problem 15.3. Within the aniline derivatives, as a rule of thumb electron-donating substituents such as $-CH_3$, $-NH_2$, and $-OCH_3$, which increase the reactivity toward electrophilic aromatic substitution, also increase the basicity. On the other hand, electron-withdrawing substituents such as $-Cl$, $-NO_2$, and $-CN$, which decrease reactivity toward electrophilic substitution, also decrease the basicity. Based on this information, rank the following sets of compounds in order of decreasing basicity:

a)

b)

c)

d)

Solution:

a) The nitro group (NO_2) has the strongest electron-withdrawing effect and therefore *p*-nitroaniline is the least reactive compound toward electrophilic substitution (see Section 14.4 of the textbook) and the weakest base. On the other side, *p*-chloroaniline has the highest basicity due the weak electron-donating resonance effect by chlorine atom. The acetyl substituent (CH_3CO) has a moderate electron-withdrawing effect which places the acetyl substituted aniline in the middle.

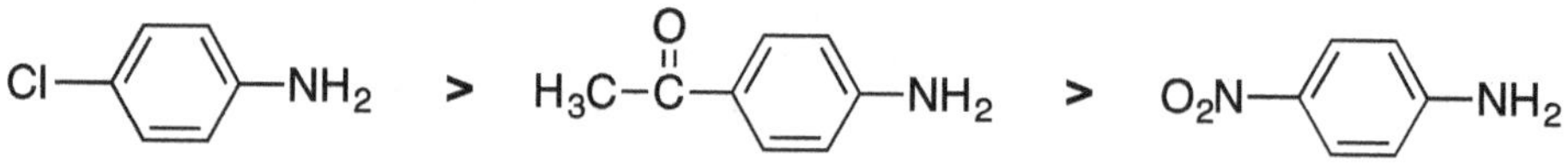

Cl—⟨benzene⟩—NH₂   >   H₃C–C(=O)—⟨benzene⟩—NH₂   >   O₂N—⟨benzene⟩—NH₂

strongest base   **weakest base**

b) The order of basicity shown below is in agreement with electron-donating ability of the substituents ($CH_3 > Br > CHO$):

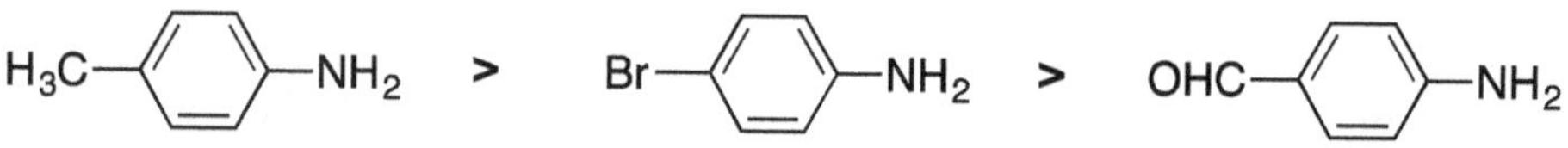

H₃C—⟨benzene⟩—NH₂   >   Br—⟨benzene⟩—NH₂   >   OHC—⟨benzene⟩—NH₂

strongest base   **weakest base**

c) The order of basicity shown below is in agreement with electron-donating ability of the substituents ($CH_3 > H > CF_3$):

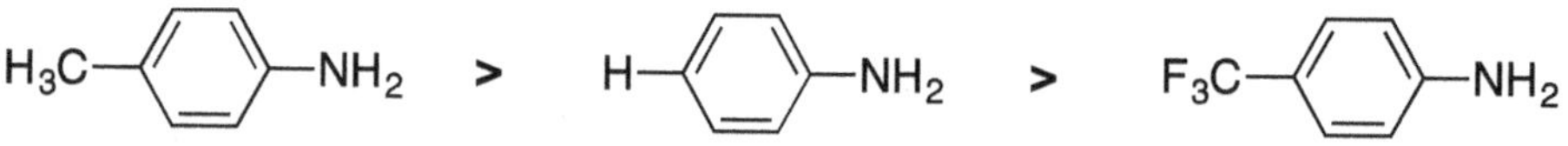

H₃C—⟨benzene⟩—NH₂   >   H—⟨benzene⟩—NH₂   >   F₃C—⟨benzene⟩—NH₂

strongest base   **weakest base**

d) The order of basicity shown below is in agreement with electron-donating ability of the substituents ($CH_3O > Cl > NO_2$):

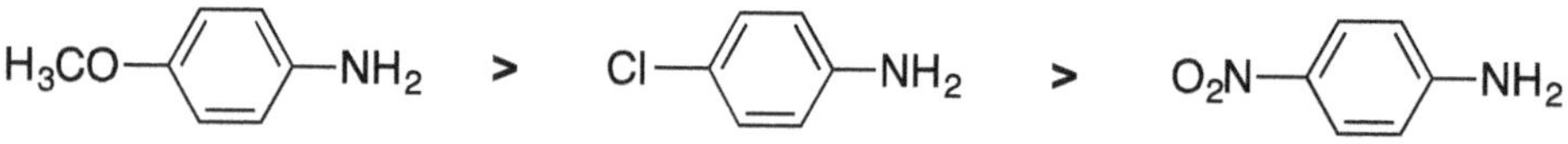

H₃CO—⟨benzene⟩—NH₂   >   Cl—⟨benzene⟩—NH₂   >   O₂N—⟨benzene⟩—NH₂

strongest base   **weakest base**

Problem 15.4. Diphenylamine (Ph$_2$NH) is an extremely weak base (pK$_a$ = 0.8), while triphenylamine (Ph$_3$N) is by ordinary standards not basic at all. Explain.

Solution:

Aniline (PhNH$_2$) is much less basic than alkylamines because the unshared electrons on nitrogen are less available for protonation due to resonance conjugation of the amino group with the phenyl ring (see Figure 15.7 and related text in Section 15.2.2 of the textbook). The presence of the second phenyl group (in Ph$_2$NH) and the third phenyl group (in Ph$_3$N) leads to further increase of the resonance delocalization of this electronic pair. As a result of such delocalization, the unshared electrons in triphenylamine (Ph$_3$N) are almost completely unavailable for protonation.

Problem 15.5. Within each molecule identify the most basic nitrogen atom:

a)

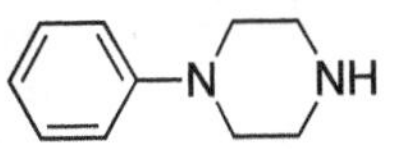

b)

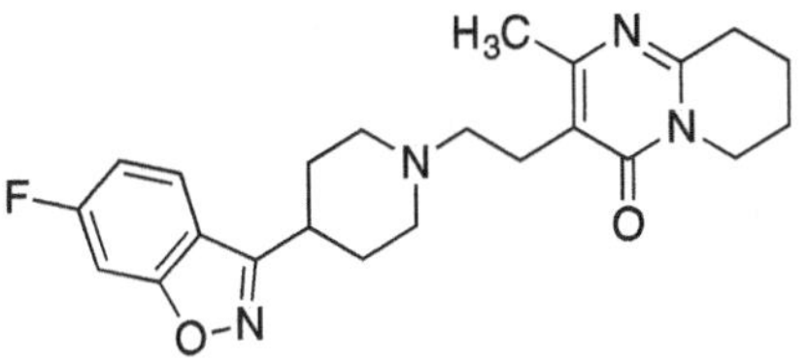

c)

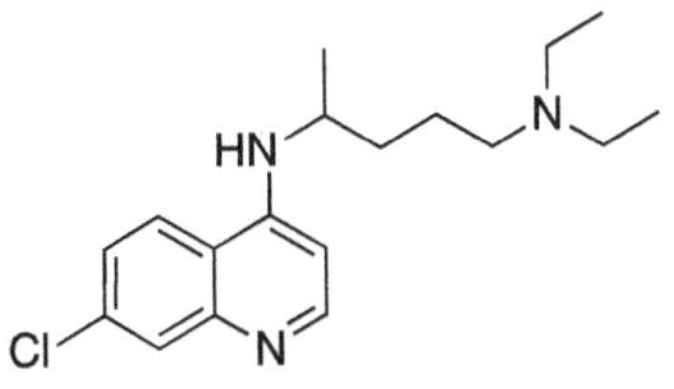

d)

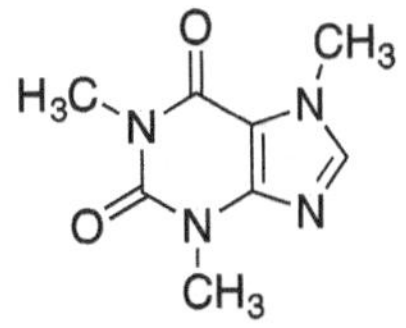

e)

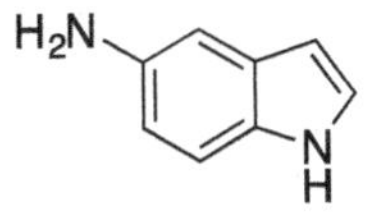

f)

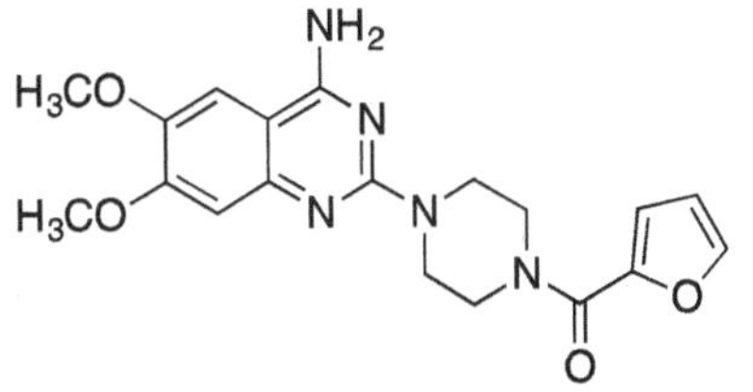

g)

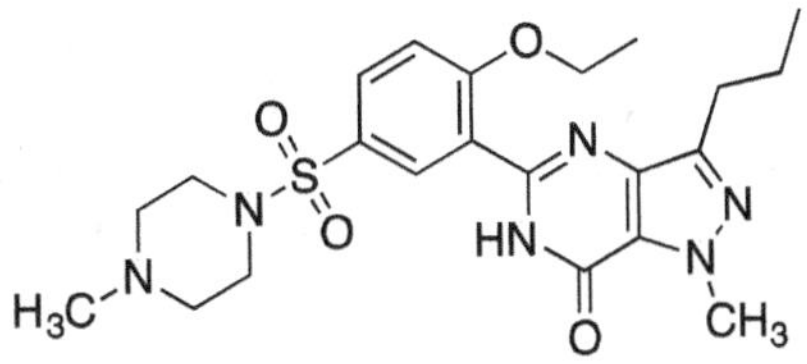

h)

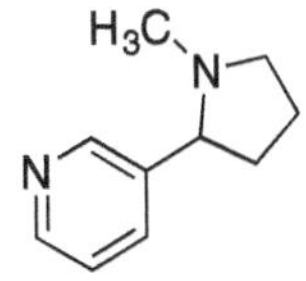

Solution:

The most basic nitrogens are circled in each structure shown below. In general, alkyl amines are more basic than aryl amines, heterocyclic amines, or amides. For comparison of the basicity of different nitrogen atoms in heterocyclic aromatic amines, the effect of protonation on the aromaticity should be considered (see Section 15.2.3 of the textbook).

a)

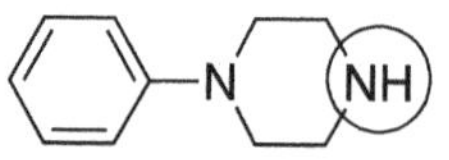

b)

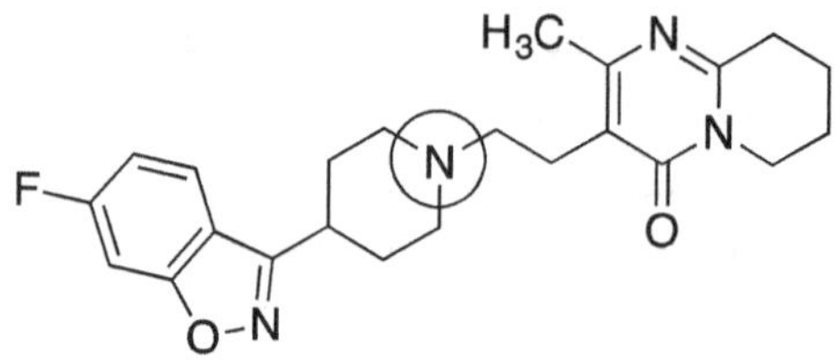

c)

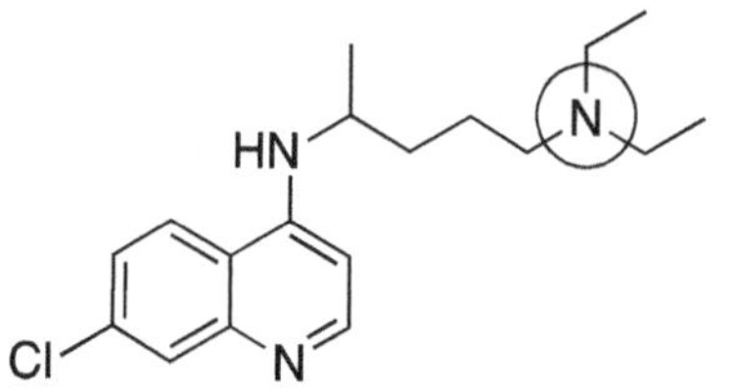

d)

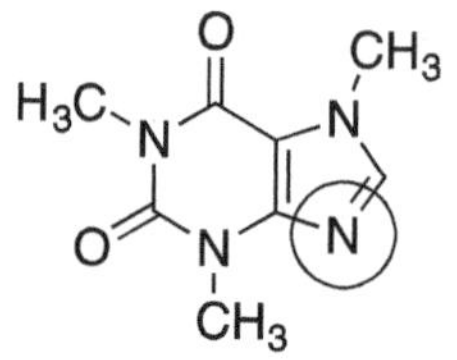

e)

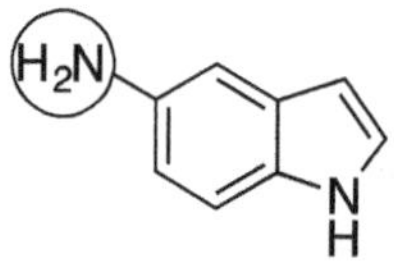

f)

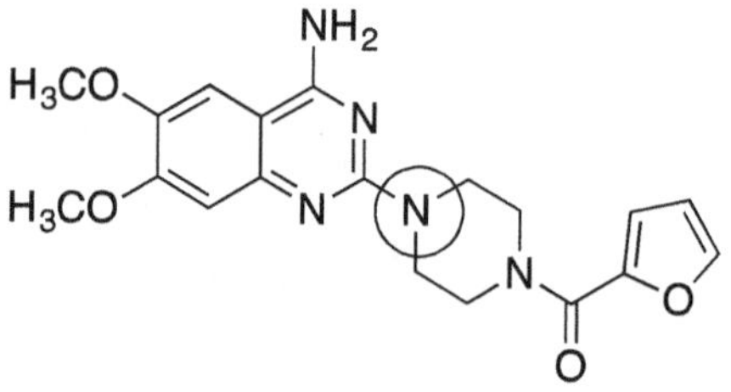

g)

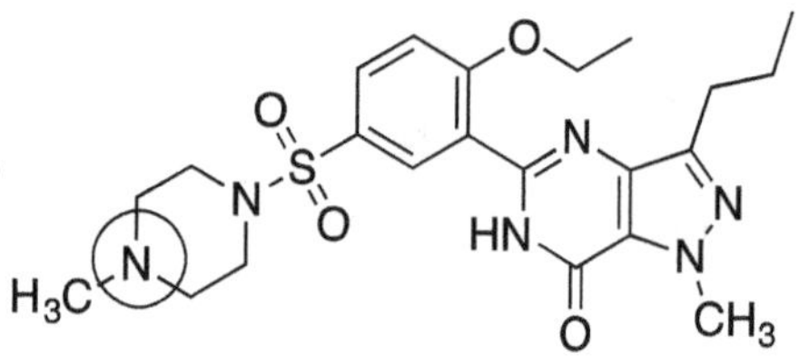

h)

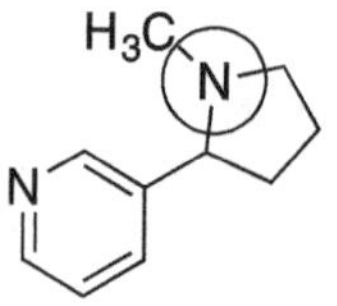

Problem 15.6. Attempts to synthesize ethylamine in high yield by treating 1 mol bromoethane with 1 mol ammonia in the presence of sodium bicarbonate as a base to neutralize the developing HBr produces a mixture of ethylamine, diethylamine, and triethylamine. Some unreacted ammonia is also recovered, but all of the bromoethane is consumed during the reaction. Use the relative basicity of the alkyl amines that form during this reaction and ammonia as measures of nucleophilicity to explain this finding.

Solution:

The sequence of reactions occurring in the mixture of 1 mol bromoethane and 1 mol ammonia is shown below. Basicity and nucleophilicity of amines (see Section 15.3 of the textbook) increases in the following order: 2° amine > 1° amine > NH_3. In agreement with this order of reactivity, the initially produced ethylamine (the 1° amine) will react with CH_3CH_2Br faster than NH_3 producing diethylamine. Finally, diethylamine (the 2° amine) which has the highest reactivity, reacts with CH_3CH_2Br forming triethylamine. The yields of produced amines depend on the rate of each reaction and on the initial concentration of nucleophilic reagents and their nucleophilicity. All these factors in combination are responsible for the exact composition of the product mixture (ethylamine, diethylamine, and triethylamine).

$$CH_3CH_2Br \ + \ NH_3 \quad \xrightarrow[\textit{slow reaction}]{\begin{array}{c}NaHCO_3 \text{ (a base for}\\ \text{neutralizing HBr)}\end{array}} \quad \begin{array}{c}CH_3CH_2NH_2\\ 1^\circ \text{ amine}\end{array}$$

$$CH_3CH_2Br \ + \ CH_3CH_2NH_2 \quad \xrightarrow[\textit{faster reaction}]{NaHCO_3} \quad \begin{array}{c}(CH_3CH_2)_2NH\\ 2^\circ \text{ amine}\end{array}$$

$$CH_3CH_2Br \ + \ (CH_3CH_2)_2NH \quad \xrightarrow[\textit{fastest reaction}]{NaHCO_3} \quad \begin{array}{c}(CH_3CH_2)_3N\\ 3^\circ \text{ amine}\end{array}$$

Order of nucleophilic reactivity (nucleophilicity):

$$NH_3 \quad < \quad CH_3CH_2NH_2 \quad < \quad (CH_3CH_2)_2NH$$

least reactive   most reactive

Problem 15.7. Provide the intermediate and final products in the following reaction sequences:

a)

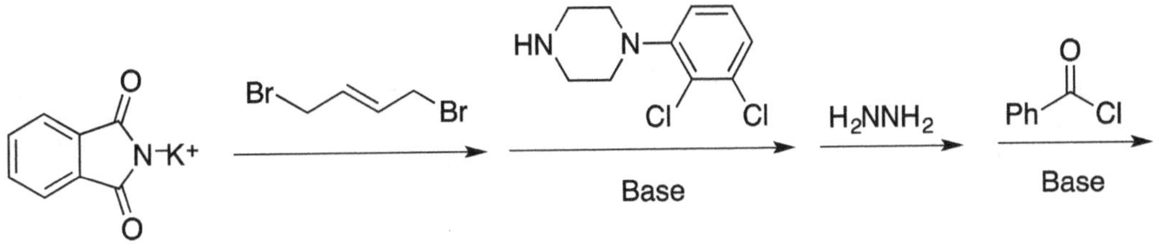

b)

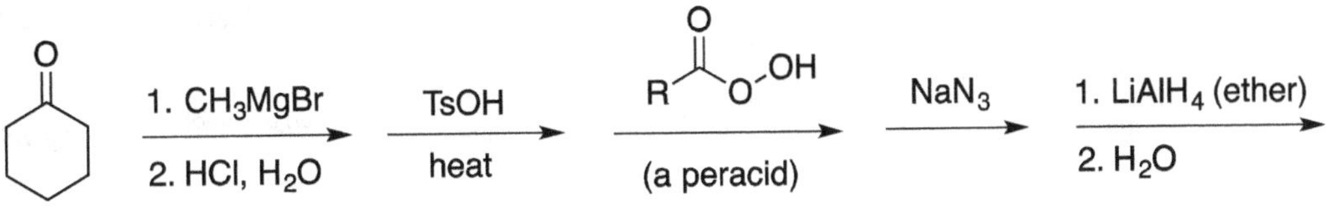

Solution:

A brief explanation of each reaction sequence is provided below:

a)

1st intermediate

2nd intermediate

H_2NNH_2

(formation of amine from N-alkylphthalimide)

3rd intermediate

Ph—C(=O)—Cl

(amide formation, Section 12.4.4)

final product

b)

1. CH_3MgBr
2. HCl, H_2O

(addition of carbon nucleophile to carbonyl, Section 11.3)

1st intermediate

TsOH
heat

(dehydration, Section 8.5)

2nd intermediate

(epoxide formation, Section 6.5.2)

3rd intermediate

NaN_3

(nucleophilic ring-opening of epoxide, Section 6.5.2)

4th intermediate

1. $LiAlH_4$ (ether)
2. H_2O

(reduction of azide)

final product

Problem 15.8. The exhaustive Hofmann degradation of 2-methyl-piperidine yields 1,5-hexadiene. Provide the structures of all intermediate products in this sequence.

1. CH_3I (excess)
2. Ag_2O, H_2O
3. heat

?

1. CH_3I
2. Ag_2O, H_2O
3. heat

+ $(CH_3)_3N$

Solution:

A brief explanation of this reaction sequence is provided below:

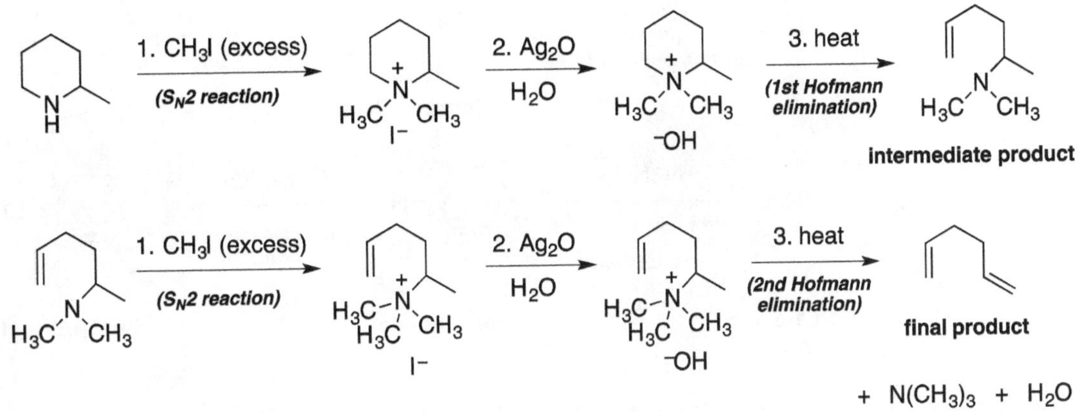

Problem 15.9. Provide the intermediate products and the final product in the following reactions:

a) 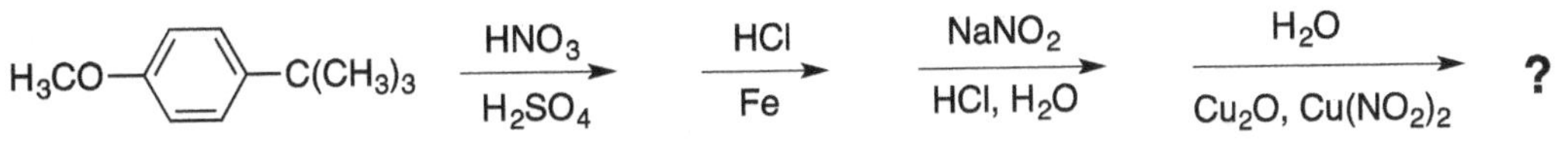 $H_3CO-\langle\rangle-C(CH_3)_3$ $\xrightarrow[H_2SO_4]{HNO_3}$ $\xrightarrow[Fe]{HCl}$ $\xrightarrow[HCl, H_2O]{NaNO_2}$ $\xrightarrow[Cu_2O, Cu(NO_2)_2]{H_2O}$ **?**

b) 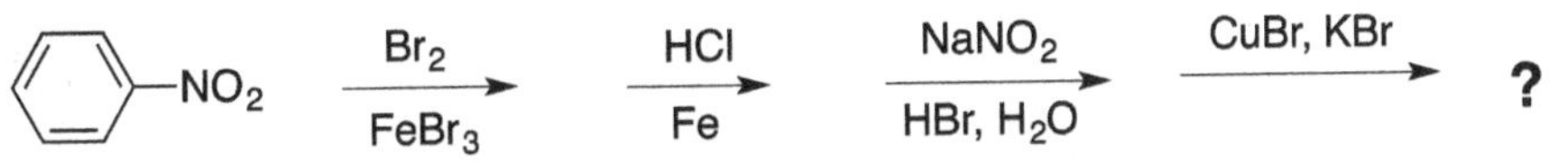 $\langle\rangle-NO_2$ $\xrightarrow[FeBr_3]{Br_2}$ $\xrightarrow[Fe]{HCl}$ $\xrightarrow[HBr, H_2O]{NaNO_2}$ $\xrightarrow{CuBr, KBr}$ **?**

Solution:

A brief explanation of each reaction sequence is provided below:

a)

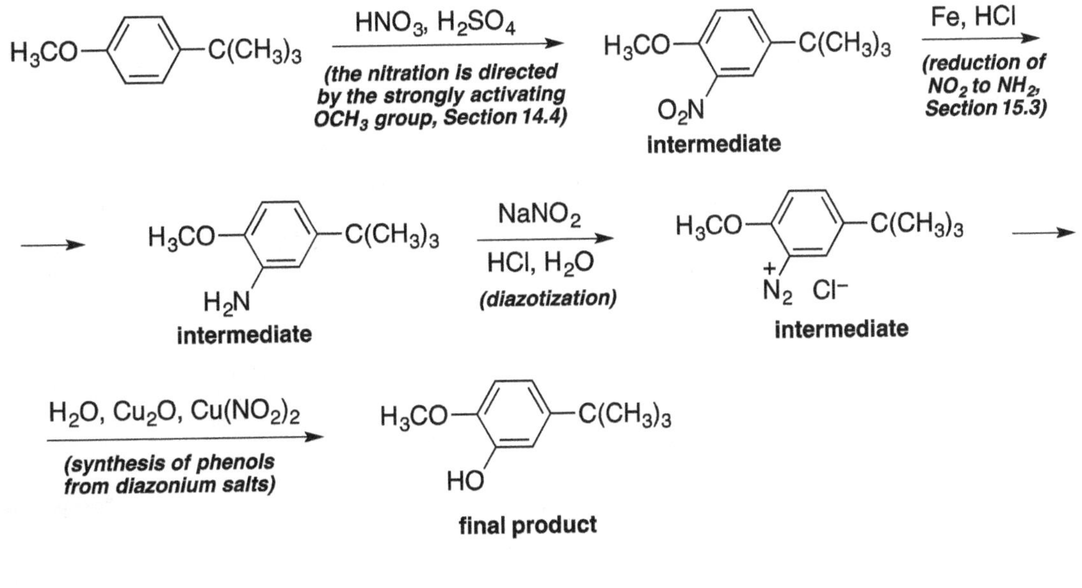

$H_3CO-\langle\rangle-C(CH_3)_3$ $\xrightarrow{HNO_3, H_2SO_4}$ $H_3CO-\langle\rangle-C(CH_3)_3$ with O_2N **intermediate** $\xrightarrow[\text{Section 15.3}]{\text{Fe, HCl}}$

(the nitration is directed by the strongly activating OCH_3 group, Section 14.4)

(reduction of NO_2 to NH_2, Section 15.3)

$\longrightarrow$ $H_3CO-\langle\rangle-C(CH_3)_3$ with H_2N **intermediate** $\xrightarrow[HCl, H_2O]{NaNO_2}$ $H_3CO-\langle\rangle-C(CH_3)_3$ with N_2^+ Cl^- **intermediate** $\longrightarrow$

(diazotization)

$\xrightarrow{H_2O, Cu_2O, Cu(NO_2)_2}$ $H_3CO-\langle\rangle-C(CH_3)_3$ with HO **final product**

(synthesis of phenols from diazonium salts)

b)

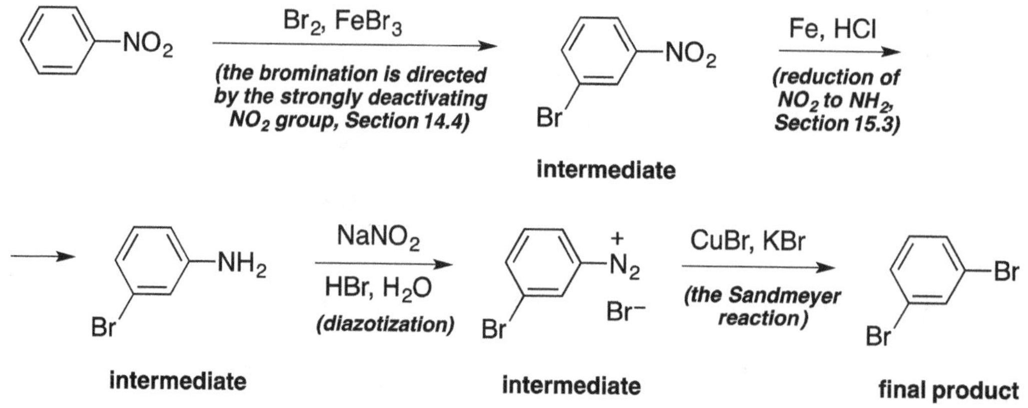

intermediate

intermediate   **intermediate**   **final product**

Problem 15.10. Provide the reagents and intermediates for the synthesis of the following compounds, using benzene as the starting material:

a) 1,3,5-tribromobenzene   b) *m*-bromophenol

Solution:

a) Synthesis of 1,3,5-tribromobenzene:

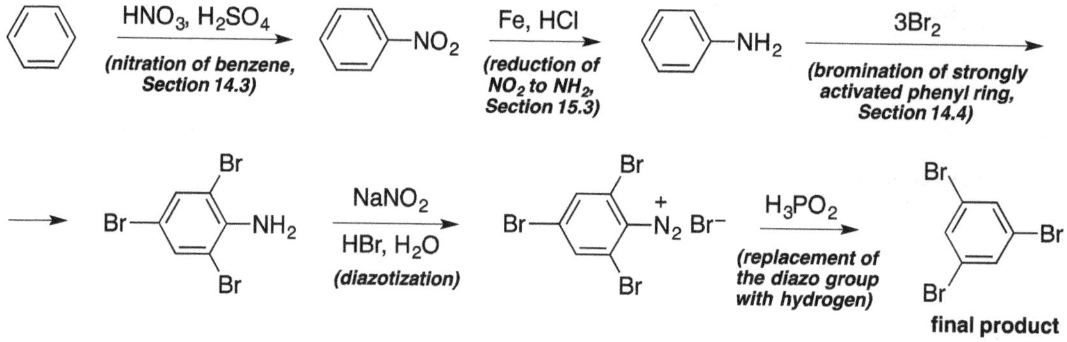

final product

b) Synthesis of *m*-bromophenol

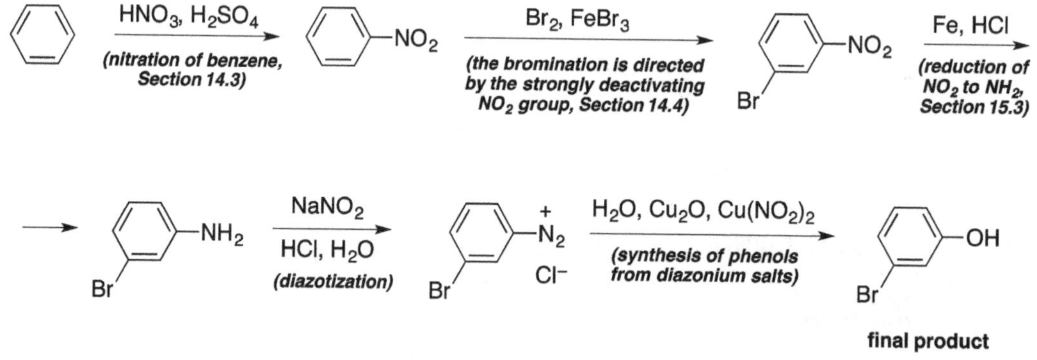

final product

Problem 15.11. The key step in the synthesis of the food coloring Citrus Red #2 is the conversion of 2,5-methoxyaniline into its diazonium salt, followed by an azo coupling using 2-naphthol. Propose a synthesis for 2,5-dimethoxyaniline from hydroquinone (benzene-1,4-diol).

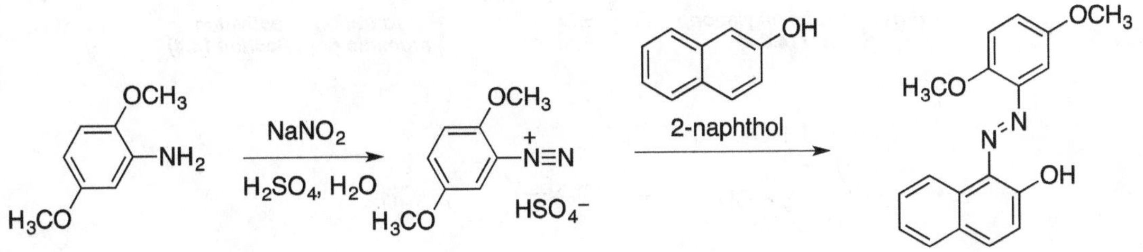

2,5-dimethoxyaniline

Citrus Red #2

Solution:

Synthesis of 2,5-methoxyaniline from hydroquinone:

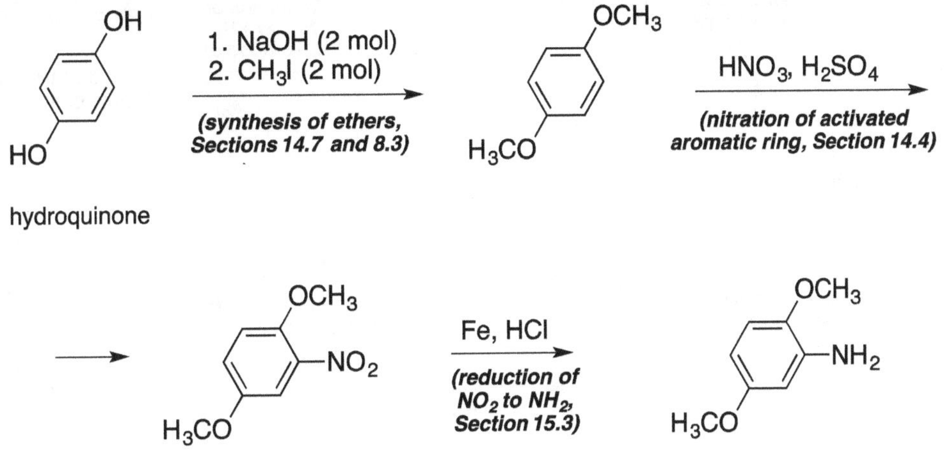

hydroquinone

Problem 15.12. The key step in the synthesis of the pH indicator methyl red is the conversion of anthranilic acid into its diazonium salt, followed by an azo coupling using *N,N*-dimethylaniline. Propose a synthesis for anthranilic acid and *N,N*-dimethylaniline from benzene.

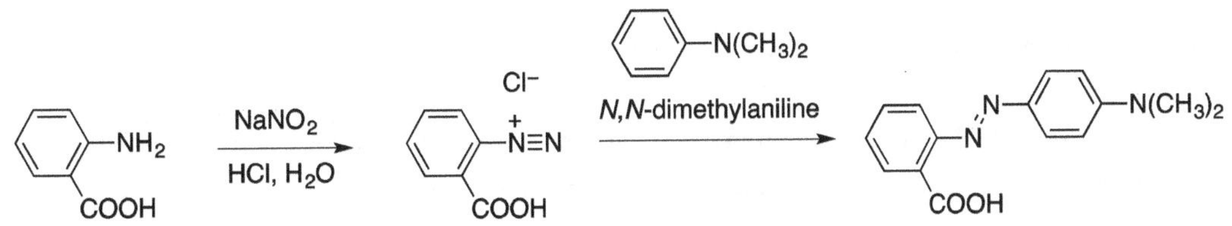

anthranilic acid
(2-aminobenzoic acid)

Methyl Red

Solution:

Synthesis of anthranilic acid from benzene:

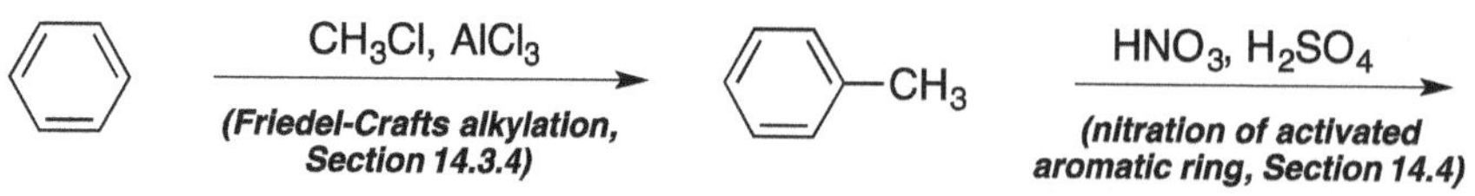

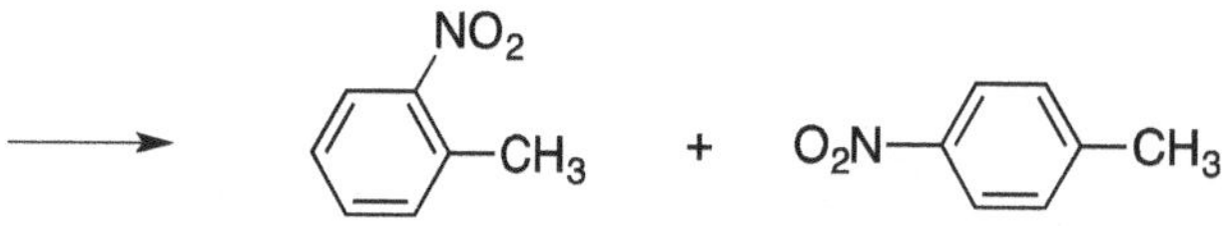

pure o-nitrotoluene can be separated by distillation of the mixture of ortho and para isomers

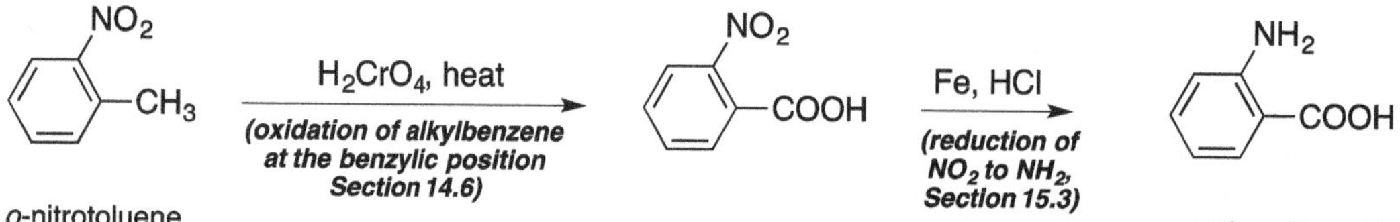

o-nitrotoluene

anthranilic acid
(2-aminobenzoic acid)

Synthesis of *N,N*-dimethylaniline from benzene:

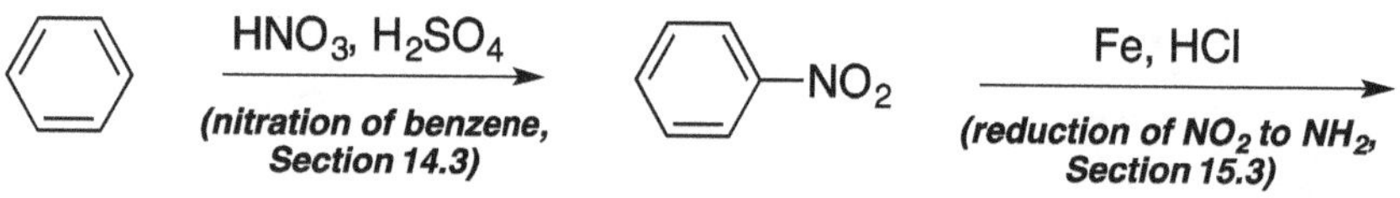

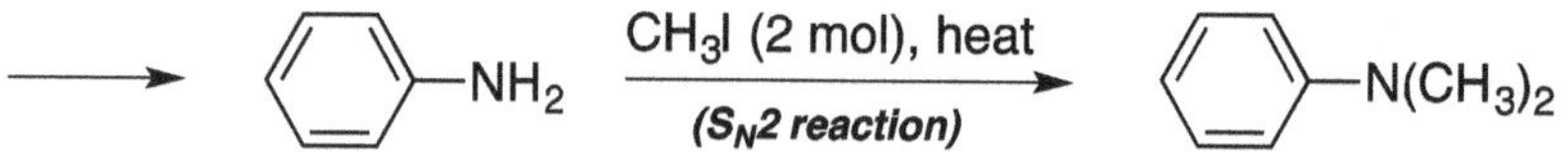

N,N-dimethylaniline

15.2. Additional Problems for Chapter 15 (for answers see Ch 17)

Problem 15.13. Propose the synthesis of the following compounds:

a) *N,N*-dimethyl-4-nitroaniline from chlorobenzene and dimethylamine
b) triethylbenzylammonium bromide from benzamide and bromoethane

Problem 15.14. Rank the following amines in decreasing order of their basicity:

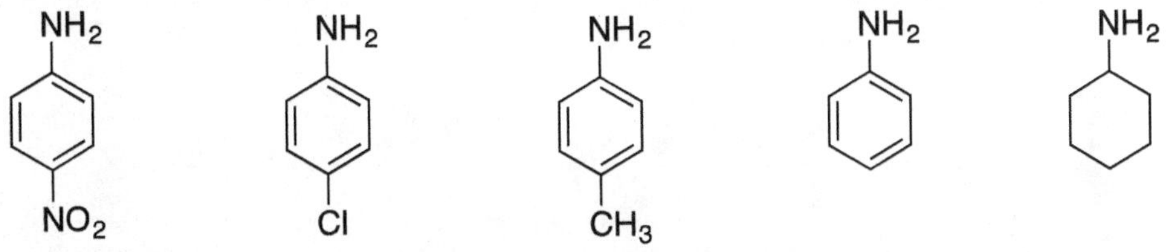

Problem 15.15. The reaction of a cyclic β-aminoalcohol with nitrous acid (HNO_2) yields a ring-expanded ketone via a molecular rearrangement. Write the complete mechanism including the rearrangement to account for the formation of cycloheptanone in the following reaction:

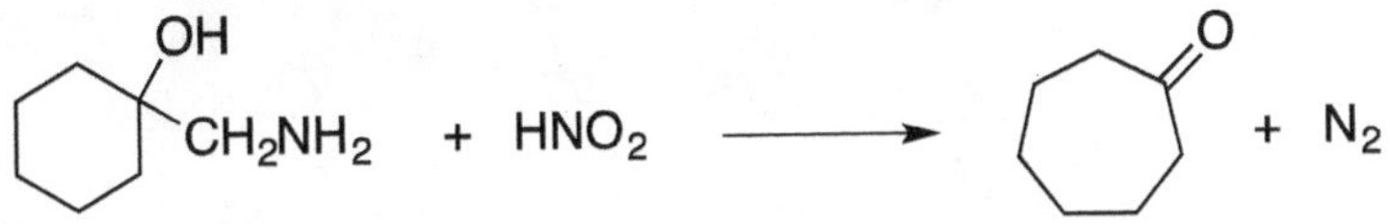

Problem 15.16. Provide a route for the conversion of benzene to the following compounds:

a) phenol   b) fluorobenzene   c) iodobenzene

Introduction to Biomolecules

16.1. Chapter 16 Problems and Solutions

Problem 16.1. Assign R or S configuration to each stereocenter present in cholesterol and prostaglandin E_1 (Figure 16.1).

Solution:

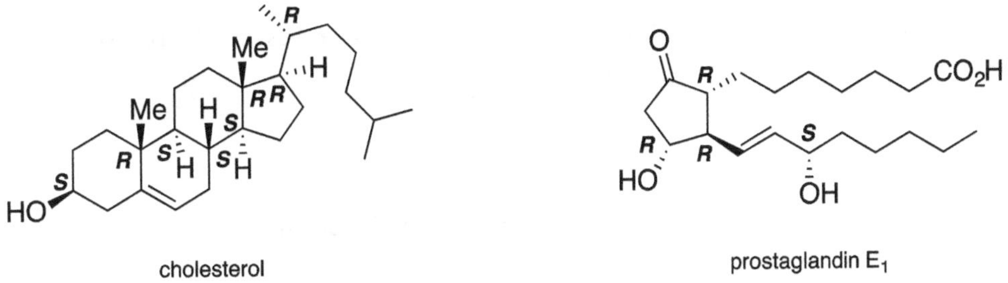

cholesterol   prostaglandin E_1

Cholesterol has eight chiral carbons and prostaglandin E_1 has four chiral carbons. Configuration of each stereocenter is shown in the picture above. See Section 4.2.1 for the rules for assignment of R/S configuration of chiral centers.

Problem 16.2. Which functional groups and heterocyclic rings are present in the simplified structure of chlorophyll (Figure 16.2)? Why is this molecule aromatic?

Solution:

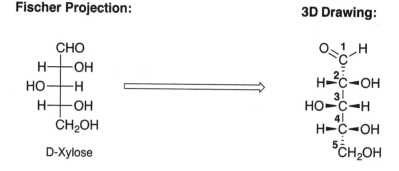

pyrrole heterocycle

ketone

ester simplified structure
of chlorophyll

9 π bonds
(18 electrons)
are involved in
the resonance

The simplified structure of chlorophyll contains functional groups of carboxylic ester, ketone, amine, and imine (see Section 1.3). It has 4 five-membered nitrogen heterocyclic rings, which are related to pyrrole (Sections 14.1 and 15.1). The molecule of chlorophyll is a completely conjugated cyclic system of 9 π bonds occupied by 18 electrons, which satisfies the requirements of Hückel's rule for aromaticity (Section 14.1). The resonance structures shown above illustrate conjugation in the macrocycle of chlorophyll.

Problem 16.3. Draw the three-dimensional structure of D-xylose and assign the IUPAC name, including the R or S configurations of each stereocenter.

Solution:

Fischer Projection: **3D Drawing:**

D-Xylose

IUPAC name: (2R,3S,4R)-2,3,4,5-tetrahydroxypentanal

See Section 4.3 of the textbook for the general concept of Fischer projections.

Problem 16.4. Draw Fischer projections of L-ribose, L-xylose, L-glucose, L-galactose and L-fructose.

Solution:

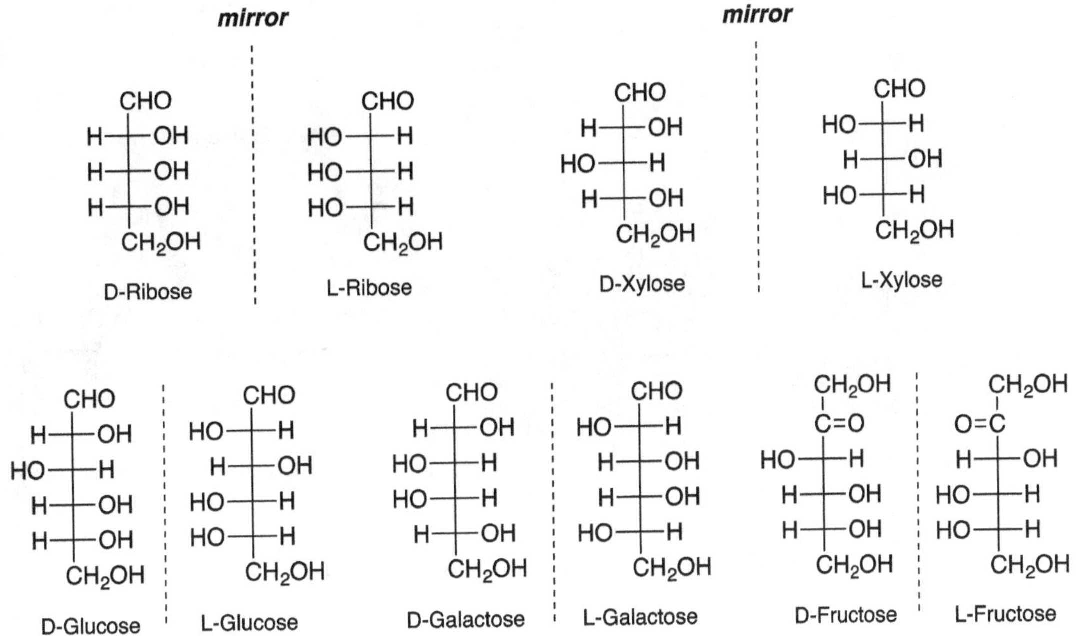

D-Ribose   L-Ribose   D-Xylose   L-Xylose

D-Glucose   L-Glucose   D-Galactose   L-Galactose   D-Fructose   L-Fructose

The L-enantiomers are mirror images of the naturally occurring D-carbohydrates as shown above. Each chiral center in L-enantiomer has opposite configuration relative to the D-enantiomer.

Problem 16.5. The optical rotation of natural glucose in aqueous solution under standard conditions (the specific rotation) is +52.7. What is the optical rotation of unnatural L-glucose?

Solution:
Since L-glucose is the enantiomer of D-glucose, its optical rotation will have the same magnitude but opposite sign: −52.7 (see Section 4.4.1).

Problem 16.6. Draw the furanose form of the two anomers of D-xylose.

Solution:

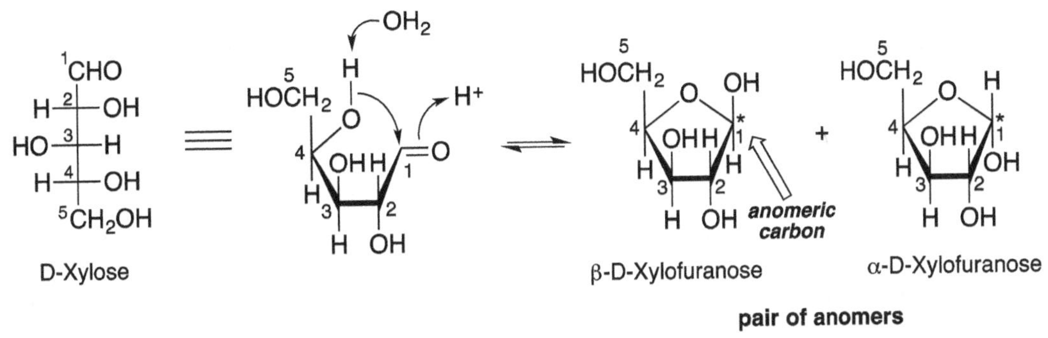

D-Xylose   β-D-Xylofuranose   α-D-Xylofuranose

pair of anomers

The formation of cyclic anomers of D-xylose is explained similar to D-ribose (see Figure 16.6 in the textbook). The only difference between D-xylose and D-ribose (in cyclic or noncyclic forms) is the configuration at carbon number 3.

Problem 16.7. Draw β-D-galactopyranose in Haworth projection and as a chair conformation.

Solution:

Fischer Projection

Haworth Projection

D-Galactose

β-D-Galactopyranose   α-D-Galactopyranose

Chair conformation of β-D-galactopyranose:

The formation of cyclic anomers of D-galactose is explained similar to D-glucose (see Figure 16.7 in the textbook). The only difference between D-galactose and D-glucose (in cyclic or noncyclic forms) is the configuration at carbon number 4. Therefore, in the chair conformation of β-D-galactopyranose the hydroxyl group at carbon number 4 is in the axial position, while β-D-glucopyranose has all non-hydrogen substituents in the equatorial position.

Problem 16.8. Draw the furanose form of the two anomers of D-fructose.

Solution:

Fischer Projection

Haworth Projection

D-Fructose

β-D-Fructofuranose   α-D-Fructofuranose

A simplified mechanism for the formation of the two anomers of D-fructose is shown above. The five-membered cyclic hemiacetal is formed via a reversible, acid-catalyzed, nucleophilic addition of the hydroxyl group at carbon number 4 to the carbonyl carbon (C-2) of D-fructose. The β-anomer (β-D-fructofuranose) has the OH at C-2 in *cis* configuration relative to the CH$_2$OH group, while the α-anomer (α-D-fructofuranose) has the OH at C-2 and the CH$_2$OH group in *trans* configuration.

Problem 16.9. Is the molecule of xylitol (Figure 16.9) chiral?

Solution:

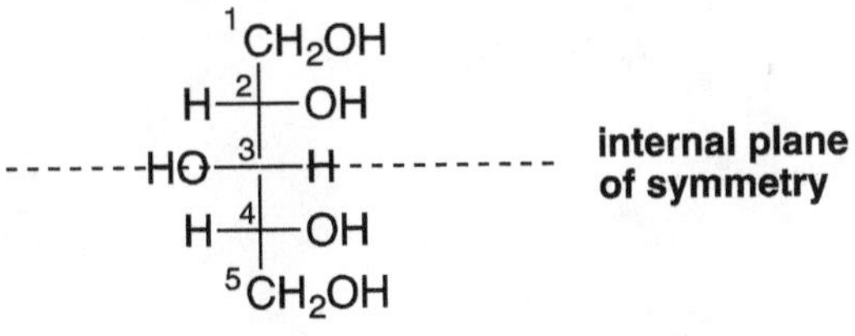

Xylitol

Xylitol has three chiral centers at C-2, C-3, and C-4 and an internal plane of symmetry as shown above. Because of the internal symmetry, mirror images of xylitol are superposable, identical molecules. Therefore, xylitol is an achiral meso compound (see Section 4.3.2).

Problem 16.10. What are the products of oxidation (with Tollens' reagent) and reduction (with NaBH$_4$) of D-ribose? Are these compounds chiral?

Solution:

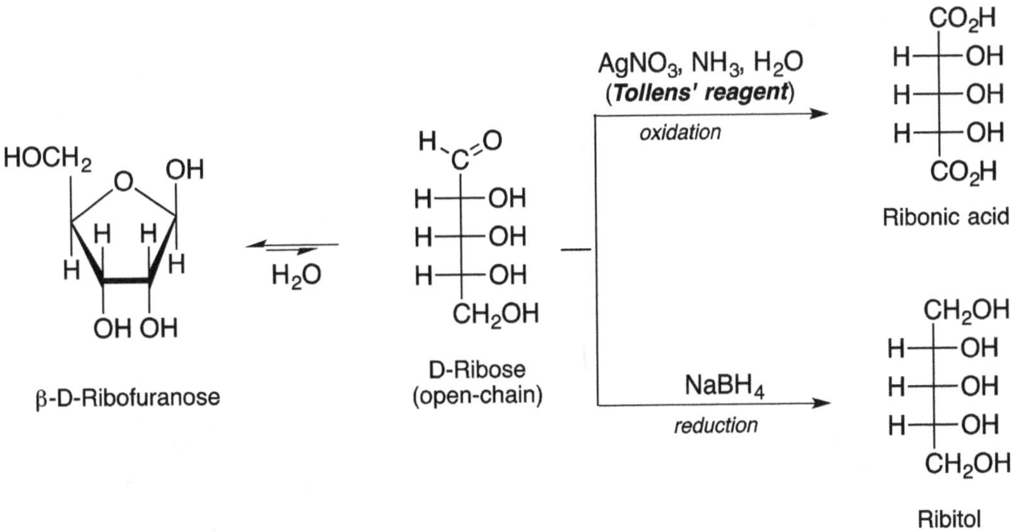

Oxidation of D-ribose forms ribonic acid and reduction produces ribitol as shown above. Both are achiral meso compounds because of the internal symmetry (see Problem 16.9).

Problem 16.11. What is a likely product of the esterification reaction of D-ribose with excess acetic anhydride?

Solution:

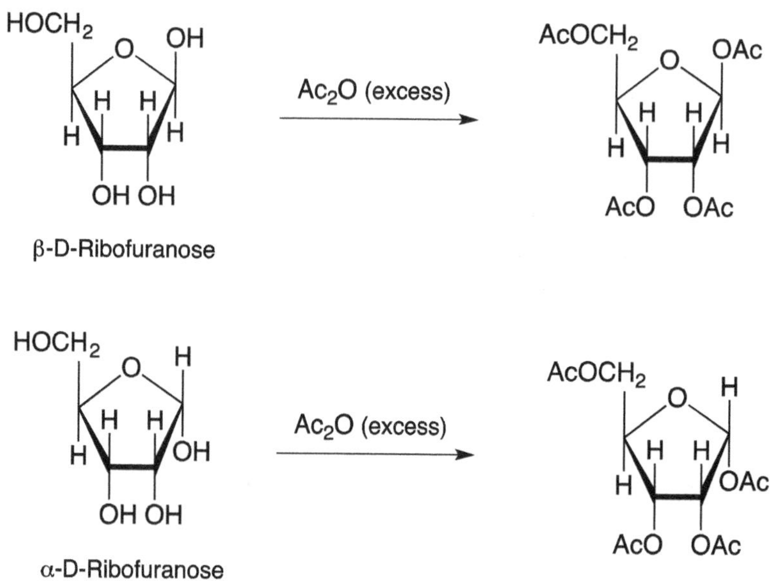

β-D-Ribofuranose

Ac₂O (excess)

α-D-Ribofuranose

Ac₂O (excess)

$Ac_2O =$

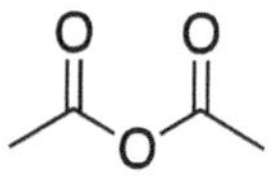

acetic anhydride

Reactions of alcohols with acid anhydrides produce esters (see Section 14.4.3 of the textbook). Each of the five hydroxyl groups in D-ribose (which exist as a mixture of two cyclic anomers) will be converted to the acetate ester. The esterification reactions of β-D-ribofuranose and α-D-ribofuranose producing the corresponding tetraacetate esters are shown above.

Problem 16.12. What is the product of the reaction of D-ribose with hydroxylamine (H_2NOH, see Figure 11.7)?

Solution:

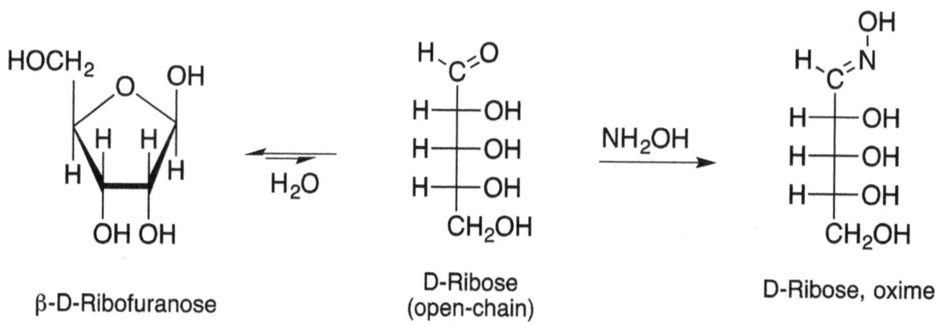

β-D-Ribofuranose

D-Ribose (open-chain)

D-Ribose, oxime

Aldehydes and ketones react with hydroxylamine in the presence of acid-producing oximes (see Section 11.6 of the textbook). The analogous reaction of D-ribose in the open-chain form yields the corresponding oxime as shown above.

Problem 16.13. Draw the structure of disaccharide maltose formed from two units of α-D-glucopyranose connected by α-1,4'-glycosidic bond. Is maltose a reducing sugar or a nonreducing sugar?

Solution:

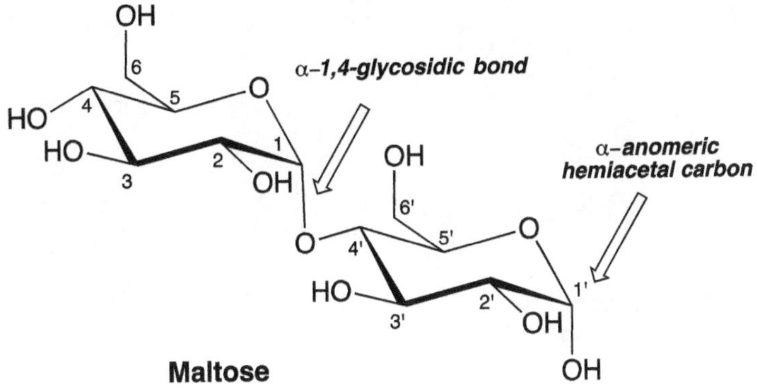

α-1,4-glycosidic bond
α-anomeric hemiacetal carbon
Maltose

The structure of maltose is shown above. Maltose has a hemiacetal group (at C-1') and therefore it is a reducing sugar.

Problem 16.14. There are three amino acids which are often referred to as basic amino acids. One of these basic amino acids is histidine, because it contains the basic imidazole moiety. Which two other amino acids are also considered to be basic? Furthermore, there are also two amino acids that are labeled as acidic amino acids because they contain an additional carboxylic acid functional group. Which ones are these?

Solution:

Basic amino acids:

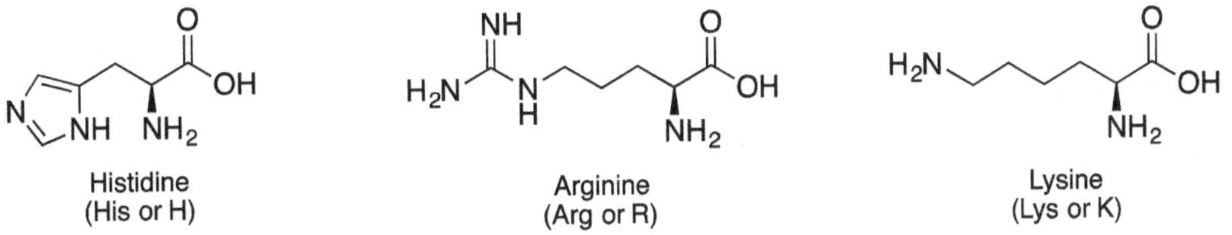

Histidine
(His or H)
Arginine
(Arg or R)
Lysine
(Lys or K)

Acidic amino acids:

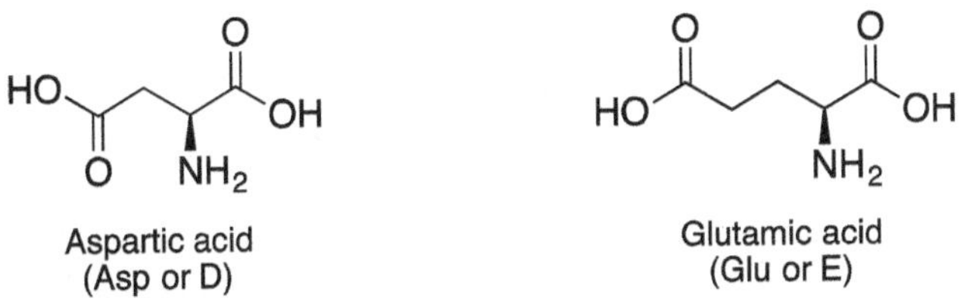

Aspartic acid
(Asp or D)
Glutamic acid
(Glu or E)

Basic amino acids have a basic amine substituent in the side chain. In histidine it is the basic imidazole moiety; arginine and lysine have a basic amino group ($-NH_2$) in their side chains. Acidic amino acids (aspartic acid and glutamic acid) have a carboxylic group ($-CO_2H$) in the side chain.

Problem 16.15. We commonly use the D/L-convention to distinguish between enantiomers of α-amino acids. The configuration of the α-carbon of all naturally occurring amino acids is L, and for most of the α-amino acids in Figure 16.14 the configuration of the α-carbon is S in the R/S convention. However, what is the configuration α-carbon in L-cysteine in the R/S convention?

Solution:

CO_2H
H_2N——H
CH_2SH

L-Cysteine
(Fischer projection)

Three-dimensional
structure of L-cysteine

*Priority of substituents
at the chiral center:*

$-NH_2 > -CH_2SH > CO_2H$

The Fischer projection of L-cysteine is in agreement with all other natural L-α-amino acids with the amino group positioned on the left side of the drawing (Figure 16.13 of the textbook). However, the α-carbon in L-cysteine has R configuration according to R/S convention (see Section 4.3 of the textbook), while all other L-amino acids have S configuration. This is explained by a different order of priority of substituents at the chiral carbon of L-cysteine compared to all other L-amino acids. Indeed, the side chain -CH_2SH has higher priority than the $-CO_2H$ group, while in all other L-amino acids the side chain has lower priority than the $-CO_2H$ group.

Problem 16.16. The following monoamines serve important functions as neurotransmitters within the central nervous system. Which amino acids are these compounds derived from?

dopamine

histamine

serotonin

Solution:

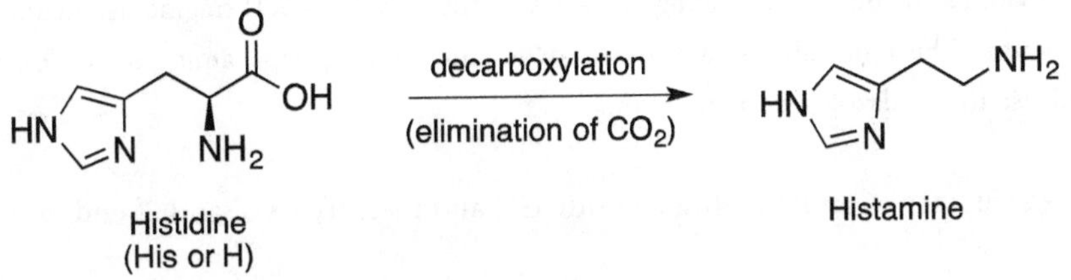

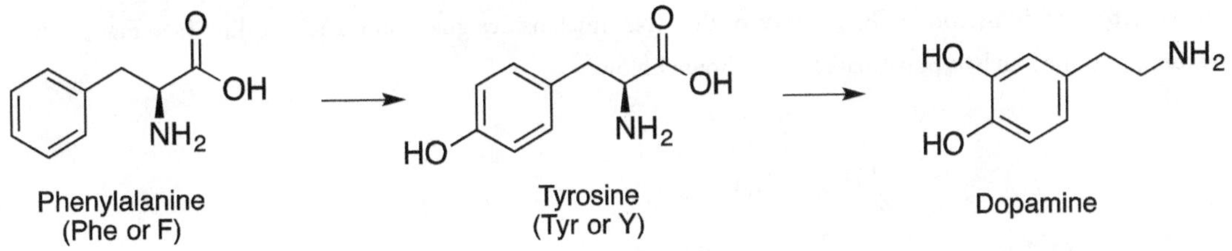

Histidine
(His or H)

decarboxylation
(elimination of CO_2)

Histamine

Phenylalanine
(Phe or F)

Tyrosine
(Tyr or Y)

Dopamine

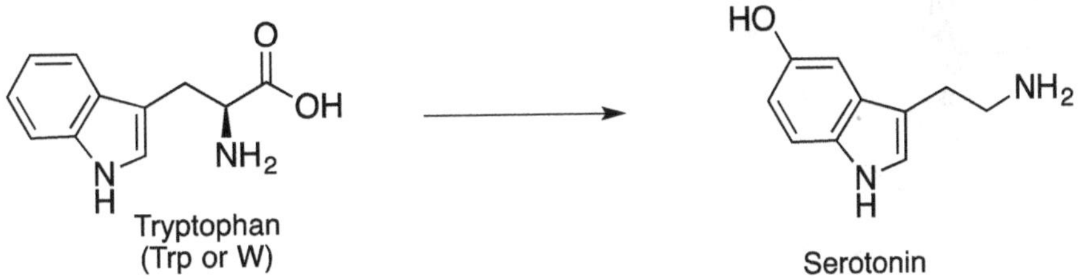

Tryptophan
(Trp or W)

Serotonin

Structures above illustrate the relationship between neurotransmitters and the amino acids. Histamine is derived from the decarboxylation of the amino acid histidine. Dopamine is related to L-tyrosine and L-phenylalanine, and serotonin is derived from tryptophan via biochemical oxidation and decarboxylation.

Problem 16.17. Draw the structure of tripeptide His-Tyr-Gln. Identify the N-terminal and C-terminal amino acids, the protein backbone, and the peptide bonds in your drawing. Which functional groups are present in this molecule?

Solution:

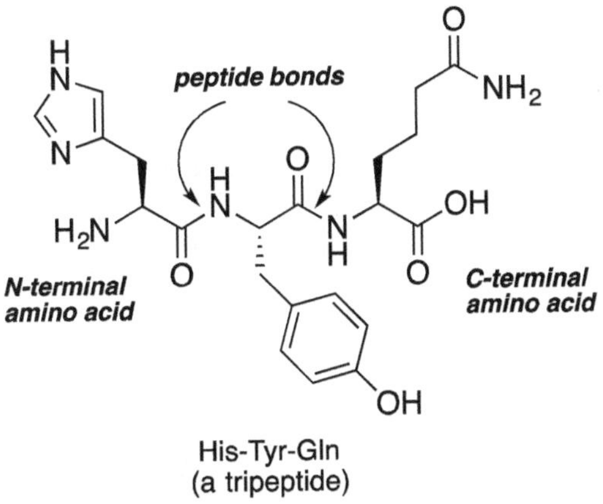

peptide bonds

*N-terminal
amino acid*

*C-terminal
amino acid*

His-Tyr-Gln
(a tripeptide)

Tripeptide His-Tyr-Gln is formed from histidine (N-terminal amino acid), tyrosine, and glutamine (C-terminal amino acid) as shown above. The chain consisting of a repeating sequence of the (–N-CH-CO) fragments, including the α-carbon, is the protein backbone. This molecule contains the following functional groups: amine, amide, carboxylic acid, phenolic hydroxyl, and also the imidazole and benzene rings.

Problem 16.18. Draw the structure of an RNA dinucleotide GC and identify its 5' and 3' ends.

Solution:

The structure of dinucleotide GC consists of the RNA nucleosides guanosine and cytidine (see Figure 16.17 of the textbook) connected by a phosphate link as shown below:

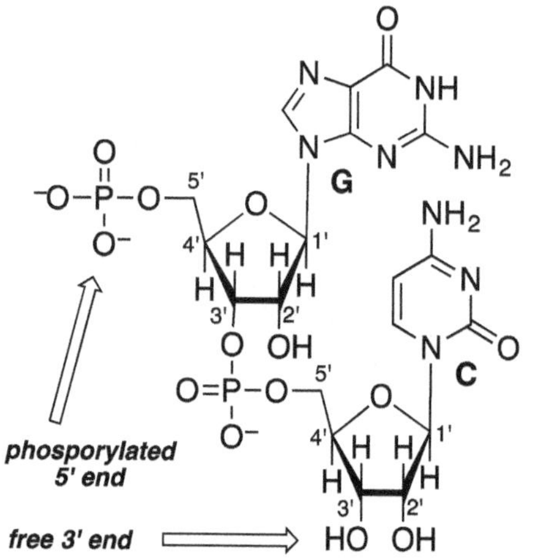

dinucleotide GC

16.2. Additional Problems for Chapter 16 (for answers see Ch 17)

Problem 16.19. Classify the two isomeric unsaturated fatty acids below as *cis* or *trans*. Which fatty acid will have a lower melting point? Explain briefly.

Problem 16.20. The following questions are based on the structure of the hexose sugar molecule given below:

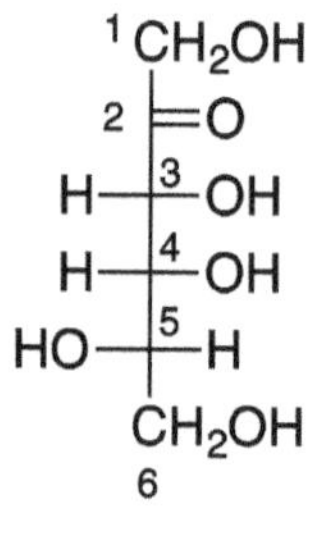

a) Identify the number of stereocenters in the molecule.

b) Determine the maximum number of stereoisomers possible for the above hexose sugar.

c) Identify the configuration (D or L) of the given structure.

Problem 16.21. Classify the following carbohydrates as reducing or nonreducing sugar.

a)

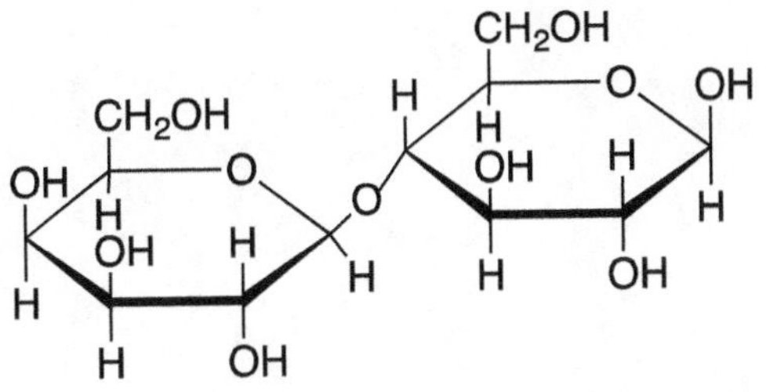

b)

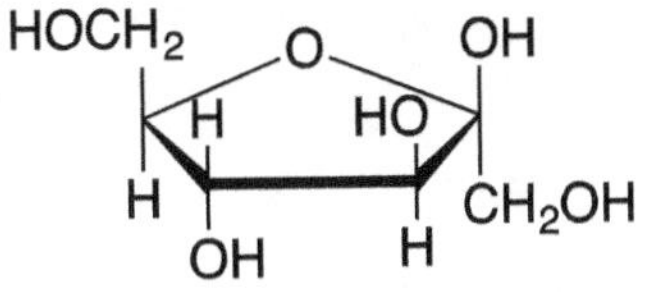

Problem 16.22. Convert the following three-dimensional line–angle structures of monosaccharides to the Fischer projections. Assign D or L designator to each molecule.

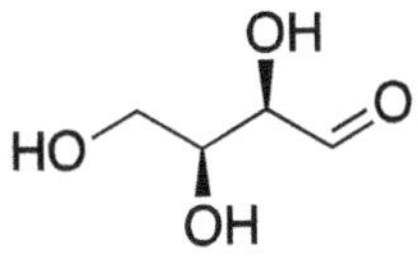

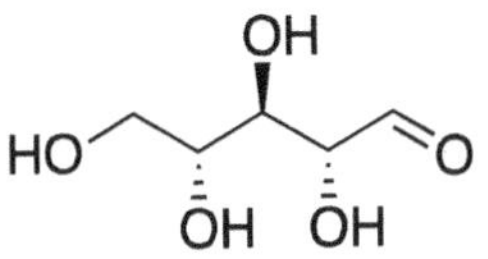

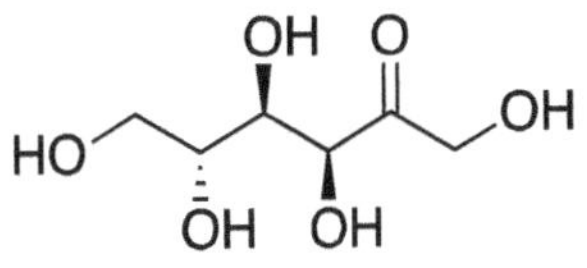

Problem 16.23. Identify the amino acid sequence in the following tripeptide and name it. Identify the N-terminal and C-terminal amino acids in this tripeptide.

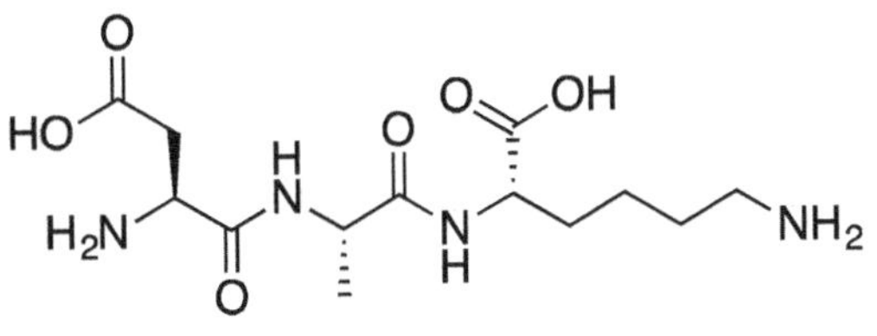

Problem 16.24. Show the formation of a peptide bond between two amino acid residues. Explain why peptide bonds in proteins are not hydrolyzed easily under physiological conditions.

CHAPTER 17

Solutions to Additional Problems

17.1. Chapter 1 Additional Problems

Problem 1.24. Determine if S–F bond is ionic, polar covalent, or nonpolar covalent. Indicate the direction of polarity in the S–F bond using the symbols δ+ and δ– on appropriate atoms.

Solution:
The electronegativity (EN) of F is 4.0 and that of S is 2.5. The difference in electronegativity ($\Delta EN = 4.0 - 2.5 = 1.5$) indicates that S–F bond is polar covalent with δ– on F due to greater EN value of F and δ+ on S.

δ+ δ–
S–F

Problem 1.25. Draw Lewis structures for the following molecules.

    a) HCN   b) a ketone with molecular formula C_3H_6O

Solution:

a)   H−C≡N:

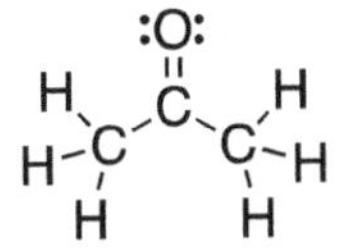

Problem 1.26. Draw the resonance contributing structure indicated by the curved arrows:

Solution:

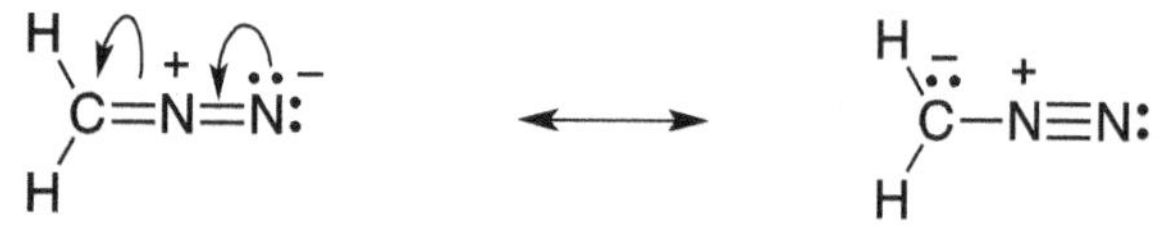

Problem 1.27. Determine the direction of molecular dipole moment in the following molecule.

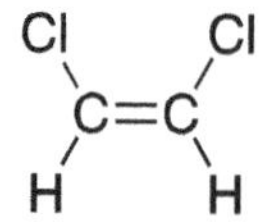

Solution:

direction of molecular
dipole moment

Problem 1.28. Identify and name all the functional groups in the following molecule.

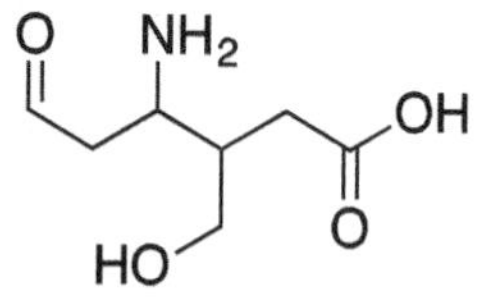

Solution:

amino group
or amine

aldehyde

carboxyl group
or carboxylic acid

hydroxyl group
or alcohol

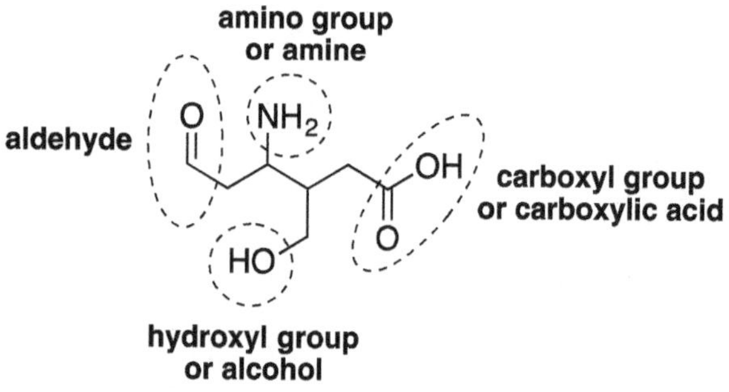

Problem 1.29. Determine the molecular formula for the structure in problem 1.28.

Solution:

The molecular formula of the structure in Problem 1.28 is $C_7H_{13}NO_4$.

17.2. Chapter 2 Additional Problems

Problem 2.9. For each pair, identify the first species as an acid or base and the second species as its conjugate acid or conjugate base.

  a) CH_3S^- and CH_3SH
  b) $H_2PO_4^-$ and HPO_4^{2-}

Solution:

  a) CH_3S^- is a base because it accepts a proton and CH_3SH is its conjugate acid.
  b) $H_2PO_4^-$ is an acid because it donates a proton and HPO_4^{2-} is its conjugate base.

Problem 2.10. For the following reaction, label each reactant and each product as acid, base, conjugate acid, or conjugate base below each structure.

Solution:

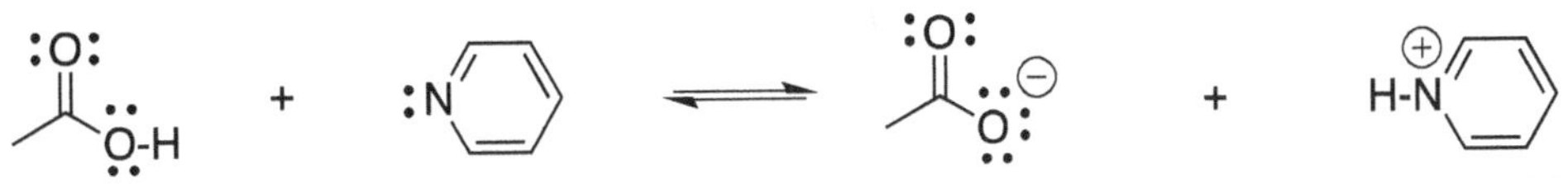

| **ACID** | **BASE** | **CONJUGATE BASE** | **CONJUGATE ACID** |
| (proton donor) | (proton acceptor) | | |

Problem 2.11. Provide the reaction of CH_3CH_2OH as a Bronsted–Lowry base with H–Cl using the curved arrow formalism.

Solution:

| **BASE** | **ACID** | **CONJUGATE ACID** | **CONJUGATE BASE** |
| (proton acceptor) | (proton donor) | | |

Problem 2.12. Select the strongest acid in each set:

a) CH_3CH_3 CH_3NH_2 CH_3OH

b) CH_3CH_3 $CH_2=CH_2$ $HC\equiv CH$

c) CH_3CH_2OH CF_3CH_2OH FCH_2CH_2OH

Solution:

a) CH_3OH is the strongest acid because its conjugate base (CH_3O^-) is more stable with the negative charge on the more electronegative O atom.

b) $HC\equiv CH$ is the strongest acid because its conjugate base $(HC\equiv C^-)$ is more stable with greater % s character to the sp hybrid orbital of the charged C atom.

c) CF_3CH_2OH is the strongest acid because its conjugate base $(CF_3CH_2O^-)$ is stabilized by the electron-withdrawing inductive effect due to the presence of three electronegative F atoms.

Problem 2.13. Provide structures of the two possible cationic intermediates in the following reactions:

a)

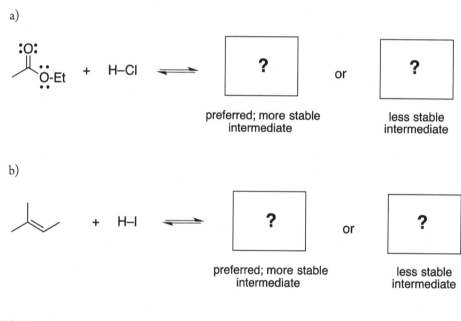

b)

Solution:

a)

b)

preferred; more stable
intermediate
(tertiary carbocation)

or

less stable
intermediate

Problem 2.14. Given pK_a (acetylene) = 25 and pK_a (H$_2$) = 35, predict whether the direction/ position of equilibrium in the following reaction will lie to the right (favors the forward reaction) or to the left (favors the backward reaction).

HC≡CH + Na$^+$H$^-$ ⇌ HC≡C$^-$Na$^+$ + H$_2$

acetylene

Solution:

The pK_a values of acetylene and H$_2$ indicate that acetylene is a stronger acid compared to H$_2$ and its conjugate base (sodium acetylide) is a weaker base compared to the conjugate base of H$_2$ (NaH). Equilibrium favors reaction of the stronger acid and stronger base to yield the weaker acid and weaker base.

HC≡CH + Na$^+$H$^-$ ⇌ HC≡C$^-$Na$^+$ + H$_2$

$pK_a = 25$ ... $pK_a = 35$

stronger acid   **stronger base**   **weaker base**   **weaker acid**

Based on the above facts, position of equilibrium in this reaction will lie to the right, favoring the forward reaction.

17.3. Chapter 3 Additional Problems

Problem 3.11. Provide the IUPAC name for each structure below.

a)

b)

SOLUTIONS TO ADDITIONAL PROBLEMS   217

Solution:

a) 5-ethyl-3,3,6-trimethyloctane

b) *trans*-1,3-dimethylcyclopentane

Problem 3.12. a) Draw the alternative chair conformation of bromocyclohexane (after the ring-flip).

A   B

b) Label Br as axial (a) or equatorial (e) in structures A and B. Which conformation is lower in energy?

Solution:

a)

A   B

b) Br is axial in structure A and equatorial in structure B after the ring-flip. Structure B with equatorial Br is more stable because of the lower 1,3-diaxial interactions.

Problem 3.13. Draw Newman projections for all staggered and eclipsed conformations of 1-chloropropane [Cl-CH_2-CH_2-CH_3] formed by rotation of groups about C1-C2 from 0° to 360° as indicated. Label each conformation A-E as anti, gauche, or eclipsed.

Solution:

A   B   C   D   E

staggered   Me-Cl   staggered   eclipsed   staggered
gauche   eclipsed   gauche   anti

Problem 3.14. Draw (a) planar conformation and (b) nonplanar (chair) conformation of *trans*-1,4-dimethylcyclohexane.

Solution:

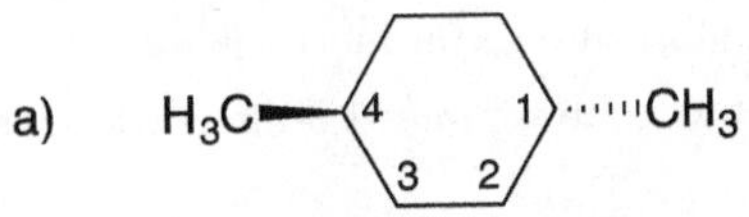

a)   H₃C━⟨4 1⟩·····CH₃
              3 2

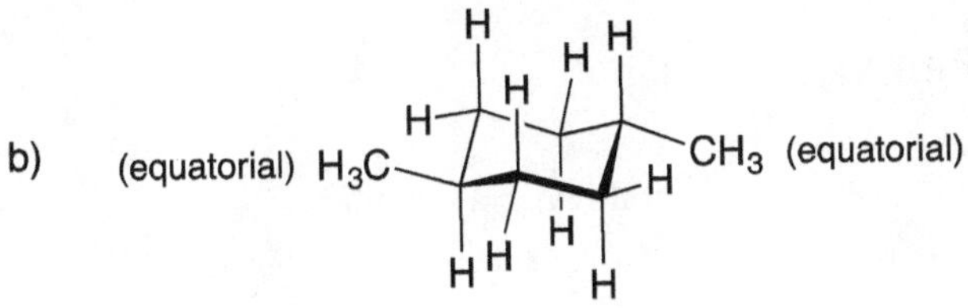

b)   (equatorial) H₃C━[chair structure]━CH₃ (equatorial)

This is the most stable chair conformation of *trans*-1,4-dimethylcyclohexane.

Problem 3.15. Draw the most stable chair conformation corresponding to the following planar structure:

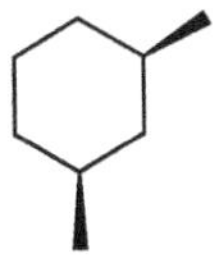

[cyclohexane structure with two methyl groups]

Solution:

(equatorial) H₃C━[chair structure]━CH₃ (equatorial)

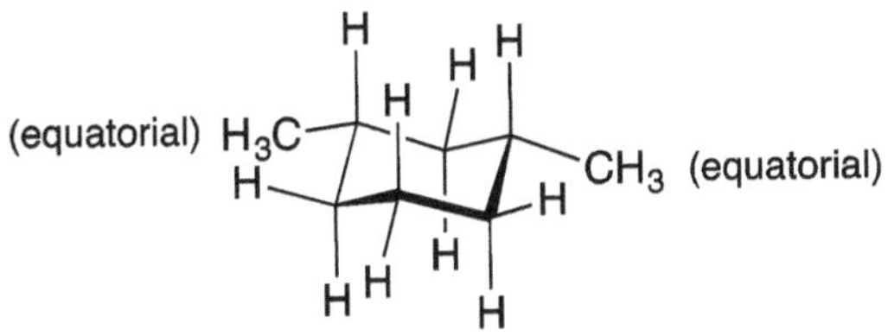

The two bulky methyl groups must be equatorial to avoid 1,3-diaxial interactions.

Problem 3.16. Identify the substituents in the chair conformations of *trans*-1,3-dimethylcyclohexane as axial or equatorial.

Solution:

The chair conformation of *trans*-1,3-dimethylcyclohexane is axial-equatorial as shown below:

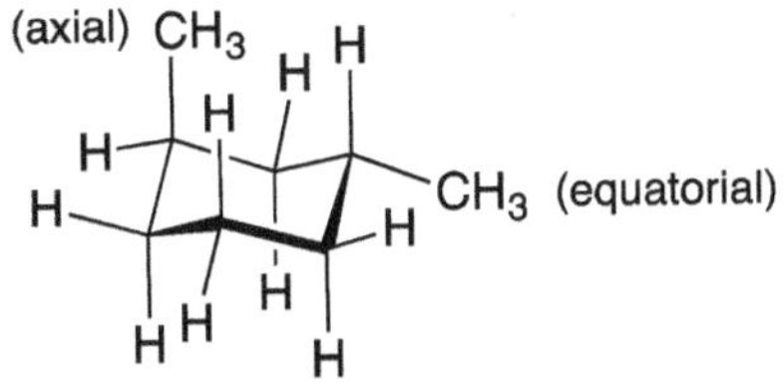

(axial) CH₃━[chair structure]━CH₃ (equatorial)

Problem 3.17. Which chair conformation of *cis* or *trans* 1,3-dimethylcyclohexanes is more stable? Explain briefly.

Solution:

The chair conformation of *cis*-1,3-dimethylcyclohexane in diequatorial conformation is the most stable because it does not have any 1,3-diaxial interactions as the methyl groups are equatorial. In contrast, *trans*-1,3-dimethylcyclohexane has one methyl group in axial position which makes it less stable.

17.4. Chapter 4 Additional Problems

Problem 4.9. How many stereoisomers are possible for the following molecule?

Solution:

This molecule has only one chiral center as indicated with an asterisk:

Maximum number of stereoisomers possible for this molecule is two.

Problem 4.10. Which of the following compounds is/are chiral?

Solution:

The second structure (from left) in the above scheme is the only chiral compound that has one chiral center and does not have a plane of symmetry.

Problem 4.11. Fill in appropriate groups in the templates so that each structure represents the specified stereoisomer:

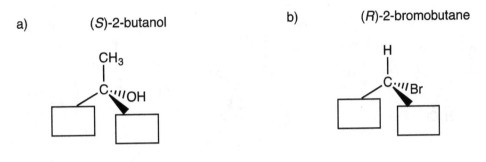

a) (*S*)-2-butanol

b) (*R*)-2-bromobutane

Solution:

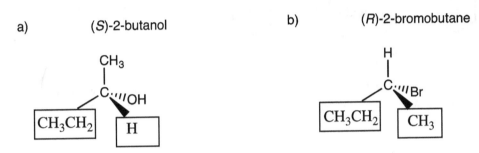

a) (*S*)-2-butanol

b) (*R*)-2-bromobutane

Problem 4.12. Which of the following structures represent the same stereoisomer?

CH₃
C······ꞮꞮꞮꞮH
(H₃C)₂HC   OH

CH(CH₃)₂
C······ꞮꞮꞮꞮH
H₃C   OH

OH
C······ꞮꞮꞮꞮH
(H₃C)₂HC   CH₃

Solution:

Structures with the same absolute configuration about the chiral center represent the same stereoisomer. Alternatively, this problem can be solved by looking at the molecular model of the actual molecule or rotating substituents in the drawing as described in Section 4.2 of the textbook.

CH₃
C······ꞮꞮꞮꞮH
(H₃C)₂HC   OH
R

CH(CH₃)₂
C······ꞮꞮꞮꞮH
H₃C   OH
S

OH
C······ꞮꞮꞮꞮH
(H₃C)₂HC   CH₃
S

same stereoisomer

Problem 4.13. Identify the relationship between the following pairs of structures as enantiomers, diastereomers, constitutional isomers, or identical molecules.

a)

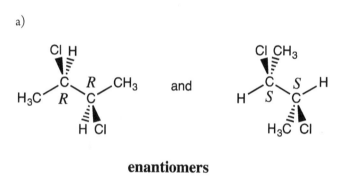

and

b)

and

Solution:

Enantiomers are stereoisomers that differ in configuration at each chiral center whereas diastereomers are stereoisomers that differ in configuration at one chiral center but have the same configuration at the other chiral center.

a)

and

enantiomers

b)

and

diastereomers

Problem 4.14. Chiral molecules interact with plane polarized light and rotate the plane of polarization of that light by a certain angle. The angle of rotation (α) of polarized light can be measured with a polarimeter. However, specific rotation ([α]) is used as a basis for comparing the optical activity of stereoisomers. **Specific rotation** is defined as the observed rotation of the plane of polarized light for a sample in a tube 1 dm in length and the concentration of the solution of 1 g/100 mL.

$$\text{Specific Rotation}[\alpha] = \frac{\text{Observed Rotation in degrees, } \alpha}{[\text{Sample Length in dm}] \bullet [\text{Concentration of solution in g/ml}]}$$

A solution containing 0.2 g/mL of a pure R enantiomer in a 1 dm polarimeter rotates plane polarized light by +3°. What is the specific rotation of the R isomer?

What will be the specific rotation of its S isomer?

Solution:

$$\text{Specific Rotation}[\alpha] = \frac{+3°}{[1\,\text{dm}] \bullet [0.2 \text{ g/ml}]} = +15°$$

The specific rotation of its S isomer will be identical in magnitude as that of the R isomer, but with the opposite sign. Therefore, the specific rotation $[\alpha]$ of the S enantiomer = −15°.

17.5. Chapter 5 Additional Problems

Problem 5.15. Select the stronger nucleophile from each pair:

a) NH_3 or $^-NH_2$ b) CH_3OCH_3 or CH_3SCH_3
c) F^- or I^- in CH_3OH d) F^- or I^- in DMF

Solution:
   a) $^-NH_2$ is the stronger nucleophile. In a series of reagents with the same nucleophilic atom, anionic reagents are stronger nucleophiles than neutral reagents.
   b) CH_3SCH_3 is the stronger nucleophile. The nonbonding electrons on S are more readily available to react with an electrophile due to its relatively large size.
   c) I^- is the stronger nucleophile. Due to its large size, I^- is the least solvated by a polar protic solvent such as CH_3OH and is more available to participate as a nucleophile.
   d) F^- is the stronger nucleophile. Polar aprotic solvents such as DMF are not very effective in solvating the anionic nucleophiles. Nucleophilicity parallels basicity in a polar aprotic solvent.

Problem 5.16. From each pair, select the halide that undergoes S_N1 solvolysis in CH_3OH more rapidly.

a)   or

b)   Br   or   Br

c)   Cl   or   Cl

d)   I   or

Solution:

a)

fast S$_N$1 reaction

**2° allylic halide forms
the resonance-stabilized
allylic carbocation**

**2° vinylic halide forms
the unstable
vinylic carbocation**

b)

**1° alkyl halide
forms the less stable
1° alkyl carbocation**

fast S$_N$1 reaction

**1° allylic halide forms
the resonance-stabilized
allylic carbocation**

c)

**1° alkyl halide
forms the less stable
1° alkyl carbocation**

fast S$_N$1 reaction

**3° alkyl halide
forms the more stable
3° alkyl carbocation**

d)

fast S$_N$1 reaction

**3° alkyl halide
forms the more stable
3° alkyl carbocation**

**the required planar geometry of carbocation is
impossible for a bridgehead position and
therefore this carbocation is very unstable**

Problem 5.17. From each pair, select the halide that undergoes S$_N$2 reaction with NaN$_3$ in acetone more rapidly.

a) or ⎯⎯CH₂Cl (2,2-dimethylpropyl chloride)

b) (1-bromocyclohexene) or (bromocyclohexane)

c) Cl or (tert-butyl chloride)⎯Cl

d) ⎯⎯Cl or ⎯⎯I

Solution:

a)

fast S$_N$2 reaction

[structure in dashed box]

1° alkyl halide

[branched structure]

this substrate is more sterically hindered because of branching of the alkyl chain

b)

[1-bromocyclohexene structure]

vinyl halide cannot react via S$_N$2 mechanism

fast S$_N$2 reaction

[bromocyclohexane structure in dashed box]

2° alkyl halide

c)

fast S$_N$2 reaction

[structure in dashed box]

1° alkyl halide

[tert-butyl chloride structure]

3° alkyl halide

d)

1° alkyl chloride

fast S_N2 reaction

**1° alkyl iodide
has a better leaving
group because I⁻ is
more stable than Cl⁻**

Problem 5.18. Provide the structure of major organic product formed in these β-elimination reactions.

a) [structure with Br] → NaOCH₃ / CH₃OH

b) [structure with Br] → KOt-Bu / t-BuOH

c) [cyclohexane with CH₃ and Cl] → NaOEt / EtOH

Solution:

a) [structure with Br] → NaOCH₃ / CH₃OH → [alkene product] **(Zaitsev elimination)**

b) [structure with Br] → KOt-Bu / t-BuOH → [alkene product] **(non-Zaitsev elimination due to the presence of a sterically hindered base; see solution to Problem 5.11)**

c) [cyclohexane with CH₃ and Cl] → NaOEt / EtOH → [methylcyclohexene] **(Zaitsev elimination)**

17.6. Chapter 6 Additional Problems

Problem 6.16. Calculate the index of hydrogen deficiency (IHD) of compounds with the following molecular formula:

a) $C_6H_{12}N_2$ b) C_5H_9Br c) C_8H_8O

Solution:

Drawing arbitrary Lewis structures corresponding to the molecular formulas shown in the question can help solve this problem (each double bond has IHD = 1 and triple bond IHD = 2):

a) $C_6H_{12}N_2$

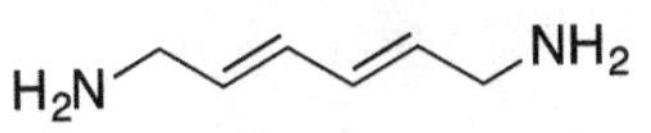

b) C_5H_9Br

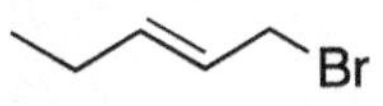

c) C_8H_8O

IHD = 2

IHD = 1

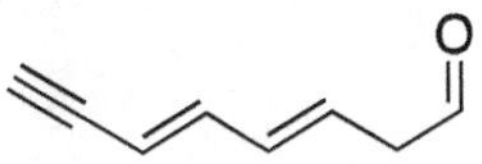

IHD = 5

Alternatively, this problem can be solved by comparing number of hydrogen atoms in these molecules with number of hydrogens in the molecular formulas of the corresponding saturated compounds containing nitrogen, oxygen, or halogen atoms:

a) IHD = $(14-10)/2 = 2$ b) IHD = $(12-10)/2 = 1$ c) IHD = $(18-8)/2 = 5$

Problem 6.17. What is the IHD value of aspartame (shown below)?

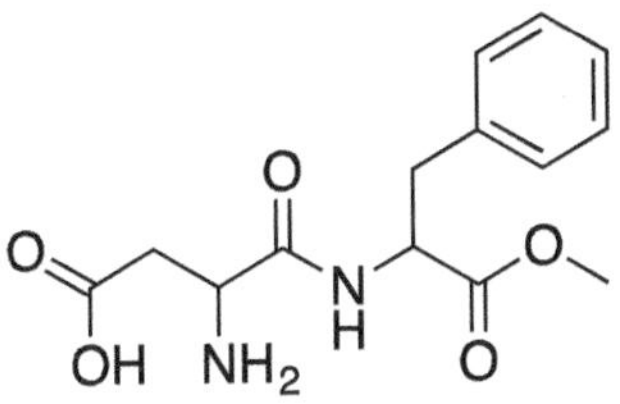

Solution:

The structure of aspartame has 6 double bonds and 1 ring. Therefore, its IHD = 6 + 1 = 7.

Problem 6.18. Provide the structures of all *cis/trans* isomers of 2,5-octadiene.

Solution:

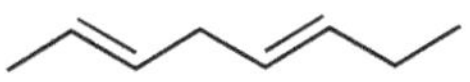

(2*E*,5*E*)-2,5-octadiene

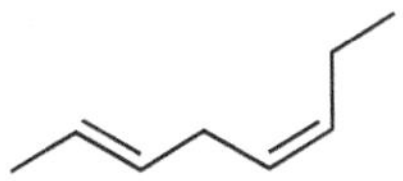

(2*E*,5*Z*)-2,5-octadiene

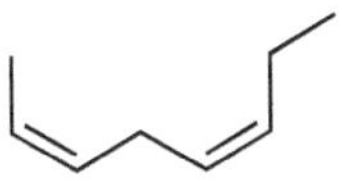

(2*Z*,5*Z*)-2,5-octadiene

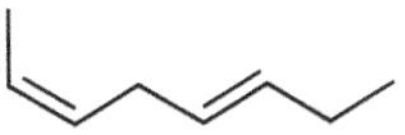

(2*Z*,5*E*)-2,5-octadiene

Problem 6.19. Select all structure(s) that will exhibit *cis–trans* isomerism.

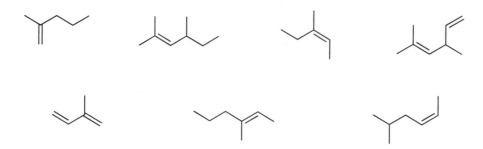

Solution:

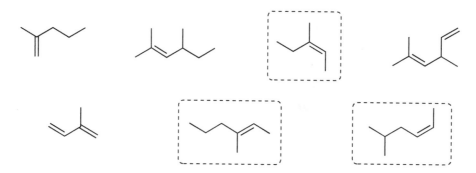

Problem 6.20. Select the most stable alkene from each set:

a)   Ph⁀═⁀Ph   Ph⁀═⁀Ph

b)   ═   ═   ═   ═

Solution:

    a) The *trans*-alkene is the most stable alkene; the *cis*-alkene has higher steric strain.

    b) The more highly substituted alkene is most stable. Thus, the tetrasubstituted alkene (the last structure) is the most stable alkene in that set.

Problem 6.21. Give reagent(s) on each arrow (one reagent per box) that can be used to convert the reactant to the indicated product in high yield.

Solution:

17.7. Chapter 7 Additional Problems

Problem 7.14. Select the most suitable sequence of reactions that can be used to convert 1-pentene to 1-pentyne.

a) treatment with HBr; followed by treatment with NaOH

b) treatment with Br_2; followed by treatment with $NaNH_2$

c) treatment with Br_2; followed by treatment with H_2SO_4

d) treatment with Br_2 and H_2O; followed by treatment with NaOH

e) treatment with Br_2; followed by treatment with NaOH

f) treatment with HBr; followed by treatment with $NaNH_2$

Solution:

Option b is the most suitable sequence of reactions to convert 1-pentene to 1-pentyne.

Problem 7.15. What is the correct assignment of the acid, base, conjugate acid, and conjugate base in the following equilibrium?

$$H_3C-C{\equiv}C-H \quad + \quad {}^-\ddot{N}H_2 \quad \rightleftharpoons \quad H_3C-C{\equiv}C{:}^- \quad + \quad {:}NH_3$$

$$\quad\quad 1 \quad\quad\quad\quad\quad 2 \quad\quad\quad\quad\quad\quad\quad 3 \quad\quad\quad\quad 4$$

Solution:

1: acid (functions as a proton donor)   **2**: base (functions as a proton acceptor)

3: conjugate base (of the acid)   **4**: conjugate acid (of the base)

Problem 7.16. What is the best choice of reagent(s) to perform the following transformation?

a) H_2/Pt

b) $H_2/Lindlar$ catalyst

c) $Na/NH_3(liq)$

d) BH_3; followed by $H_2O_2/NaOH$

e) Br_2; followed by 2 mol $NaNH_2$

Solution:

Hydrogenation of an alkyne in the presence of Lindlar catalyst is a stereoselective reaction yielding the corresponding *cis*-alkene. So option b must be used for the above transformation.

Problem 7.17. Fill one reagent in each box to complete the transformation in the following scheme.

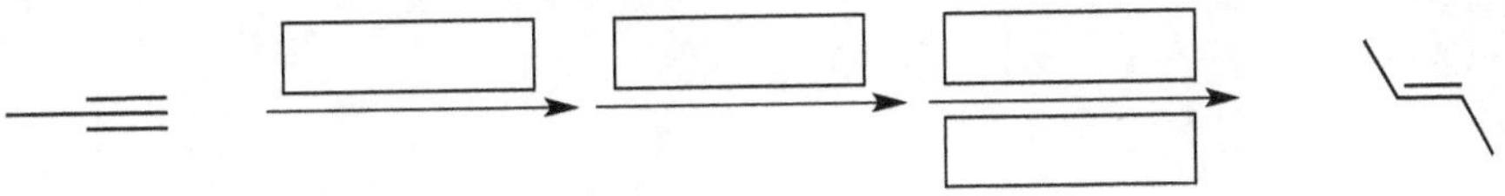

Solution:

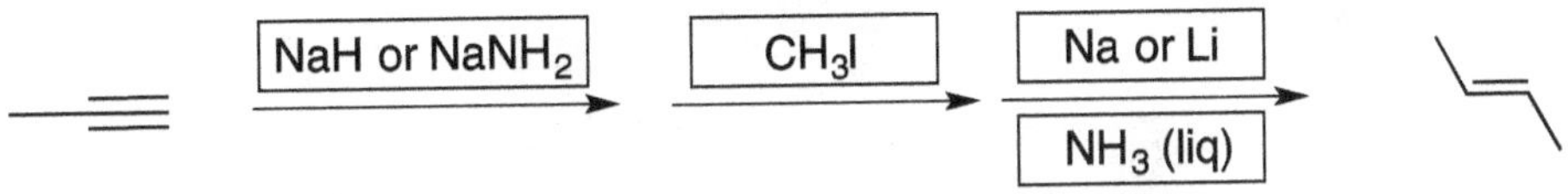

17.8. Chapter 8 Additional Problems

Problem 8.16. Complete the following reactions by filling in the reagent(s) or the product(s) for each reaction.

a)

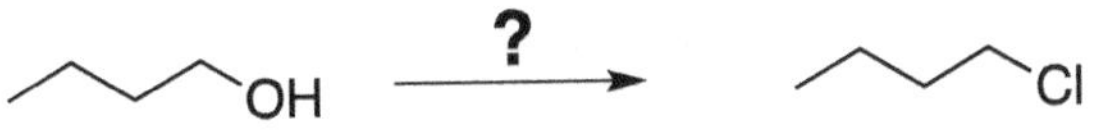

b)

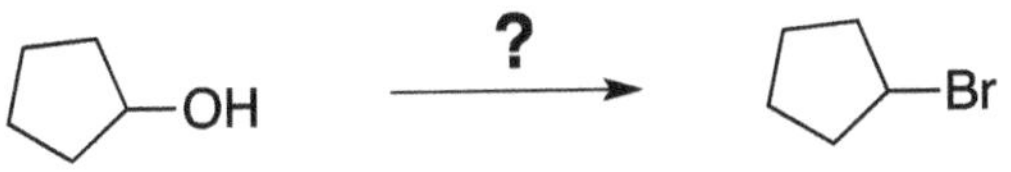

c)

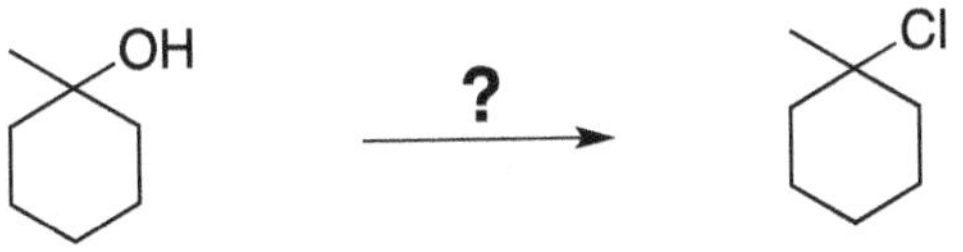

d)

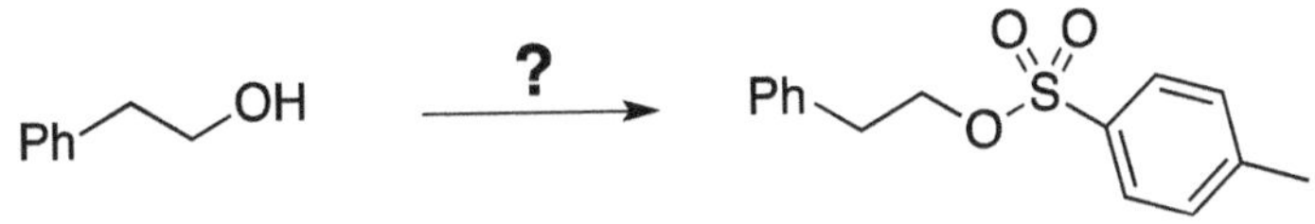

e)

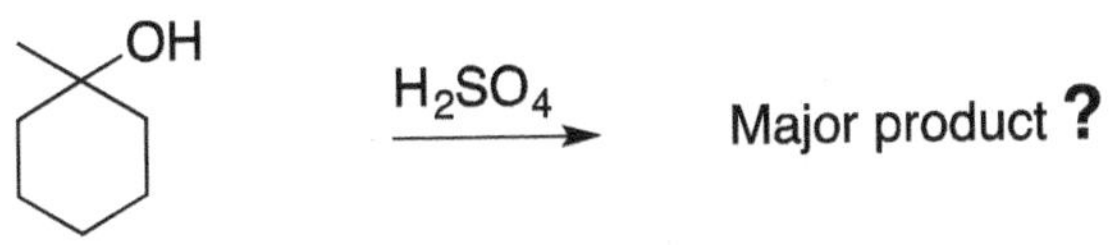

f)

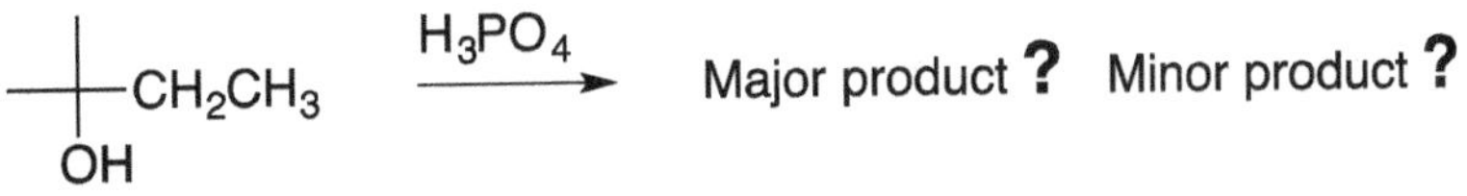

g) 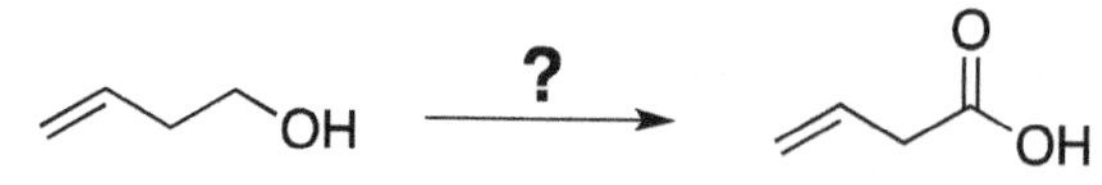 **?**

h) 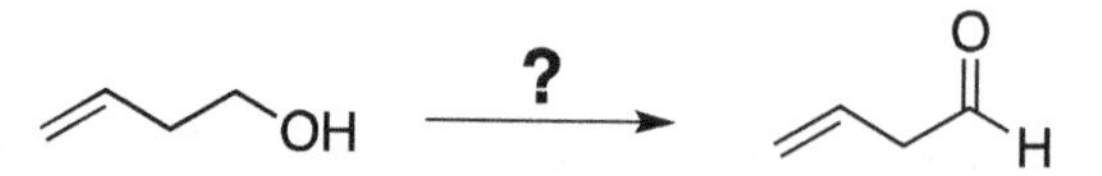 **?**

i)  **?**

Solution:

a) 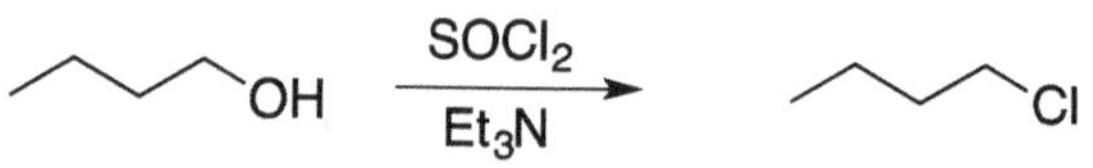 $\xrightarrow[\text{Et}_3\text{N}]{\text{SOCl}_2}$

b) 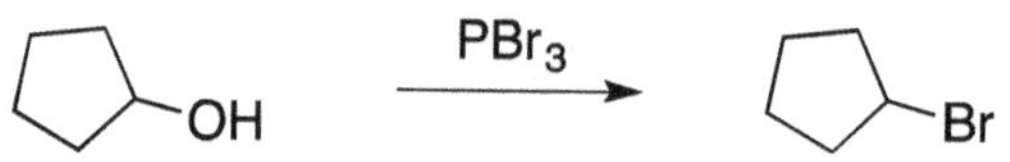 $\xrightarrow{\text{PBr}_3}$

c) 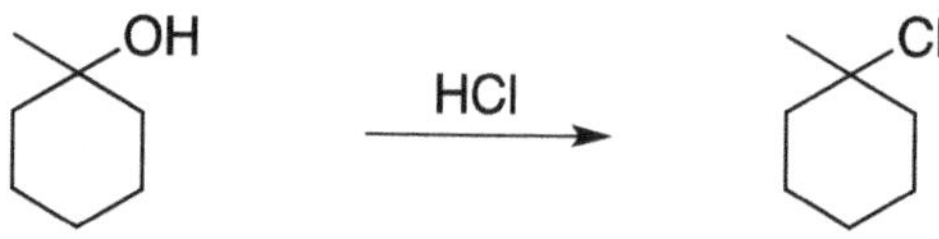 $\xrightarrow{\text{HCl}}$

d)  Ph $\xrightarrow[\text{pyridine}]{\text{TsCl}}$ Ph

e) 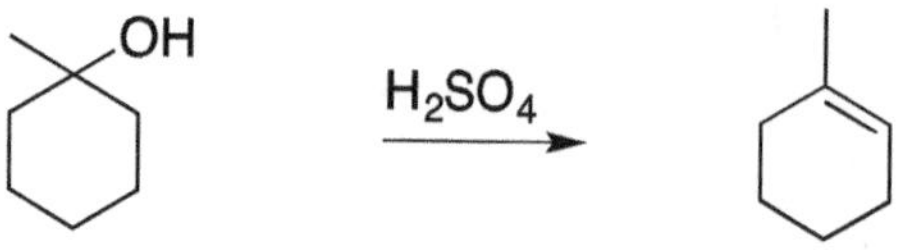 $\xrightarrow{\text{H}_2\text{SO}_4}$

f) 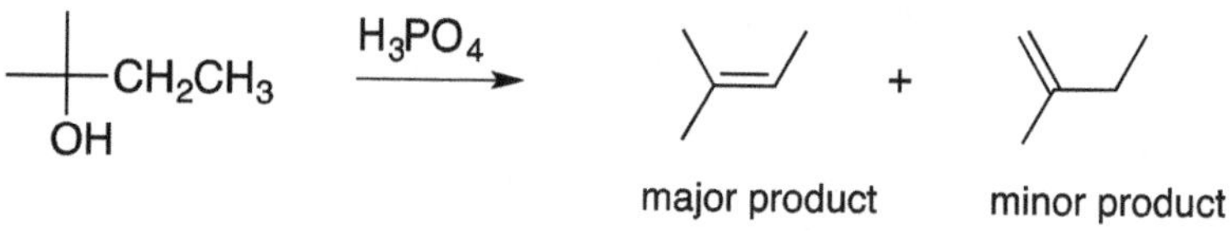 $\xrightarrow{\text{H}_3\text{PO}_4}$ +

major product   minor product

g) $\xrightarrow{\text{H}_2\text{CrO}_4}$

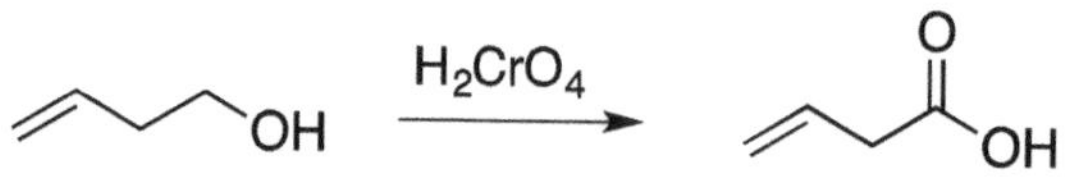

h) $\xrightarrow{\text{PCC}}$

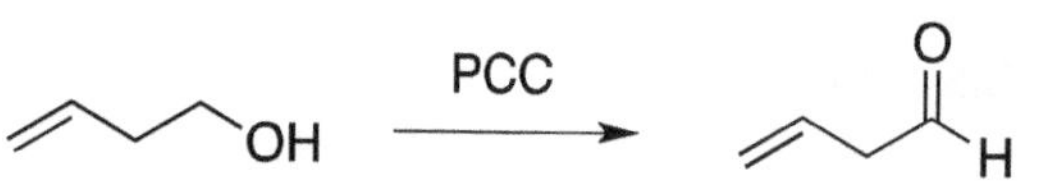

i) 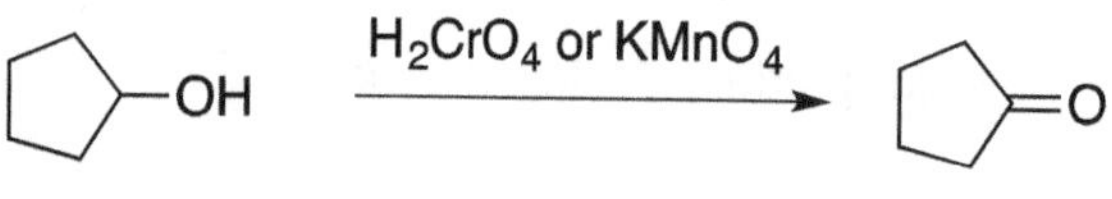 $\xrightarrow{\text{H}_2\text{CrO}_4 \text{ or KMnO}_4}$

Problem 8.17. Provide reagents that can be used in each nucleophilic substitution reaction in the following scheme to achieve the desired stereochemical outcome.

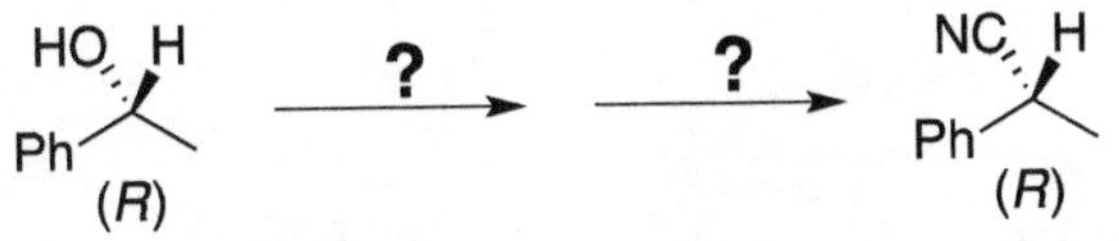

(NOTE: Net retention in configuration at the chiral center in the substitution product)

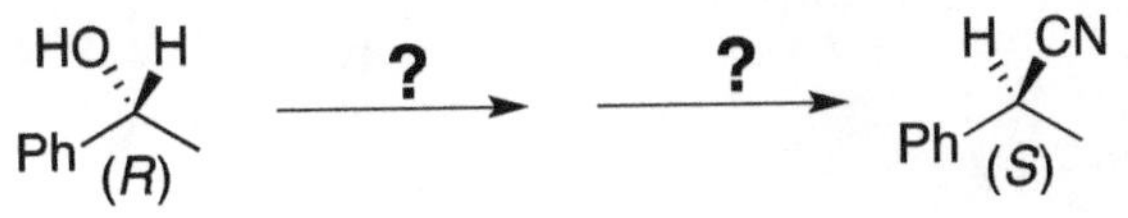

(NOTE: Net inversion in configuration at the chiral center in the substitution product)

Solution:

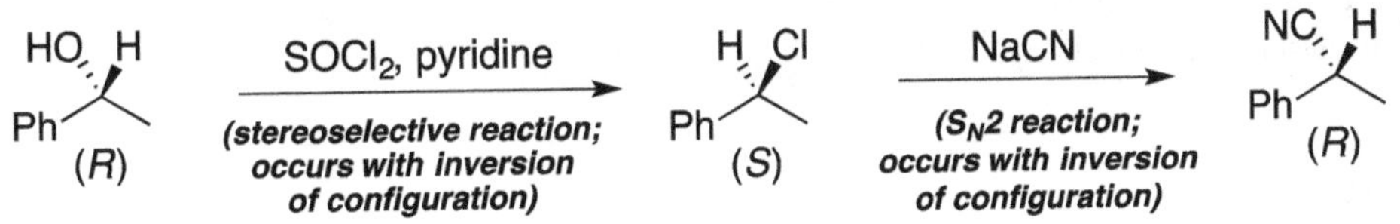

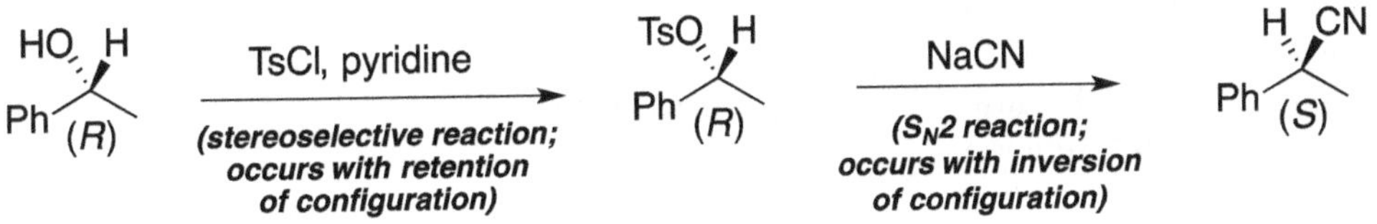

17.9. Chapter 9 Additional Problems

Problem 9.12. Determine/ identify (a) number of signals in the ¹H NMR spectrum, (b) number of signals in the ¹³C NMR spectrum, (c) splitting pattern (also known as multiplicity) of all the ¹H NMR signals, (d) the most deshielded H(s), and (e) the most deshielded C in the following three structures.

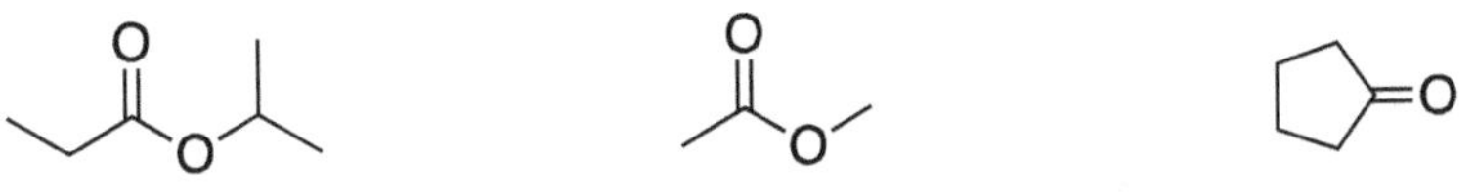

Solution:

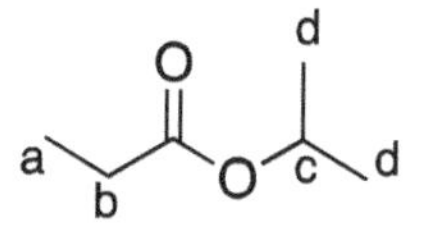

(structure: an ester — propanoate type with labels a, b on the acyl side and c, d on the isopropyl group, with O=)

a) number of signals in the ¹H NMR spectrum: 4
b) number of signals in the ¹³C NMR spectrum: 5
c) multiplicity of ¹H NMR signals: triplet (H-a), quartet (H-b), septet (H-c), doublet (H-d)
d) the most deshielded H(s): H-c
e) the most deshielded C: carbonyl C

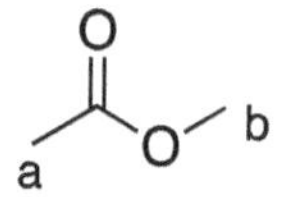

(structure: methyl acetate with labels a and b, O=)

a) number of signals in the ¹H NMR spectrum: 2
b) number of signals in the ¹³C NMR spectrum: 3
c) multiplicity of ¹H NMR signals: singlet (H-a), singlet (H-b)
d) the most deshielded H(s): H-b
e) the most deshielded C: carbonyl C

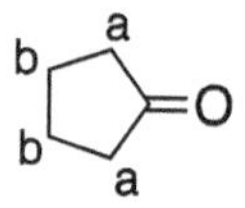

(structure: cyclopentanone with labels a, a adjacent to C=O and b, b)

a) number of signals in the ¹H NMR spectrum: 2
b) number of signals in the ¹³C NMR spectrum: 3
c) multiplicity of ¹H NMR signals: triplet (H-a), quintet (H-b)
d) the most deshielded H(s): H-a
e) the most deshielded C: carbonyl C

Problem 9.13. Determine if the indicated hydrogens in the following structures are related as homotopic, enantiotopic, or diastereotopic.

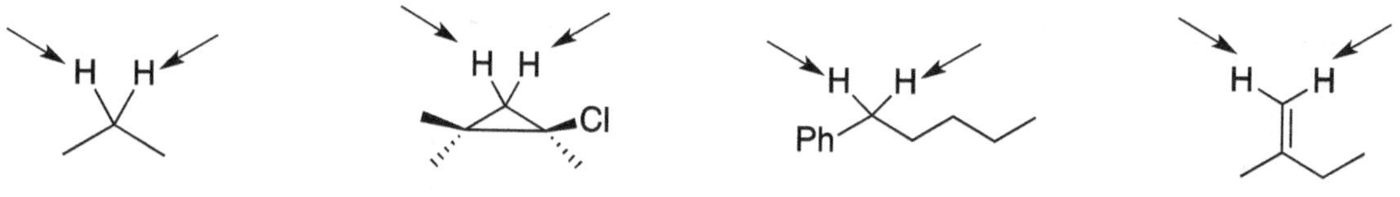

Solution:

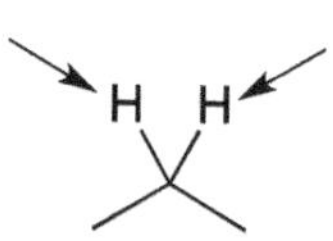

homotopic

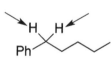

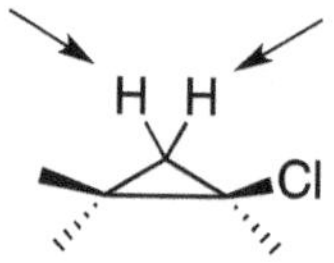

diastereotopic

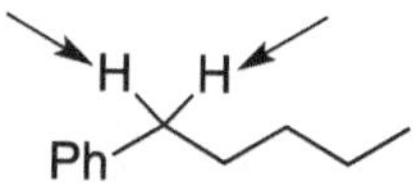

enantiotopic

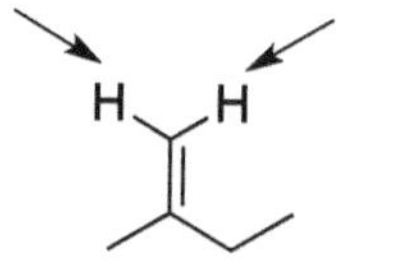

diastereotopic

Problem 9.14. Choose **one** structure from the given set that agrees with the given IR and NMR spectral data:

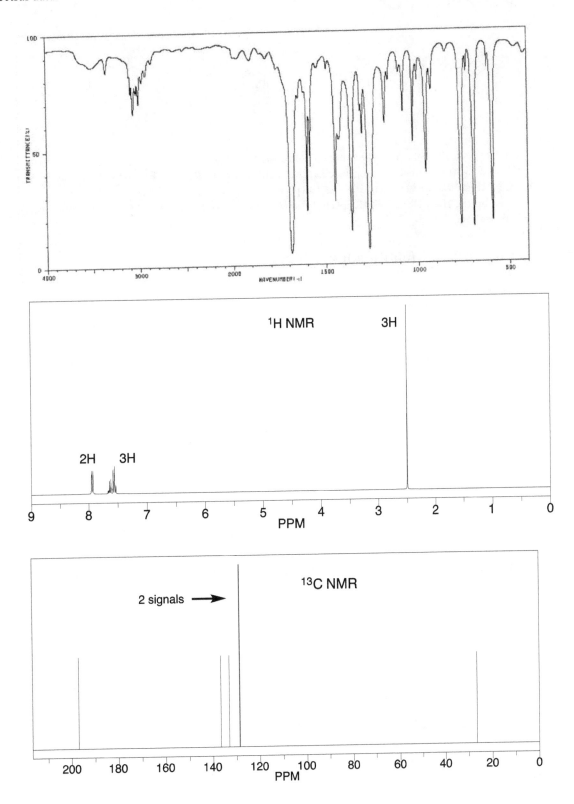

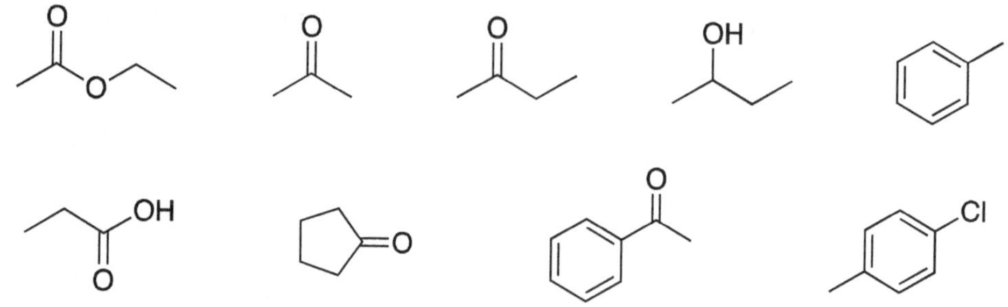

Solution:

Characteristic IR peaks: C=O present and O-H absent;

^{1}H NMR signals: aromatic hydrogens present; characteristic –CHO and –COOH signals absent;

^{13}C NMR signals: C=O present at about 196 ppm; aromatic carbons present.

Based on the given IR and NMR spectral data analysis, the structure of $PhCOCH_3$ (acetophenone) agrees with the data.

17.10. Chapter 10 Additional Problems

Problem 10.7. What is the major organic product obtained from the following sequence of reactions?

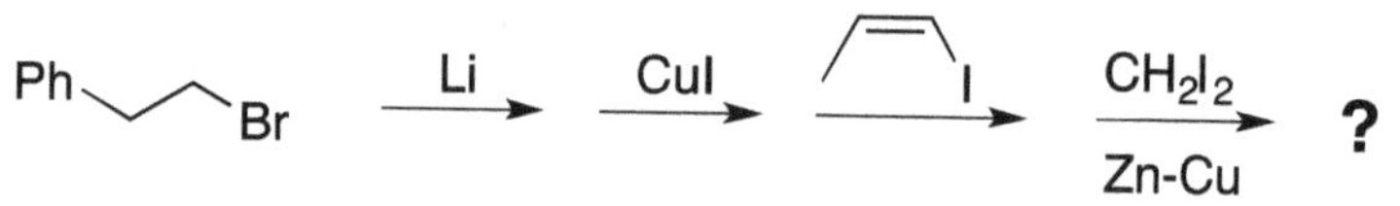

Solution:

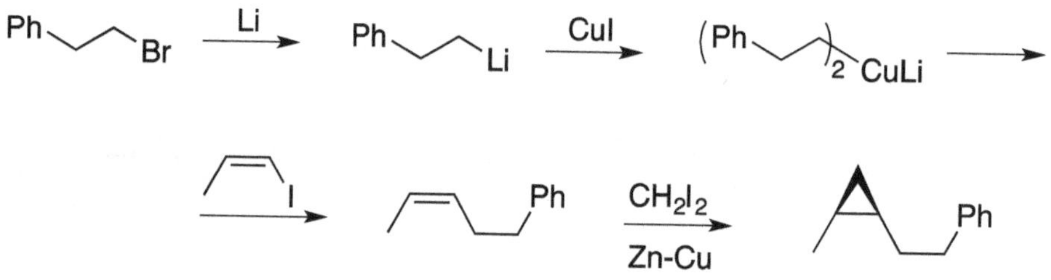

Problem 10.8. Propose a mechanism to account for the formation of product in the following reaction:

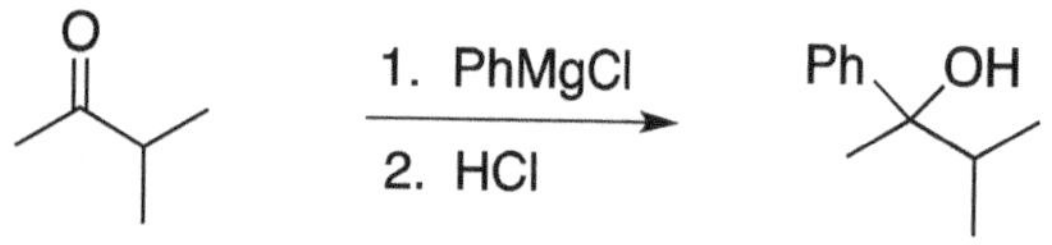

Solution:

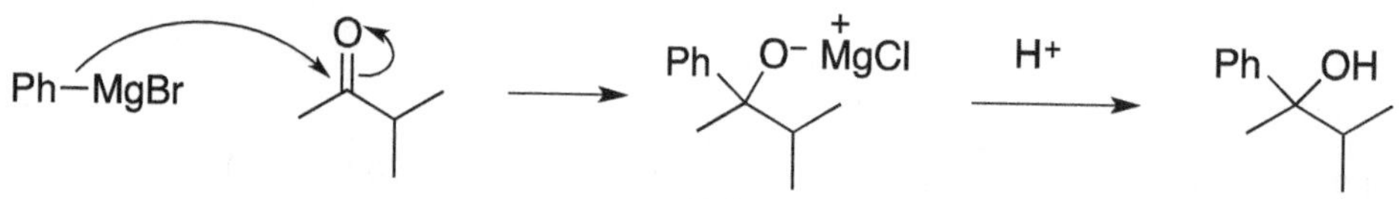

Problem 10.9. Identify the reagent(s) required to convert the reactant to the indicated product in each reaction.

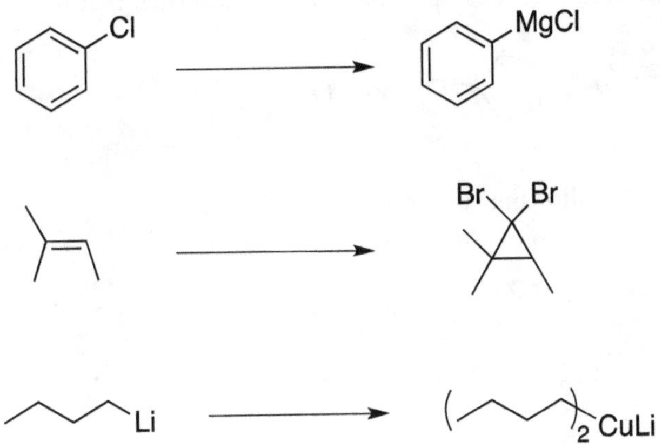

Solution:

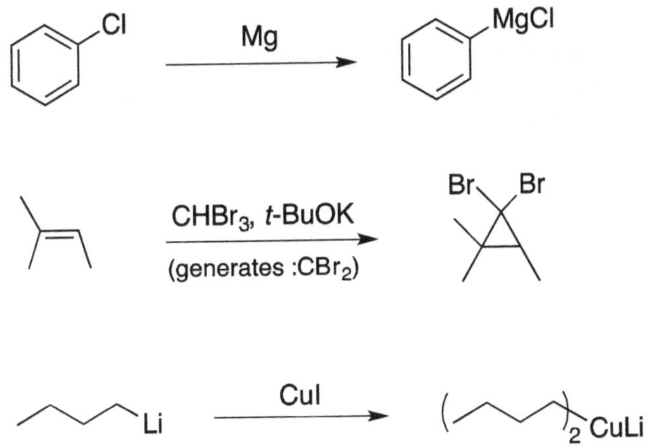

17.11. Chapter 11 Additional Problems

Problem 11.25. Select one compound from the given set that fits **all** of the following descriptions:

a) has the molecular formula C_8H_{14}, and

b) absorbs 1 mole of H_2 when exposed to excess H_2 and Pt, and

c) produces **two different ketones** upon ozonolysis.

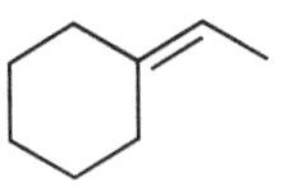

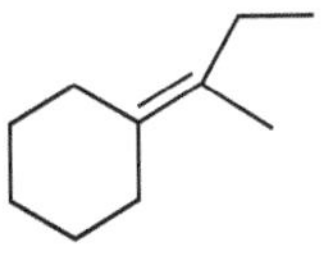

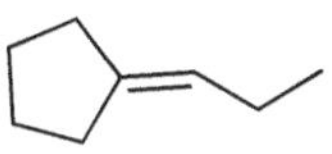

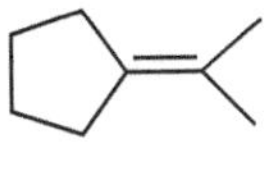

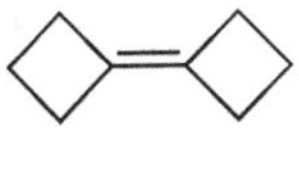

Solution:

Structure **d** agrees with all the descriptions. It has molecular formula C_8H_{14}, the C=C can be reduced with H_2/Pt, and it produces two different ketones upon ozonolysis as shown below:

O3
(CH3)2S
O
+
O

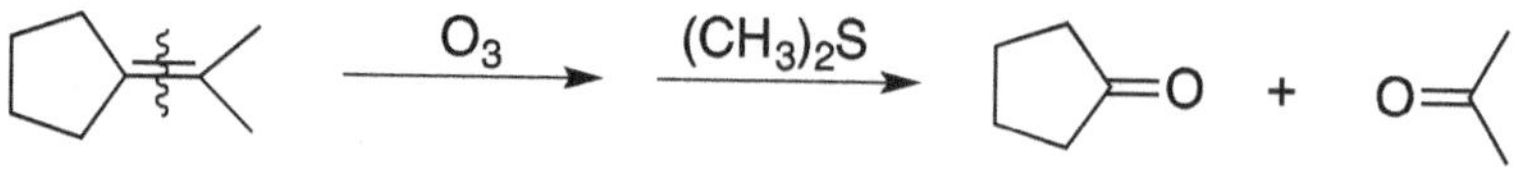

Problem 11.26. Provide the product(s) in the following reaction.

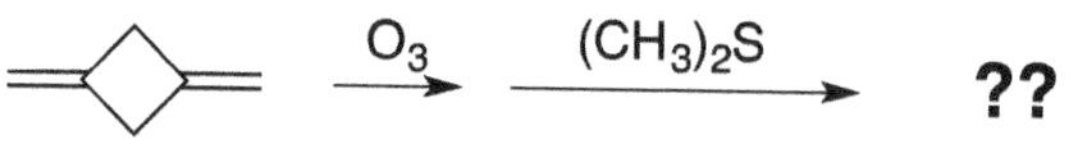

O3
(CH3)2S
??

Solution:

O3
(CH3)2S
O
O
+ 2
O
H
H

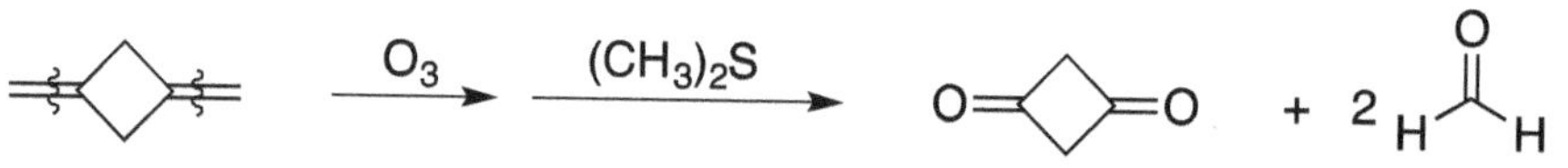

Problem 11.27. Provide structures of A, B, C, and D based on the following details.
Compound **A**, molecular formula C_6H_{10}, absorbs one equivalent of H_2 to form **B**, molecular formula C_6H_{12}. Ozonolysis of A yields cyclopentanone and formaldehyde:

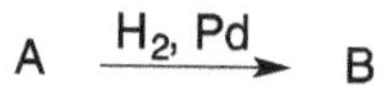

A
H2, Pd
B

A
O3
(CH3)2S
O
+
H
O
H

A also reacts with HBr to form **C**, molecular formula $C_6H_{11}Br$.

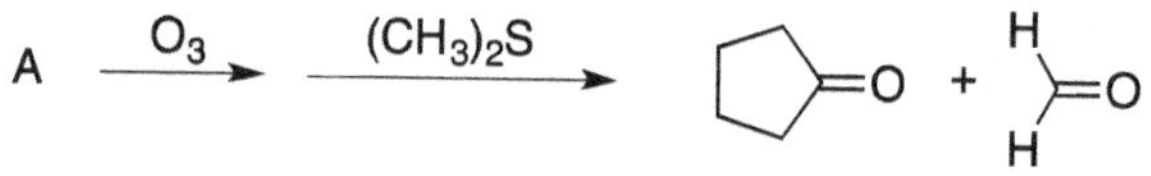

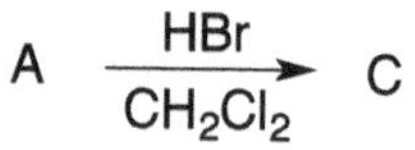

A
HBr
CH2Cl2
C

C undergoes elimination to produce **D**, molecular formula C_6H_{10}.

C
KOH
ethanol-H2O
D

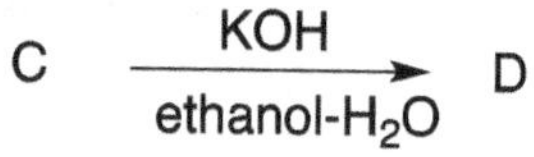

D undergoes cleavage upon ozonolysis to yield the keto-aldehyde shown below.

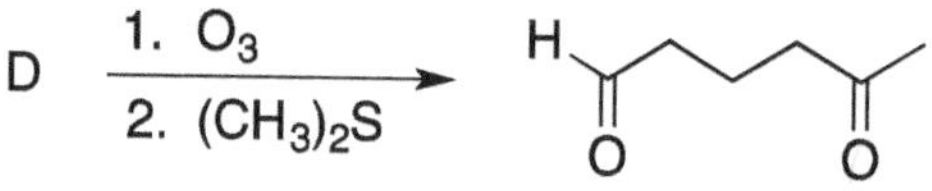

D
1. O3
2. (CH3)2S
H
O
O

Solution:

H
H
CH3
Br
CH3
CH3

A B C D

17.12. Chapter 12 Additional Problems

Problem 12.29. Structures A and B undergo decarboxylation readily under mild thermal condition compared to structure C.

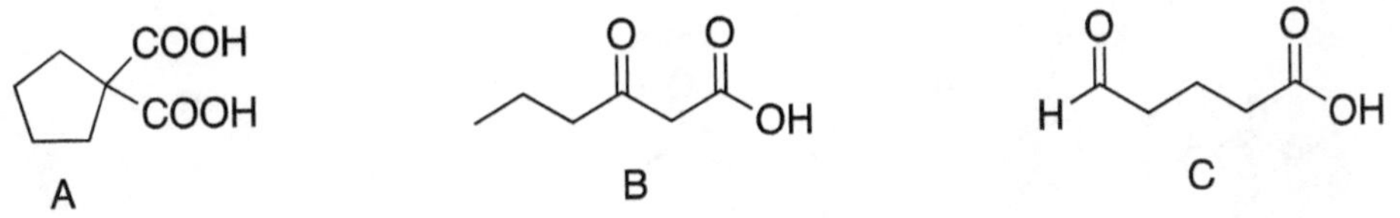

Identify the factor(s) that facilitate thermal decarboxylation in structures A and B. Also, provide the mechanism to account for this process.

Solution:

Structures A and B have a carbonyl group (C=O), located β to the –COOH which assists in the decarboxylation process. Such molecules are called β-ketoacids. The mechanism for this process involves the formation of a six-membered cyclic transition state which is stabilized by the intramolecular hydrogen bond between the carboxyl H and the O atom of the β-carbonyl group as shown below:

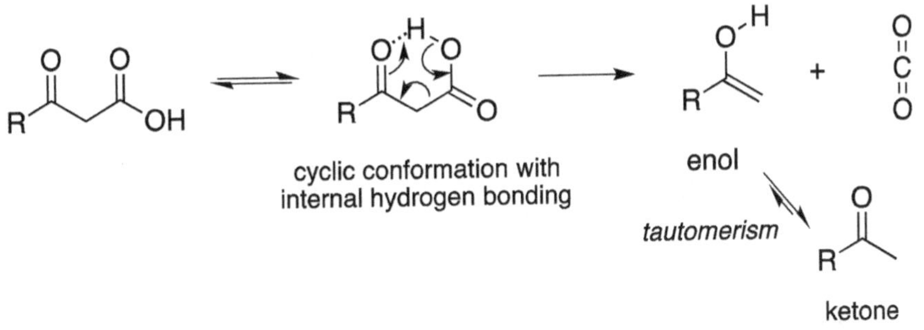

Problem 12.30. Provide the structure of products obtained via thermal decarboxylation of A and B in the above problem.

Solution:

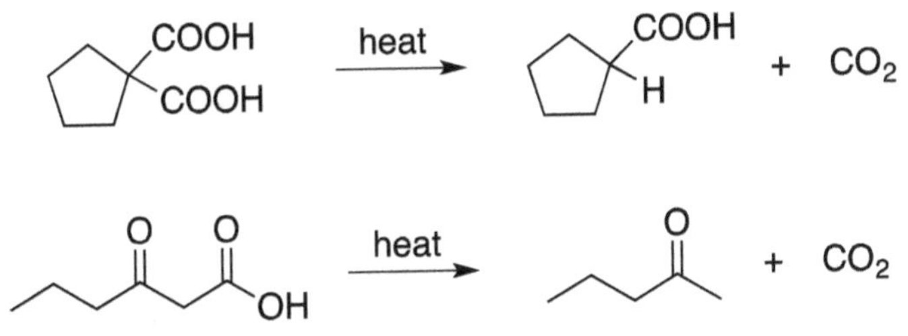

Problem 12.31. Determine appropriate reducing agent for each reaction that can be used to selectively obtain the indicated product in high yield.

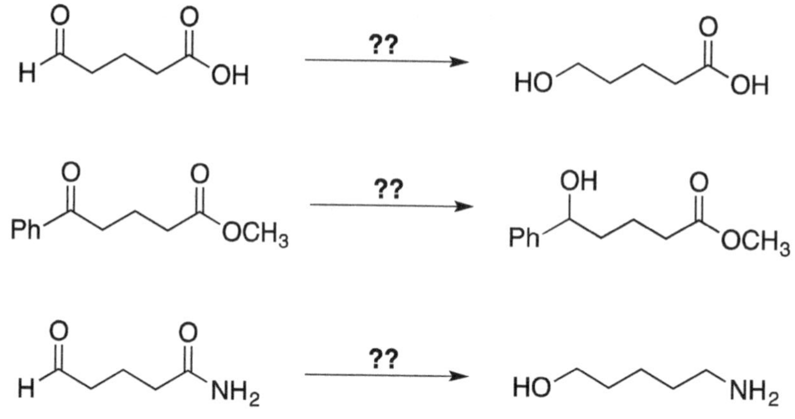

Solution:

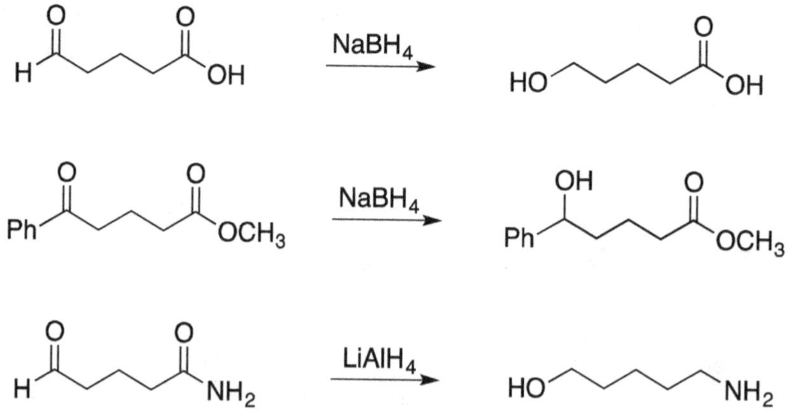

Problem 12.32. Provide the structures of unknowns A, B, C, D, E in the following reaction scheme.

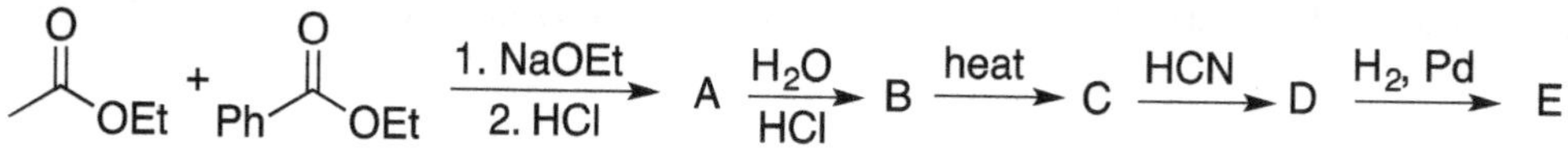

Solution:

A:

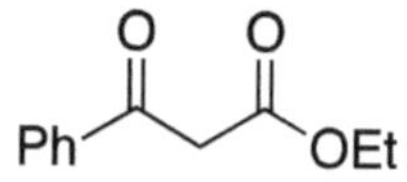

B:

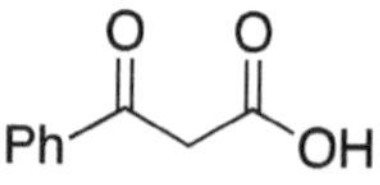

C:

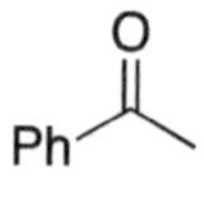

D:

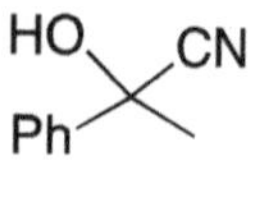

E:

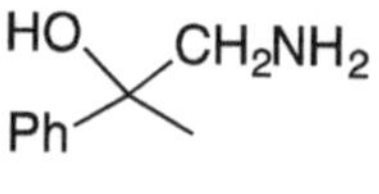

17.13. Chapter 13 Additional Problems

Problem 13.9. Consider the addition of 1 mole of HBr to 1,3-butadiene to answer the following questions a-c.

  a) Provide the reaction mechanism and structures of 1,2- and 1,4-addition products formed in this reaction.

  b) Which is more stable, the 1,2- or 1,4-addition product?

  c) Which addition product in the above reaction will be the major product when the reaction is under thermodynamic control? Explain your reasoning.

Solution:

  a)

Resonance stabilized allylic carbocation:

secondary allylic
(more stable)

primary allylic
(less stable)

+ Br⁻

Br⁻

Br⁻

Br

1,2-addition product
(less stable product)

Br

1,4-addition product
(more stable product)

  b) The 1,4-addition product is more stable because it is a more highly substituted, disubstituted alkene.

  c) The more stable, 1,4-addition product will be the major product when the reaction is under thermodynamic control. In this reaction, 1,4-addition product is the thermodynamic product (most stable) and 1,2-addition product is the kinetic product (fastest formed). Stability of the products dictates the outcome of a thermodynamically controlled reaction.

Problem 13.10. Determine if the following dienes will react with a dienophile in a Diels–Alder reaction.

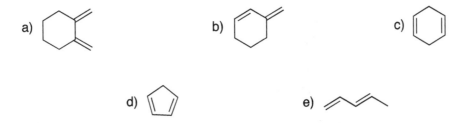

a)

b)

c)

d)

e)

Solution:

The Diels–Alder reaction requires s-*cis* conformation of the diene for effective orbital overlap between diene and dienophile. Dienes that cannot exist in s-*cis* conformation are unreactive in a Diels–Alder reaction.

a) Diene is in the desired s-*cis* conformation and will therefore react with a dienophile in a Diels–Alder reaction.

b) Diene is in s-*trans* conformation and cannot assume s-*cis* conformation due to rigidity of the cyclic structure. The diene will therefore never react in a Diels–Alder reaction.

c) Diene is not a conjugated diene and therefore cannot react in a Diels–Alder reaction.

d) Diene is in the desired s-*cis* conformation and will therefore react with a dienophile in a Diels–Alder reaction.

e) Diene is in the more stable s-*trans* conformation but is always in equilibrium with the less stable s-*cis* conformation. The diene can react in a Diels–Alder reaction as long as it can assume the s-*cis* conformation.

Problem 13.11. Identify the diene and dienophile that can be used to synthesize the following compound using a Diels–Alder reaction.

Solution:

diene   dienophile (*trans*)

17.14. Chapter 14 Additional Problems

Problem 14.18. Imidazole is a biologically important molecule and a commonly used base in organic synthesis. The structure of this heterocyclic aromatic amine is provided below for your reference. Explain why the reaction of imidazole with an acid always involves the N atom at the C=N in preference to the other N atom in the structure.

Imidazole   Conjugate Acid

Solution:

The other N atom of imidazole that does not react with an acid has the lone electron pair in a p orbital, parallel to the other p orbitals in the molecule. This lone electron pair actually contributes to the aromaticity of imidazole. If this lone pair is used to form a bond with proton during reaction with an acid, the molecule will lose its aromatic character. In contrast, the lone pair on N atom at the C=N occupies an sp^2 orbital and does not contribute to the aromaticity of imidazole. That lone electron pair is available to react with an acid resulting in the formation of the conjugate acid shown above.

Problem 14.19. n-Butylbenzene can be prepared from benzene *directly* via Friedel–Crafts alkylation or *indirectly* via Friedel–Crafts acylation followed by subsequent reduction of the carbonyl group in the acylated product as shown in the following scheme.

Direct synthesis via Friedel-Crafts alkylation:

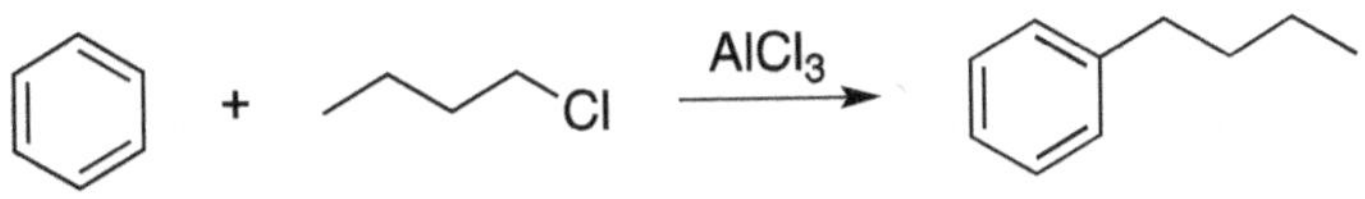

Synthesis via Friedel-Crafts acylation - reduction sequence:

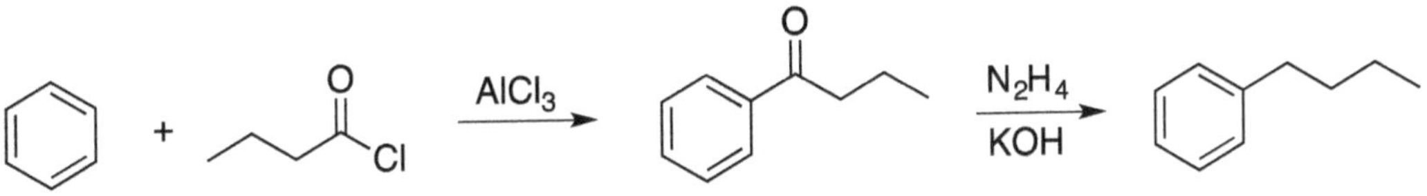

Which synthetic strategy will yield n-butylbenzene in high yield? Explain your reasoning.

Solution:

Indirect synthesis via Friedel–Crafts acylation–reduction sequence will lead to high yield of n-butylbenzene. Direct synthesis of n-butylbenzene by Friedel–Crafts alkylation proceeds via the formation of carbocation intermediate which is very susceptible to rearrangement through 1,2-hydride shift or 1,2-alkyl shift depending on its structure. Formation of rearranged product(s) via carbocation rearrangement will lower the yield of n-butylbenzene. In contrast, Friedel–Crafts acylation does not involve carbocation intermediate which eliminates the issue with carbocation rearrangement and lower yield of n-butylbenzene.

Problem 14.20. Provide reagent(s) that can be used to convert toluene to the following aromatic compounds:

a) benzyl bromide   b) *o*-Bromotoluene   c) benzoic acid

Solution:

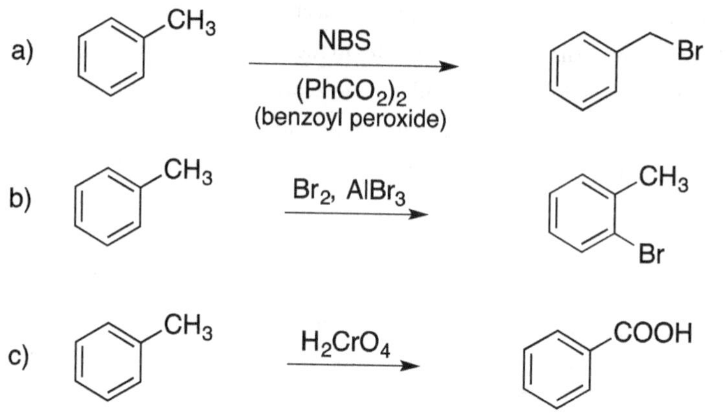

a)

b)

c)

Problem 14.21. Provide a route for the conversion of benzene to the following compounds:

a) aniline

b) styrene (vinylbenzene)

c) *m*-chlorobenzoic acid

d) *m*-bromonitrobenzene

Solution:

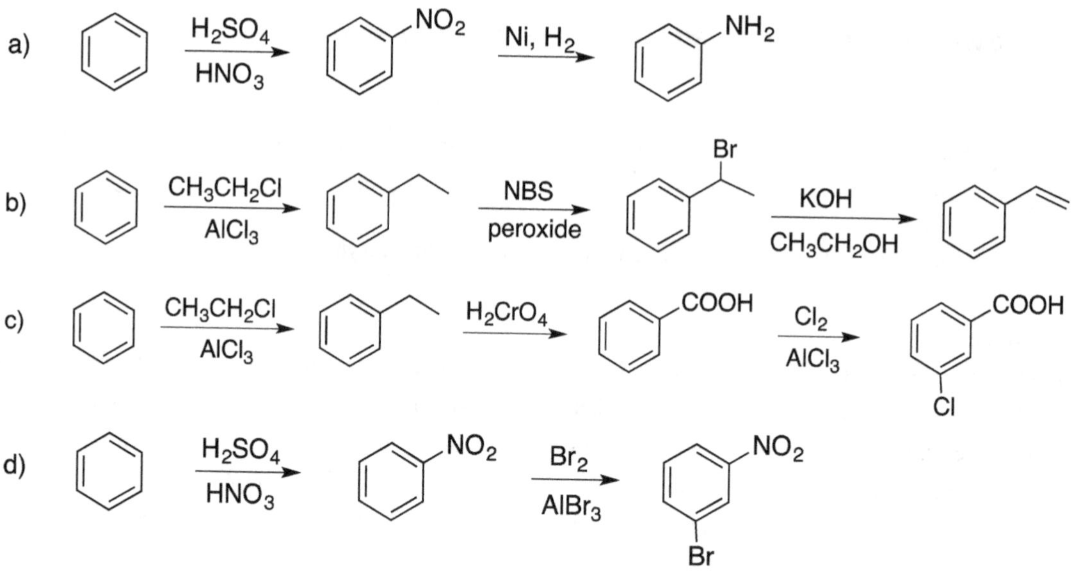

a)

b)

c)

d)

17.15. Chapter 15 Additional Problems

Problem 15.13. Propose the synthesis of the following compounds:

a) *N,N*-dimethyl-4-nitroaniline from chlorobenzene and dimethylamine

b) triethylbenzylammonium bromide from benzamide and bromoethane

Solution:

a)

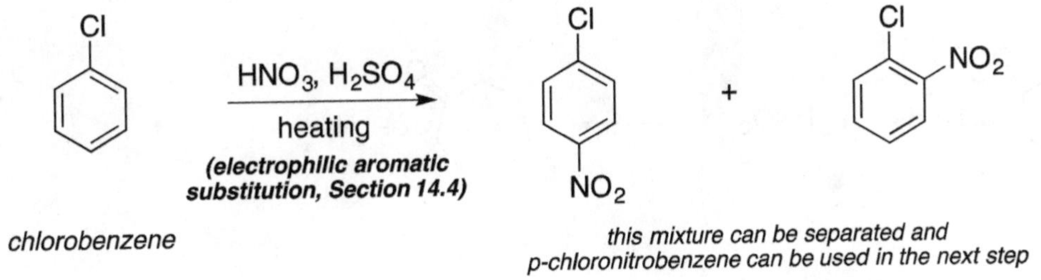

Cl
HNO3, H2SO4
heating
(electrophilic aromatic substitution, Section 14.4)
Cl
NO2
+
Cl
NO2
chlorobenzene
this mixture can be separated and
p-chloronitrobenzene can be used in the next step

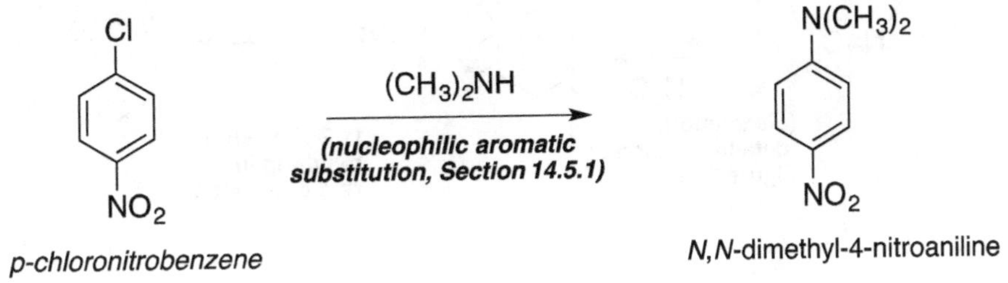

Cl
NO2
(CH3)2NH
(nucleophilic aromatic substitution, Section 14.5.1)
N(CH3)2
NO2
p-chloronitrobenzene
N,N-dimethyl-4-nitroaniline

b)

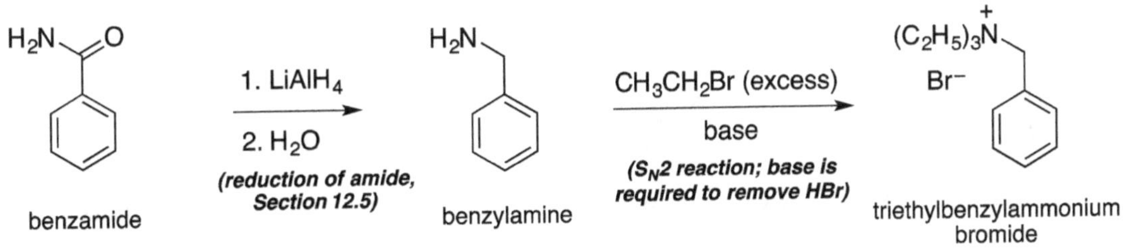

H2N
O
1. LiAlH4
2. H2O
(reduction of amide, Section 12.5)
H2N
CH3CH2Br (excess)
base
(SN2 reaction; base is required to remove HBr)
(C2H5)3N
+
Br−
benzamide
benzylamine
triethylbenzylammonium bromide

Problem 15.14. Rank the following amines in the decreasing order of their basicity:

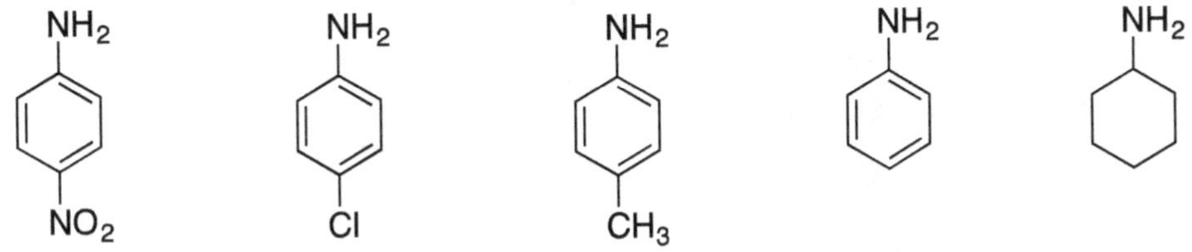

NH2
NO2
NH2
Cl
NH2
CH3
NH2
NH2

Solution:

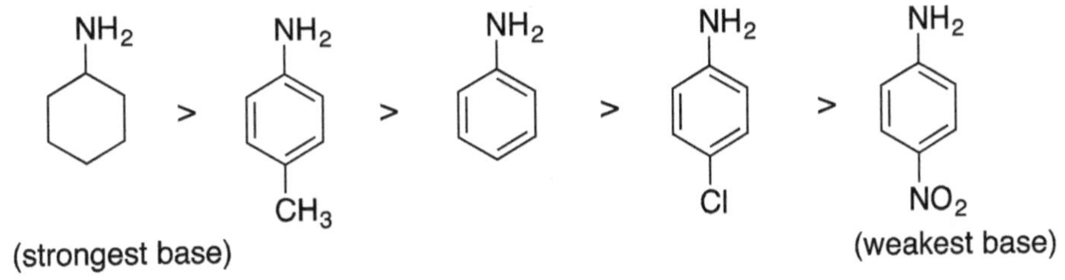

NH2
>
NH2
CH3
>
NH2
>
NH2
Cl
>
NH2
NO2
(strongest base)
(weakest base)

Problem 15.15. The reaction of a cyclic β-aminoalcohol with nitrous acid (HNO_2) yields a ring-expanded ketone via a molecular rearrangement. Write the complete mechanism including the rearrangement to account for the formation of cycloheptanone in the following reaction:

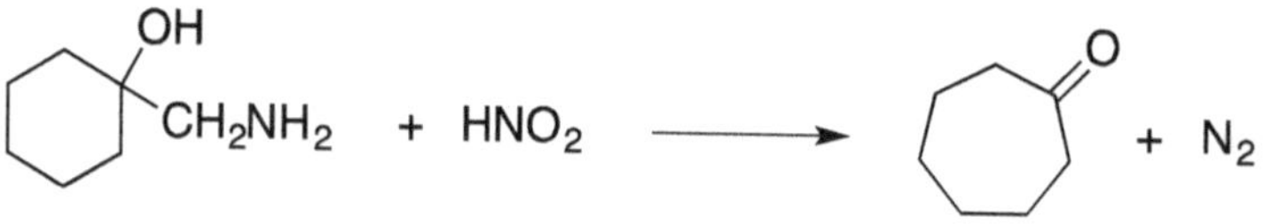

OH
CH2NH2
+ HNO2
O
+ N2

Solution:

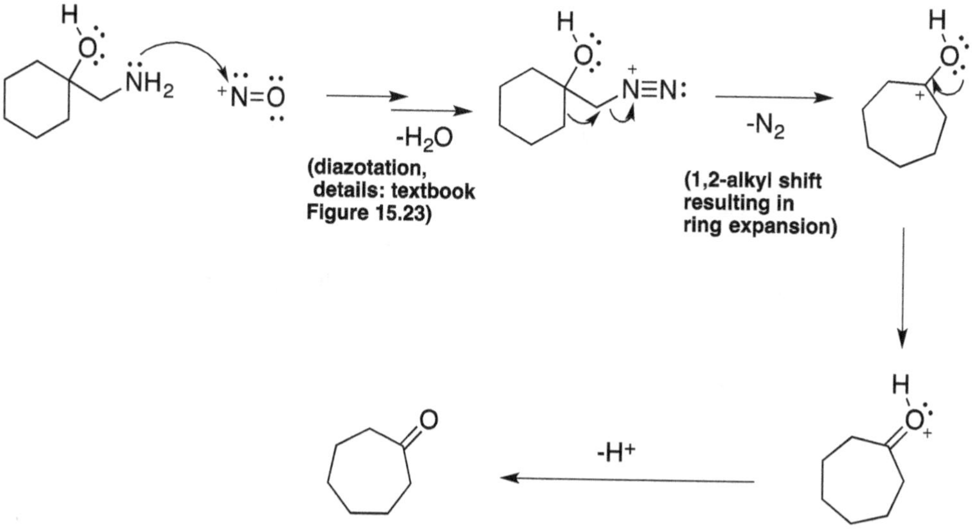

-H2O
(diazotation, details: textbook Figure 15.23)
-N2
(1,2-alkyl shift resulting in ring expansion)
-H+

Problem 15.16. Provide a route for the conversion of benzene to the following compounds:

a) phenol b) fluorobenzene c) iodobenzene

Solution:

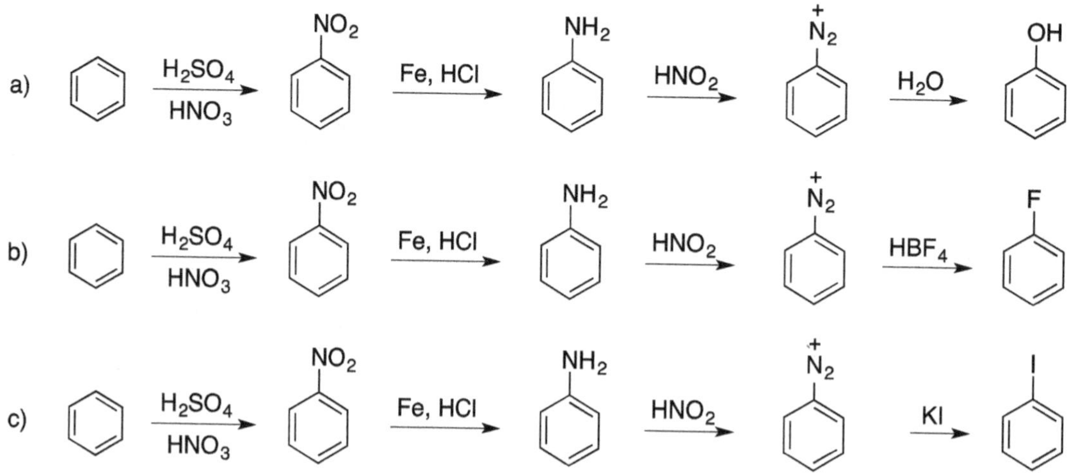

a)
H2SO4
HNO3
NO2
Fe, HCl
NH2
HNO2
N2
H2O
OH
b)
H2SO4
HNO3
NO2
Fe, HCl
NH2
HNO2
N2
HBF4
F
c)
H2SO4
HNO3
NO2
Fe, HCl
NH2
HNO2
N2
KI
I

17.16. Chapter 16 Additional Problems

Problem 16.19. Classify the two isomeric unsaturated fatty acids below as *cis* or *trans*. Which fatty acid will have a lower melting point? Explain briefly.

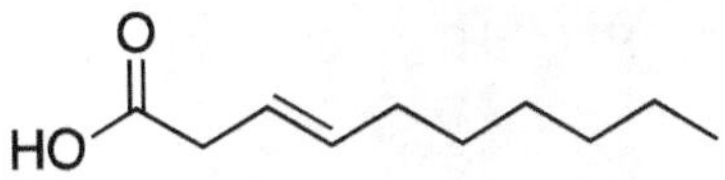

Solution:
The classification of fatty acids as *cis* or *trans* refers to the geometry of the C=C in each structure:

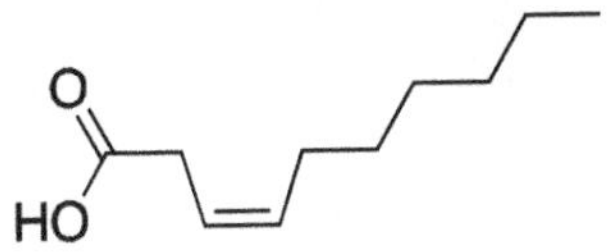

cis 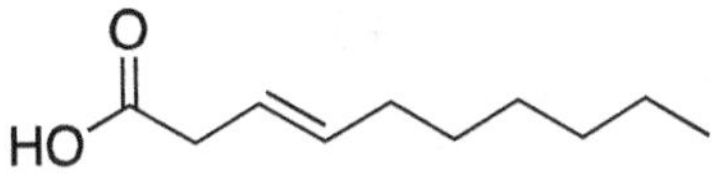   trans

The *cis* double bond in the fatty acid introduces a "kink" in its shape, which makes it more difficult to pack the molecules together in a stable repeating array. The kink in the structure of *cis* unsaturated fatty acid does not allow the close packing and interactions between the hydrocarbon chains as in the case of *trans* unsaturated fatty acid or saturated fatty acid. Therefore, *cis* fatty acid will have the lower melting point.

Problem 16.20. The following questions are based on the structure of the hexose sugar molecule given below:

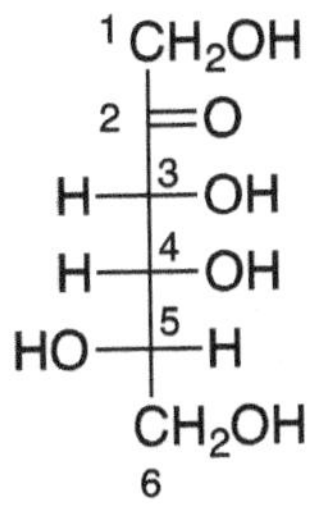

a) Identify the number of stereocenters in the molecule.
b) Determine the maximum number of stereoisomers possible for the above hexose sugar.
c) Identify the configuration (D or L) of the given structure.

Solution:

a) The molecule has three stereocenters (C-3, C-4, C-5).
b) There are three stereocenters, therefore the maximum number of stereoisomers possible for this molecule is $2^3 = 8$.
c) If the stereocenter farthest away from the carbonyl C has the OH group to the right of the vertical backbone, the configuration of the structure is D. If the OH group is to the left of the vertical backbone, the configuration of the structure is L. The configuration of the given hexose sugar is L as the OH group on C-5 appears to the left of the vertical carbon backbone.

Problem 16.21. Classify the following carbohydrates as reducing or nonreducing sugar.

a)

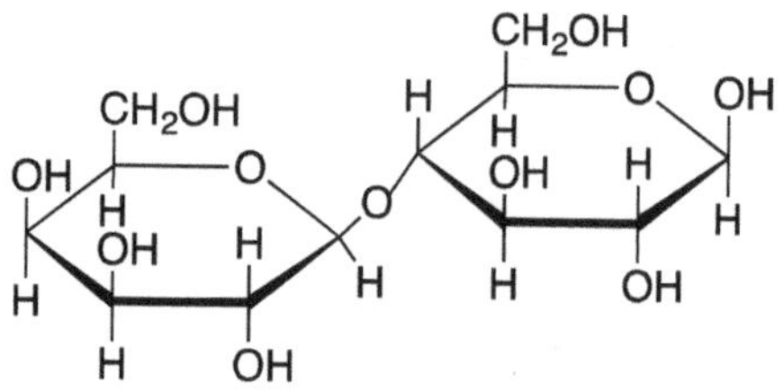

b)

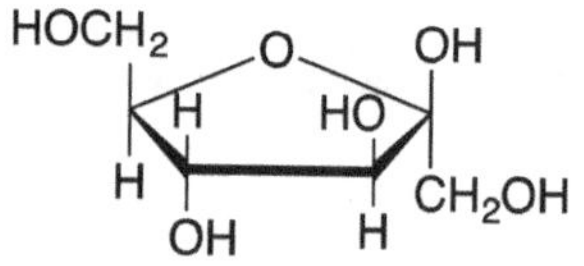

Solution:

Carbohydrates a and b are both reducing sugar as they have a free/unmodified OH group at the anomeric carbon which allows them to revert to the open chain form. The open chain form has a free –CHO group which is oxidized to –COOH.

Problem 16.22. Convert the following three-dimensional line–angle structures of monosaccharides to the Fischer projections. Assign D or L designator to each molecule.

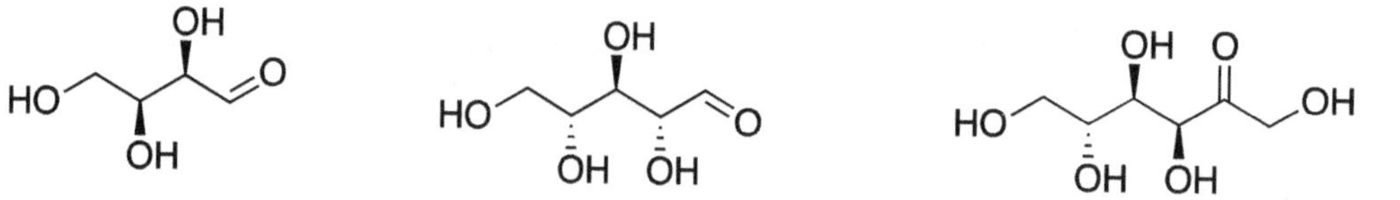

Solution:

Assigning R or S configuration to each stereocenter in the three-dimensional drawings will help to convert these structures to the Fischer projections as shown below. In general, the carbon with R configuration will have the hydroxyl group on the right side corresponding to the D designator. The carbons with S configuration will have OH on the left side of the Fischer projection. Alternatively, this problem can be solved by looking at the molecular model of the actual molecule.

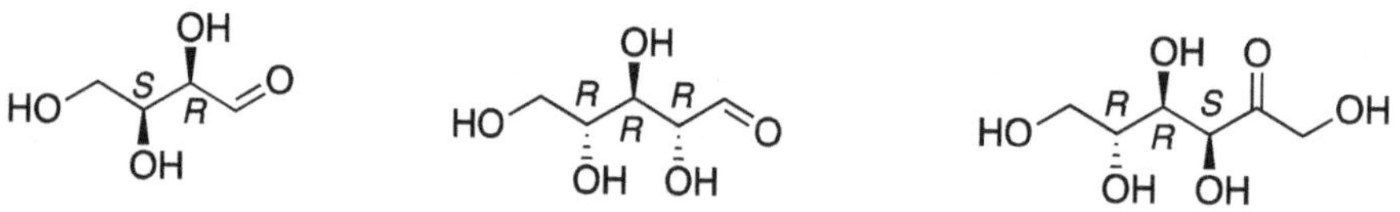

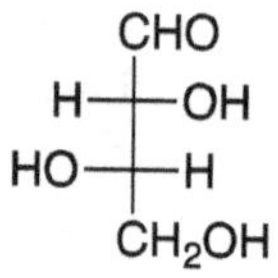

L-Threose

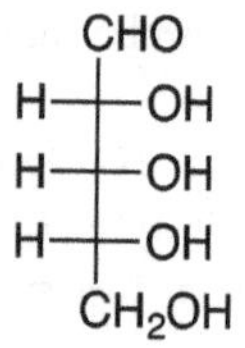

D-Ribose

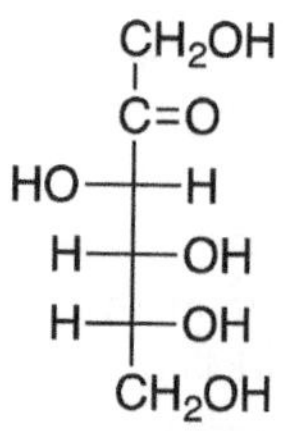

D-Fructose

Problem 16.23. Identify the amino acid sequence in the following tripeptide and name it. Identify the N-terminal and C-terminal amino acids in this tripeptide.

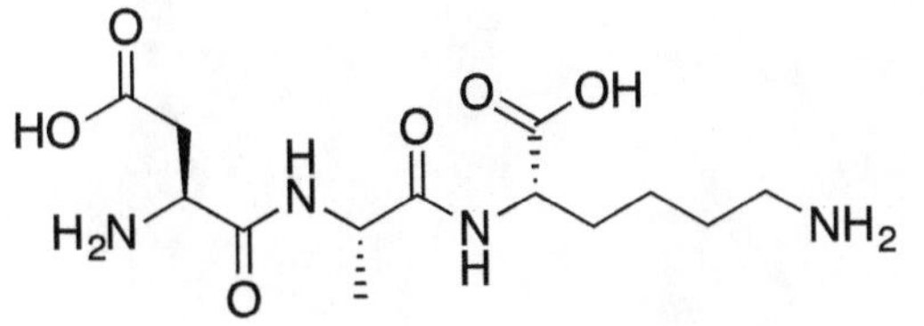

Solution:

This tripeptide is formed from the following amino acids: glutamic acid (N-terminal), alanine, and lysine (C-terminal).

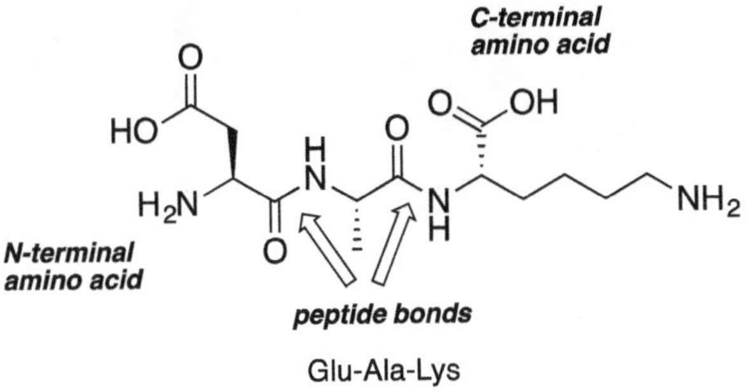

Glu-Ala-Lys

Problem 16.24. Show the formation of a peptide bond between two amino acid residues. Explain why peptide bonds in proteins are not hydrolyzed easily under physiological conditions.

Solution:

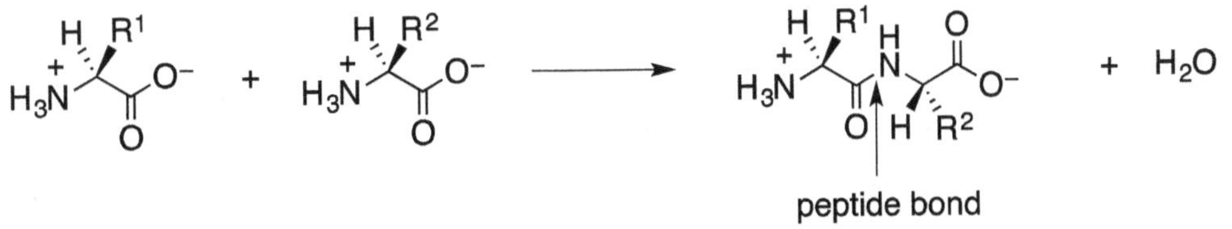

Peptide bond has partial double bond character due to resonance as shown below. The rigidity of peptide bonds provides stability to proteins and prevents their hydrolysis under physiological conditions.

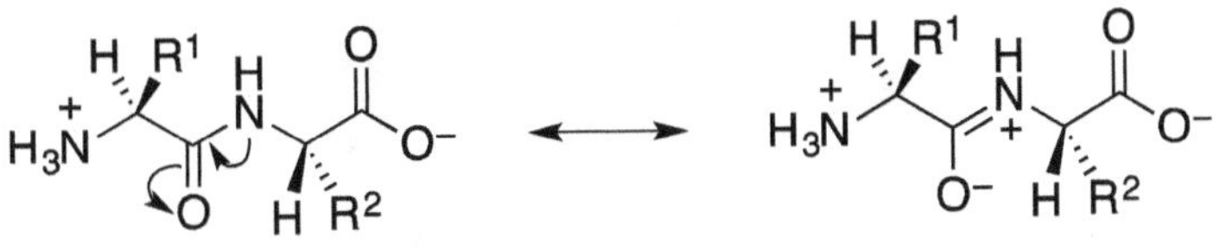

CPSIA information can be obtained
at www.ICGtesting.com
Printed in the USA
FSHW010317200719
60203FS

9 781516 524563